SCOTT FORESMAN · ADDISON WESLEY

Mathematics

Grade 1

Assessment Sourcebook

PEARSON

Scott Foresman

Editorial Offices: Glenview, Illinois • Parsippany, New Jersey • New York, New York

Sales Offices: Needham, Massachusetts • Duluth, Georgia • Glenview, Illinois
Coppell, Texas • Ontario, California • Mesa, Arizona

Table of Contents

ISBN: 0-328-11686-6

3 4 5 6 7 8 9 10 V004 12 11 10 09 08 07 06 05 04

Table of Contents

continued on next page

Table of Contents

Table of Contents

Overview of the
Assessment Sourcebook

Assessment and instruction are interwoven strands in the fabric of mathematics education. The primary purpose of assessment is to promote learning, so assessment may be referred to as the glue that holds curriculum and instruction together. As a result, the various instructional methods used in Scott Foresman–Addison Wesley Mathematics are supported by different assessment methods. This overview is a brief introduction to the kinds of assessment available in this Assessment Sourcebook, including both formal and informal types of assessment.

Formal Written Tests

A variety of formal written tests are provided to assess students' mastery of important mathematics concepts and skills.

Materials Provided
Blackline masters (starting on page 1)

- **Diagnosing Readiness** in Grades 1–6 to assess students' understanding of mathematical concepts developed in the previous grade level.

- **Chapter Tests** for use with all individual chapters in the student text. In Grades K–2 there are two forms of the Free Response and the Multiple Choice chapter tests. In Grades 3–6 these tests are called Mixed Formats because they contain free-response, multiple-choice, and writing in math questions. There are two forms of each chapter test.

- **Cumulative Tests** provided for use after Chapters 3, 6, 9, and 12.

- **A bubble-form Answer Sheet** to allow students to practice answering test questions on a separate response sheet.

Journal Writing

Journal Writing encourages students to use mathematical language as they reflect on what they are learning. It also provides an opportunity for you, the teacher, to gain insight as to how students approach problem-solving.

Materials Provided
(starting on page viii)

- Tips for assessing and responding to journal entries
- Ideas for Journal Prompts

Portfolio Assessment

Portfolio Assessment provides a way of tracking a student's growth and progress over time. A portfolio should include many types of assessment.

Materials Provided
(starting on page xiii)

- Tips and ideas for compiling and managing mathematics portfolios
- Inside My Mathematics Portfolio (blackline master) serves as a table of contents for the portfolios
- A Mathematics Portfolio Assessment Sheet (blackline master) to record how student portfolios track growth in various areas

Performance Assessment

Performance tests give a way to assess students' qualities of imagination, creativity, and perseverance. By using performance assessment, you can evaluate how students

- reason through problems,
- make and test conjectures,
- use number sense to predict reasonable answers, and
- utilize alternative strategies.

Materials Provided
(starting on page xviii)

- Performance Assessment tasks to be used after each chapter
- Notes that identify the mathematical concepts and skills needed
- A four-point Scoring Rubric

Basic-Facts Timed Tests

Basic-Facts Timed Tests provide students with the opportunity to review and practice basic facts.

Materials Provided
(starting on page 25)

- Tips for administering the tests
- Tips on adjusting time limits
- Additional materials
- Basic-Facts Timed Tests to be used before each chapter

Journal Writing

In a mathematics journal, students have the opportunity to explore their thoughts about a particular mathematics topic, to construct and crystallize their understanding of mathematical concepts and procedures, and to explain their ideas about mathematics. As a result, mathematics journals can provide an enormous amount of information about student thinking and are a valuable component of a comprehensive assessment program.

The Purpose of Journal Writing

Journals can be used to reflect, summarize, or generalize about mathematics lessons. They can also be used as a vehicle to apply mathematical concepts or skills. Some other reasons to incorporate journal writing into your mathematics assessment program include

- improving students' skills in communicating their mathematical thinking,
- encouraging application and transfer of previous knowledge to new situations,
- helping students improve creative writing skills,
- helping students explore their thoughts about mathematics,
- providing you with information about students' prior knowledge and what they do or do not understand,
- building and deepening student understanding of mathematical concepts, and
- helping students review and restate just-learned information.

Opportunities for Journal Writing

Journal writing can be incorporated as a natural extension of daily lessons. A few of the opportunities provided throughout the program are listed below.

- Have students respond in their journals to the *Writing in Math* questions presented in most lessons.

- Have students keep a list of new vocabulary that appears in each lesson. Suggest that they include a definition or an example.

- After Problem-Solving lessons, suggest that students write about ways in which the skills and strategies they are learning apply to their everyday lives.

Getting Started with Journal Writing

- Discuss the purpose of each mathematics journal entry and the audience for which it is intended. Students should know before beginning an assignment whether or not their entries will be shared with peers.

- Have students begin each assignment with a 3–5 minute brainstorming session. Then have students free-write about the assignment. During this time, students should jot down ideas, impressions, computations, drawings, or problems they are having with the assignment.

- Allow limited-English-speaking students to first write in the language in which they feel most comfortable. If students are fluent in two languages, encourage them to write in English.

- Include opportunities for students to express their thoughts about assignments in writing.

Assessing Journal Writing and Providing Feedback

When reading student journals, it's important to provide constructive feedback. You may choose to write comments and suggestions right in the journal or on removable note-pad paper. Include questions you have about the entry, and ideas you have about other topics the student might consider. Encourage the student to reply in his or her next entry.

If journal entries are destined for inclusion in the display portfolio, you might wish to have a formal revision stage in the journal writing process in which students revise their entries.

Ideas for Journal Prompts

Periodically during the school year give students a journal prompt and encourage them to write about the subject provided. This activity will provide opportunities for students to communicate their mathematical thinking as well as reinforce their writing skills. Some suggested journal prompts include:

- Today in math I learned…
- My math goals for this year are…
- The math I learned today can be used to…
- You should go back and check your math work because…
- When I need help with my math homework, I…
- My favorite math lesson is…
- I can use a number line to…
- If I had a hundred (thousand, million) dollars, I would…
- All squares are rectangles but not all rectangles are squares because…
- If I were one centimeter tall, I would…
- It is important to read data from a graph because…
- It is important to figure some math problems in your head because…
- Subtraction is the opposite of addition because…
- To find the mean (average) of five numbers, I would…
- It is faster to count to 100 by 10s rather than by 5s because…
- Using coupons at a grocery store can save on the family budget because…
- Since I know that 36 divided by 9 is 4, I can find the quotient of 3,600 divided by 900 by…
- $\frac{1}{2}$ is greater than $\frac{1}{4}$ because…
- When I think about all the possible numbers between 3 and 4, I know that there are…

Name_____

Date_____

Student Self-Assessment

Assignment _____

Write about what you did.

What were you trying to learn? _____

_____

_____

How did you start your work? _____

_____

_____

What materials did you need? _____

What did you learn?_____

_____

_____

Check the sentences that describe your work.

_____ I made a plan before I began my work.

_____ I was able to do the work.

_____ I did not understand the directions.

_____ I followed the directions but got the wrong answer.

_____ I found a different way to do this assignment.

_____ I could explain how to do this to someone else.

_____ The work was easier than I thought it would be.

_____ The work was harder than I thought it would be.

_____ Other: _____

Name_____

Date_____

My Math Experiences

Math that interests me: _____

_____

_____

_____

_____

My math goals: _____

_____

_____

_____

_____

Math skills I just learned and can do: _____

_____

_____

_____

_____

Math skills I need to work on: _____

_____

_____

_____

_____

Math rewards I have received: _____

_____

_____

_____

_____

Portfolio Assessment

What is a Portfolio?

A portfolio is a carefully chosen collection of a student's work that exhibits the student's efforts, achievements, and thinking. A portfolio can include many different types of assessment, including formal and informal assessments. Unlike a test, which gives a picture of a student's achievements at one certain point, a portfolio provides evidence of progress over time. Some pieces of work might remain in the portfolio for the entire school year, if you are going to chart progress over time.

Portfolios should only be used for assessment when

- an assessment purpose is defined,
- a method of determining what is to be put into the portfolio, by whom, and when, is detailed, and
- criteria for assessing individual pieces or the collection as a whole are identified.

The Purposes of Portfolio Assessment

Before making a portfolio, have a clear idea of how you want to use it for assessment. For example, a portfolio may be used

- to help you assess student understanding and progress,
- to help your students monitor their own progress, or
- to aid in teacher-student and teacher-parent conferences.

In addition to these basic purposes, the portfolio can also

- give you insight into your students' views of themselves through the specific pieces they choose to include,
- encourage your students to join with you in assessing their work, and
- provide a tool for evaluating your instruction and the mathematics curriculum.

Getting Started Using Portfolio Assessment

Help students understand what a portfolio is and what they will do to build their own portfolios. You may want to discuss with students the differences between types of portfolios. A *working* portfolio contains ALL the student's work for a particular chapter, group of chapters, and other work related to the mathematics that the students are learning. An *assessment* or *display* portfolio is a selection of work that is chosen by the student, the teacher, and by teacher and student agreeing together. Parents can also participate in their child's *assessment* or *display* portfolio by choosing a few pieces of work to be included.

• Have students begin by compiling a working portfolio that holds *all* their work for particular chapter, group of chapters, and other math-related work. Set aside time each week or at the end of a chapter for students to review their working portfolios in order to select pieces they wish to include in a display portfolio of finished products.

• Have students help set the standards for selection of pieces for the display portfolio. Some should be chosen by the teacher, some by the student, and some by mutual agreement. Talk about choosing quality over quantity. You may also invite parents to choose two or three of their child's pieces of work to include.

• Make sure students consider many kinds of work to include, such as artwork, graphics, audio- and videotapes, project results, journal writings, and self-assessments.

• Identify those items that you will require in each student's assessment portfolio, such as Chapter Tests and Performance Assessments.

Organizing Pieces for the Display Portfolio

• **Inside My Mathematics Portfolio** (blackline master) provides students a place to list, date, and explain the inclusion of each piece.

• Be sure that each piece in the portfolio is dated. The portfolio then becomes an ongoing record of student progress.

Assessing Portfolios

Decide when you want to assess students' display portfolios. Logical checkpoints might be quarterly, after chapters 3, 6, 9, and 12. On the next page are some possible criteria to use for assessing math portfolios. The **Mathematics Portfolio Assessment Sheet** (blackline master) helps you summarize how each student's portfolio demonstrates growth in these areas.

Growth Area	Definitions
Reasoning and Problem Solving	Includes interpreting and analyzing problems, choosing successful problem-solving strategies, and using higher-order thinking skills (interpretation, analysis, justification)
Communication	Includes explaining ideas clearly, using mathematical terms and symbols correctly, and organizing mathematical information effectively (models, diagrams, graphs)
Applying Concepts and Procedures	Includes selecting appropriate concepts, procedures, and materials to solve problems, and applying the concepts and procedures correctly

It is helpful to meet with students as you assess their portfolios. Have some leading statements prepared, such as:

Show me something you are proud of and explain why.
Show me something you revised.
Show me something you enjoyed doing and tell why.

Let students know if you plan to use the display portfolios during conferences with family members, other teachers, or school administrators.

Name_____

Inside My Mathematics Portfolio

My work   Why I Kept It

1. _____   _____

   _____   _____

2. _____   _____

   _____   _____

3. _____   _____

   _____   _____

4. _____   _____

   _____   _____

5. _____   _____

   _____   _____

6. _____   _____

   _____   _____

7. _____   _____

   _____   _____

8. _____   _____

   _____   _____

9. _____   _____

   _____   _____

10. _____   _____

    _____   _____

Name_____

Date_____

Mathematics Portfolio Assessment Sheet

Growth Area   **How Portfolio Demonstrates Growth**

Reasoning and
Problem Solving
_____
_____
_____
_____

Communication
_____
_____
_____
_____

Applying Concepts
and Procedures
_____
_____
_____
_____

Summary
_____
_____
_____
_____

Additional
Comments
_____
_____
_____
_____

Performance Assessment

Performance assessment allows you to assess how well students apply their mathematical knowledge and skills in different contexts and realistic situations.

Performance Assessment Opportunities Provided in Scott Foresman–Addison Wesley Mathematics

* Many of these tests provide information about a realistic situation and ask students to use new information along with their mathematics power to solve problems. Most of the problems are open-ended problems, with an emphasis on finding meaningful solutions rather than calculating one and only one correct response.

Administering a Performance Assessment Task

Managing performance assessment projects may be more difficult than managing other types of assessment. The following tips may help you with classroom management during performance assessment administration.

* Consider having students work in groups to complete a performance assessment.

* Move among students as they work to collect anecdotal information during the test. Ask questions that will give you information about thought processes.

* Spend time at the beginning of the test to be sure all students understand the purpose.

* Review the Scoring Rubric. These rubrics, customized to each performance assessment, provide one way of qualifying your assessment of student results. You may wish to distribute this rubric to each student before beginning the assessment task. In this way, students will understand how they will be assessed on their performance.

During the Performance Assessment

* Consider using the **Observation Checklist Group Skills** on page xix as you observe students working on the task.

Assessing Performance

* Answers to the activities and questions included in the task are provided on the Scoring Rubric page.

* Use the Scoring Rubric to evaluate student performance.

Observation Checklist **Group Skills**

Student	Encourages and Listens to Others	Participates in Discussion	Communicates Clearly	Shares Tasks	Takes Initiative	Shares Responsibility/ Accountability	Cooperates with Others
_____	☐	☐	☐	☐	☐	☐	☐
_____	☐	☐	☐	☐	☐	☐	☐
_____	☐	☐	☐	☐	☐	☐	☐
_____	☐	☐	☐	☐	☐	☐	☐
_____	☐	☐	☐	☐	☐	☐	☐
_____	☐	☐	☐	☐	☐	☐	☐
_____	☐	☐	☐	☐	☐	☐	☐
_____	☐	☐	☐	☐	☐	☐	☐
_____	☐	☐	☐	☐	☐	☐	☐
_____	☐	☐	☐	☐	☐	☐	☐
_____	☐	☐	☐	☐	☐	☐	☐
_____	☐	☐	☐	☐	☐	☐	☐
_____	☐	☐	☐	☐	☐	☐	☐
_____	☐	☐	☐	☐	☐	☐	☐
_____	☐	☐	☐	☐	☐	☐	☐
_____	☐	☐	☐	☐	☐	☐	☐
_____	☐	☐	☐	☐	☐	☐	☐
_____	☐	☐	☐	☐	☐	☐	☐
_____	☐	☐	☐	☐	☐	☐	☐
_____	☐	☐	☐	☐	☐	☐	☐
_____	☐	☐	☐	☐	☐	☐	☐
_____	☐	☐	☐	☐	☐	☐	☐
_____	☐	☐	☐	☐	☐	☐	☐

Name _____

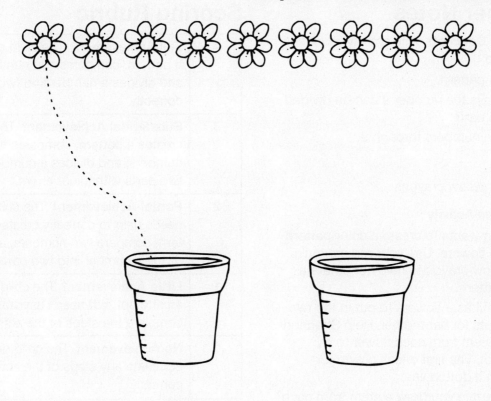

_____   _____

1 Color the flowers red and yellow to show a pattern.

2 Draw a stem from each flower to a flowerpot.
   Put flowers in both pots.

3 Count how many flowers are in each flowerpot.
   Write the number below each flowerpot.

4 Circle the number that is the least.

5 Write the numbers that show the way you made 9.

   _____ and _____

Teacher Notes

Skills and Concepts This activity requires children to:

- create a pattern.
- show ways the number 9 can be divided into two parts.
- compare numbers through 9.

Materials

- red and yellow crayons

Guiding the Activity

- Shannon wants to create a color pattern with the flowers. Use your red crayon and yellow crayon to help her create a color pattern.
- Shannon has 9 flowers to put in the two flowerpots for her mother. Help Shannon draw a stem from each flower to a flowerpot. The first one is drawn for you with a dotted line.
- Make certain you draw a stem from each flower to one of the pots.
- Each flowerpot must have some flowers in it.
- How many flowers did you put in each flowerpot?
- Write the number of flowers below each flowerpot.
- Draw a circle around the number that is the least.
- Write the missing numbers to show the way you made 9.

Answers

- Check that the child's colored flowers create a pattern. 1 stem should be drawn from each of the 9 flowers to one of the 2 flowerpots. The number of flowers in each pot should be written below each pot. The number that is the least should be circled. The number of flowers in each pot should be written to show how to make 9.

Scoring Rubric

4	**Full Achievement** The child creates a pattern, compares two numbers, and divides a number into two parts correctly.
3	**Substantial Achievement** The child creates a pattern, compares two numbers, and divides a number into two parts with minor errors.
2	**Partial Achievement** The child needs help to correctly create a pattern, compare two numbers, and divide a number into two parts.
1	**Little Achievement** The child makes an attempt, but needs assistance to complete the steps of the activity.
0	**No Achievement** The child does not complete any steps of the activity correctly.

Name _____

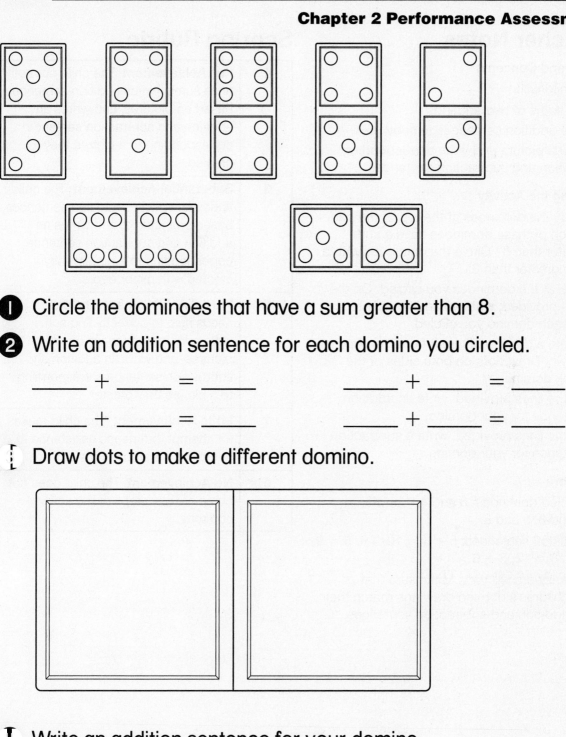

1 Circle the dominoes that have a sum greater than 8.

2 Write an addition sentence for each domino you circled.

_____ + _____ = _____   _____ + _____ = _____

_____ + _____ = _____   _____ + _____ = _____

3 Draw dots to make a different domino.

4 Write an addition sentence for your domino.

_____ + _____ = _____

5 Write a subtraction sentence for your domino.

_____ − _____ = _____

Teacher Notes

Skills and Concepts

The child will:

- find sums of two addends.
- write addition sentences to show joining.
- draw a picture and write corresponding addition and subtraction sentences.

Guiding the Activity

- Study the dominoes at the top of the page. Which of these dominoes have a sum greater than 8? Circle the dominoes with a sum greater than 8.
- Look at the dominoes you circled. On the lines provided, write an addition sentence for each domino you circled.
- Create a domino different from the ones shown. Draw dots on both sides of the blank domino.
- On the lines provided, write an addition sentence for your domino.
- On the lines provided, write a subtraction sentence for your domino.

Answers

1. Circled dominoes: 6 and 4, 4 and 5, 6 and 6, 5 and 6.

2. Addition sentences: $6 + 4 = 10$, $4 + 5 = 9$, $6 + 6 = 12$, $5 + 6 = 11$

3–5. Answers will vary. Make sure that children's domino drawings match their addition and subtraction sentences.

Scoring Rubric

4	**Full Achievement** The child correctly finds sums, writes addition sentences based on pictures, and writes an addition and subtraction sentence corresponding to a picture they created.
3	**Substantial Achievement** The child finds sums, writes addition sentences based on pictures, and writes an addition and subtraction sentence corresponding to a picture they created with minor errors.
2	**Partial Achievement** The child needs help to correctly find sums, write addition sentences based on pictures, and write an addition and subtraction sentence corresponding to a picture they create.
1	**Little Achievement** The child makes an attempt, but needs assistance to complete the steps of the activity.
0	**No Achievement** The child does not complete any steps of the activity correctly.

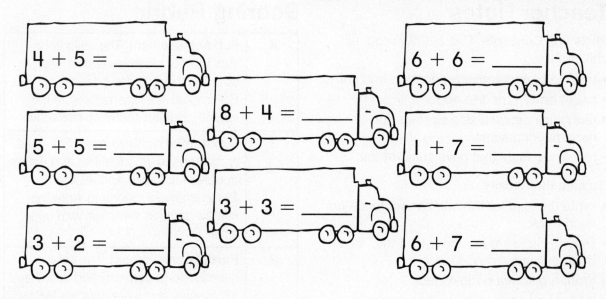

4 + 5 = _____

8 + 4 = _____

6 + 6 = _____

5 + 5 = _____

1 + 7 = _____

3 + 2 = _____

3 + 3 = _____

6 + 7 = _____

 Write the sum on each truck.

2 Circle the trucks that have doubles facts.

3 Write a different doubles fact on this truck.

_____ + _____ = _____

4 Write the sum on the first truck. Write the addition sentence another way on the other truck.

5 + 6 = _____

_____ + _____ = _____

5 Write a different addition sentence with a sum of 10 on each truck.

_____ + _____ = _____

_____ + _____ = _____

Teacher Notes

Skills and Concepts This activity requires children to:

- use the commutative property to find sums.
- count on 1, 2, or 3 to add.
- recognize doubles as a strategy for remembering sums.
- recognize facts that have sums of ten.

Guiding the Activity

- Write the sum for the number sentence on each truck.
- Draw a circle around the trucks that have doubles facts.
- Write a different doubles fact.
- Write the sum for the number sentence in the first truck.
- Show another way to write this number sentence in the second truck.
- Write two different addition sentences with sums of 10. Put one of the addition sentences on each truck.

Answers

1. $4 + 5 = 9$, $8 + 4 = 12$, $5 + 5 = 10$,
   $3 + 2 = 5$, $6 + 6 = 12$, $3 + 3 = 6$,
   $1 + 7 = 8$, $6 + 7 = 13$

2. Trucks with $5 + 5 = 10$, $6 + 6 = 12$,
   $3 + 3 = 6$ should be circled.

3. Answers will vary but must be a doubles fact that is not shown: $4 + 4 = 8$,
   $3 + 3 = 6$, etc.

4. $5 + 6 = 11$, $6 + 5 = 11$

5. Answers will vary. Addition facts must have a sum of 10, and the facts cannot be related.

Scoring Rubric

4	**Full Achievement** The child finds sums to 10, identifies and writes doubles facts, and applies the Commutative Property to write the related addition sentence correctly.
3	**Substantial Achievement** The child finds sums to 10, identifies and writes doubles facts, and applies the Commutative Property to write the related addition sentence with minor errors.
2	**Partial Achievement** The child needs help to correctly find sums to 10, identify and write doubles facts, or apply the Commutative Property to write the related addition sentence.
1	**Little Achievement** The child makes an attempt but needs assistance to complete the steps of the activity.
0	**No Achievement** The child does not complete any of the steps in the activity correctly.

Name _____

1 Draw less than 6 🍊 in the empty basket.

2 How many fewer oranges than apples are there?
Write a subtraction sentence to answer the question.

_____ – _____ = _____ fewer oranges

3 Write the fact family for the apples and oranges.

_____ + _____ = _____   _____ – _____ = _____

_____ + _____ = _____   _____ – _____ = _____

Teacher Notes

Skills and Concepts This activity requires students to:

- solve a problem by writing a subtraction sentence.
- write the addition and subtraction sentences that make up a fact family.
- review and apply concepts, skills, and strategies learned in this and previous chapters.

Guiding the Activity

- Look at the baskets at the top of the page. How many apples are in the basket? Draw some oranges in the empty basket. Draw fewer than six oranges.
- Count the apples and oranges. How many fewer oranges than apples are there? Write a subtraction sentence to answer this question.
- Write the fact family for the numbers of apples and oranges on the lines.

Answers

Sample answers are given.

1. Drawing of 2 oranges
2. 6 – 2 = 4 fewer oranges
3. 6 – 2 = 4, 6 – 4 = 2, 2 + 4 = 6, 4 + 2 = 6

Scoring Rubric

4	**Full Achievement** The child correctly draws less than six oranges in the empty basket, writes a subtraction sentence to answer the question, and writes all four related facts for the number of apples and oranges in the basket.
3	**Substantial Achievement** The child draws less than six oranges in the empty basket, writes a subtraction sentence to answer the question, and writes all four related facts for the number of apples and oranges in the basket with only a minor error.
2	**Partial Achievement** The child draws less than six oranges in the empty basket, writes a subtraction sentence to answer the question, and writes all four related facts for the number of fruit with errors.
1	**Little Achievement** The child needs assistance to draw less than six oranges in the empty basket, to write a subtraction sentence, or to write related facts.
0	**No Achievement** No attempt was made to accomplish the tasks.

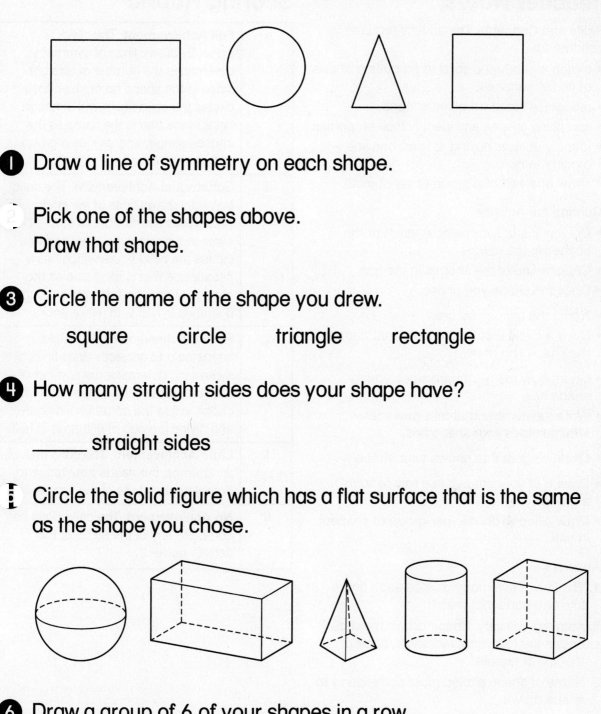

1 Draw a line of symmetry on each shape.

2 Pick one of the shapes above.
Draw that shape.

3 Circle the name of the shape you drew.

square   circle   triangle   rectangle

4 How many straight sides does your shape have?

_____ straight sides

5 Circle the solid figure which has a flat surface that is the same as the shape you chose.

6 Draw a group of 6 of your shapes in a row.
Draw a line to divide the group in half.

Teacher Notes

Skills and Concepts The activity requires children to:

- match a geometric solid to an outline of one of its flat surfaces.
- recognize standard plane shapes.
- sort plane shapes and identify their properties.
- identify objects having at least one line of symmetry.
- show one-half of a group of six objects.

Guiding the Activity

- Draw a line of symmetry on each of the shapes in the row.
- Choose one of the shapes in the row.
- Draw the shape you chose.

- Name the shape you drew.
- Draw a circle around the word that names the shape you drew.

- Count how many straight sides your shape has.
- Write the number that tells how many straight sides your shape has.

- Circle a figure that shows your shape.

- Draw 6 of your shapes in a row to form a group.
- Draw a line to divide your group of shapes in half.

Answers

1. The line of symmetry divides each figure into two parts that match.
2. Answers will vary. Shape drawn must be one of the following: rectangle, circle, triangle or square.
3. Name of shape circled must correspond to shape drawn.
4. Answers will vary, but must correspond to shape drawn. Possible answers are 0, 3, or 4.
5. Answers will vary; the solid chosen has a face like shape drawn. Rectangular prism may be circled for rectangle or square.
6. Answers will vary, but shapes drawn replicate original shape drawn. Line drawn must divide group of shapes into two sets of three.

Scoring Rubric

4	**Full Achievement** The child correctly draws lines of symmetry, determines the number of straight sides in the shape he or she chose, circles the solid figure which has a flat surface that is the same as the chosen shape, and divides a group of 6 shapes in half.
3	**Substantial Achievement** The child correctly draws lines of symmetry, determines the number of straight sides in the shape he or she chose, circles the solid figure which has a flat surface that is the same as the chosen shape, and divides a group of 6 shapes in half with minor errors.
2	**Partial Achievement** The child needs help to correctly draw lines of symmetry, determine the number of straight sides of the shape he or she chose, circle the correct solid figure, and divide a group of 6 shapes in half.
1	**Little Achievement** The child makes an attempt, but needs assistance to complete the steps of the activity.
0	**No Achievement** The child does not complete any of the steps of the activity correctly.

Name _____

1   2   3

_____   _____   _____

1 Write the time under each picture to tell when the activity
happened. Use these times.

8:00 morning   4:00 afternoon   9:30 night

2 Draw a circle around one of the above pictures.
Draw the hands on the clock face for
the time of that activity.
Write the time on the other clock.

3 Look at picture number 3.
Circle the month that goes with picture number 3.

July   September

February   May

4 Which month comes after May?

_____

Teacher Notes

Skills and Concepts

This activity requires students to:

- identify the hour and minute hands on a clock and tell time to the hour.
- determine whether an event takes place in the morning, afternoon, or night.
- identify and order the months of the year.

Guiding the Activity

- Look at the pictures of the activities at the top of the page.
- On the line under each picture write the time to tell when each activity happened. Use 8:00 morning, 4:00 afternoon, 9:30 night.

- Draw a circle around one of the pictures.
- Draw the hands on the clock face for the time of that activity.
- Write the time for the activity on the other clock.

- Look at picture number 3. Which month of the year does picture number 3 show? Circle the month from the four months shown.

- Which month comes after May? Write the month on the line.

Answers

1. 9:30 night, 8:00 morning, 4:00 afternoon
2. Answers for activity circled will vary. Time drawn on clocks must correspond to activity circled.
3. February
4. June

Scoring Rubric

4	**Full Achievement** The child correctly labels the three pictures with the appropriate time of day, shows the time on an analog and digital clock for the chosen picture, chooses a winter month, and identifies June as the month that follows May.
3	**Substantial Achievement** The child labels the three pictures, shows the time on an analog and digital clock for a chosen picture, chooses a winter month, or names June as the month that follows May with only minor errors.
2	**Partial Achievement** The child may need help to label the three pictures with the appropriate time of the day, show the time on an analog and digital clock for a chosen picture, choose a winter month, and name June as the month that follows May.
1	**Little Achievement** The child makes an attempt, but needs assistance to complete the steps of the activity.
0	**No Achievement** The child does not complete any of the steps of the activity correctly.

Name _____

50 51 52 53 54 55 56 57 58 59

① Write 3 **even** mailbox numbers.   _____ , _____ , _____

② Write 3 **odd** mailbox numbers.   _____ , _____ , _____

③ Write the number that comes after 59.   _____

④ Write the number that comes before 50.   _____

⑤ Write the numbers that come between. 54, _____ , _____ , 57

⑥ Circle 2 mailboxes at the top of
the page. Write the numbers you
chose on these 2 mailboxes

Show each number as groups of 10 and some left over.

_____
mailbox number

_____
mailbox number

⑦ Write each number as groups of 10 and some left over.

_____ is _____ groups of 10 and _____ left over.
mailbox number

_____ is _____ groups of 10 and _____ left over.
mailbox number

Teacher Notes

Skills and Concepts

This activity requires children to:

- make and count groups of tens and leftovers.
- write the numbers before, after, or between the given numbers.
- determine if a number less than 60 is odd or even.

Guiding the Activity

- Look at the numbers on the mailboxes at the top of the page.
- Write three mailbox numbers that are even.
- Write three mailbox numbers that are odd.
- Write the number that comes after 59.

- Write the number that comes before 50.
- Write the numbers that come between 54 and 57.

- Write the numbers of the mailboxes you circled.
- Show each of your numbers as groups of tens and some left over.
- Write each of your numbers as groups of tens and some left over.

Answers

1. Answers will vary. Possible answers are 50, 52, 54, 56, 58.
2. Answers will vary. Possible answers are 51, 53, 55, 57, 59.
3. 60
4. 49
5. 55, 56
6–8. Answers will vary. Groups of 10 and some left over must correspond to numbers on circled mailboxes. Sample answer: 51; 5 groups of 10 and 1 leftover is shown; **5** groups of 10 and **1** left over.

Scoring Rubric

4	**Full Achievement** The child correctly identifies even and odd numbers, writes the numbers before, after, and between given numbers, pictures and writes numbers as groups of 10 and some left over.
3	**Substantial Achievement** The child identifies even and odd numbers and writes the numbers before, after, and between given numbers with minor errors. The child may have difficulty picturing and writing the numbers as groups of 10 and some left over.
2	**Partial Achievement** The child needs help to correctly identify even and odd numbers, write the numbers before, after, and between given numbers, and picture the numbers as groups of 10 and some left over.
1	**Little Achievement** The child makes an attempt, but needs assistance to complete the steps of the activity.
0	**No Achievement** The child does not complete any of the steps of the activity correctly.

Name _____

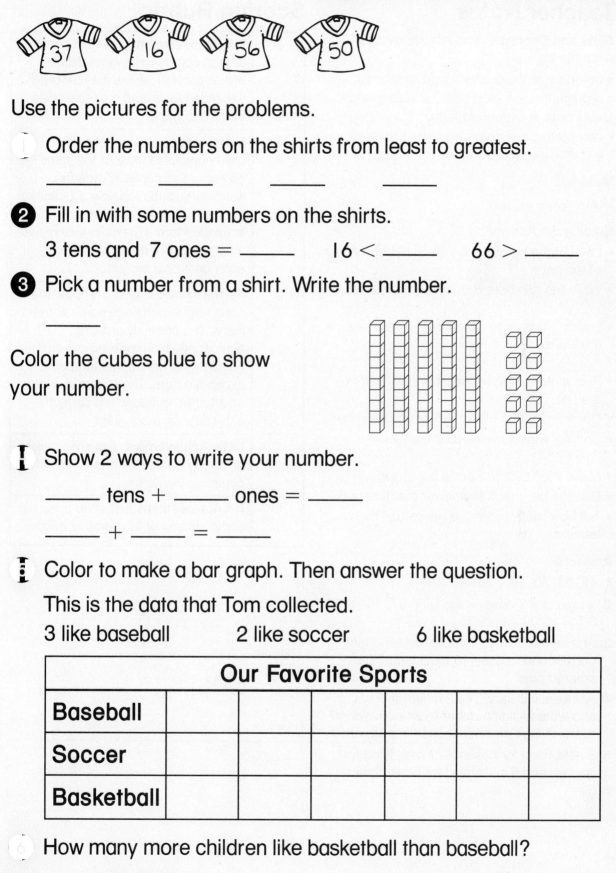

Use the pictures for the problems.

1 Order the numbers on the shirts from least to greatest.

_____   _____   _____   _____

2 Fill in with some numbers on the shirts.

3 tens and 7 ones = _____   16 < _____   66 > _____

3 Pick a number from a shirt. Write the number.

_____

Color the cubes blue to show
your number.

4 Show 2 ways to write your number.

_____ tens + _____ ones = _____

_____ + _____ = _____

5 Color to make a bar graph. Then answer the question.

This is the data that Tom collected.

3 like baseball   2 like soccer   6 like basketball

Our Favorite Sports					
Baseball					
Soccer					
Basketball					

6 How many more children like basketball than baseball?

_____ children

Teacher Notes

Skills and Concepts This activity requires students to:

- compare and order two-digit numbers.
- represent a two-digit number with models and write in expanded form.
- complete a bar graph and use it to answer a question.

Materials

blue crayon

Guiding the Activity

- Look at the numbers on the shirts at the top of the page.
- Write the numbers from least to greatest.

- Use >, <, or = to compare the numbers on the shirts.

- Pick a number from a shirt and write it on the line.
- Color the cubes blue to show your number.
- Show 2 ways to write your number.

- Make the Favorite Sports bar graph.
- Use the bar graph to answer the question.
- Tell how many more like basketball than baseball.

Answers

1. 16, 37, 50, 56
2. 3 tens and 7 ones = 37; 16 < 37, 50, or 56; 66 > 16, 37, 50, or 56
3. Answers will vary. Number chosen must correspond to base 10 blocks that are colored blue.
4. Answers will vary. The 2 different ways to show the 2-digit number must correspond to the 2-digit number chosen in problem 3.
5. 3 cells filled for baseball, 2 cells filled for soccer, and 6 cells filled for basketball
6. 3

Scoring Rubric

4	**Full Achievement** The child correctly orders, compares, and models a 2-digit number, writes the number in expanded form, and organizes data into a bar graph.
3	**Substantial Achievement** The child completes most of the items correctly, i.e., correctly ordering, comparing, and modeling a 2-digit number and writing the number in expanded form. The child may make an attempt, but does not correctly enter data on a bar graph.
2	**Partial Achievement** The child may need help to complete some of the items, i.e., correctly ordering, comparing, and modeling a 2-digit number and writing the number in expanded form. The child may make an attempt, but does not correctly enter data on a bar graph.
1	**Little Achievement** The child makes an attempt, but needs assistance to complete the items.
0	**No Achievement** The child does not complete any of the items correctly.

Name _____

Bananas	Oranges	Apples	Grapes

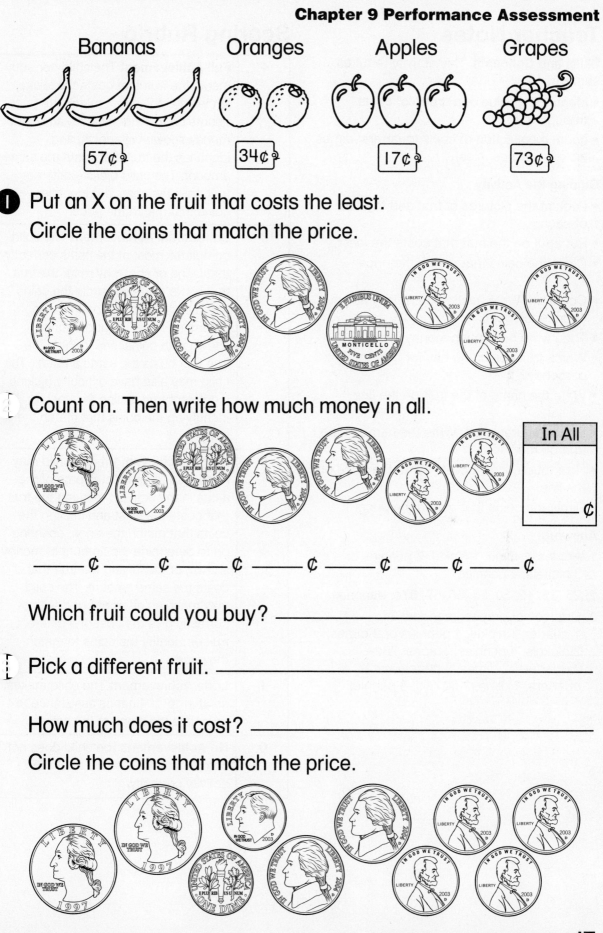

57¢   34¢   17¢   73¢

1 Put an X on the fruit that costs the least.
Circle the coins that match the price.

2 Count on. Then write how much money in all.

In All

_____ ¢

_____ ¢ _____ ¢ _____ ¢ _____ ¢ _____ ¢ _____ ¢ _____ ¢

Which fruit could you buy? _____

3 Pick a different fruit. _____

How much does it cost? _____

Circle the coins that match the price.

Teacher Notes

Skills and Concepts This activity requires students to:

- identify the value of a group of coins through 99¢.
- count a collection of coins (quarters, dimes, nickels, and pennies).

Guiding the Activity

- Look at the pictures of fruit and the cost of each.
- Put an *X* on the fruit that costs the least.
- Circle the coins that match the price.

- Count on. Write how much money as you count each coin.
- Then write how much money in all.
- Which fruit could you buy for this amount of money?
- Write the name of the fruit on the line.

- Pick a different fruit. Write the name of the fruit on the line.
- How much does it cost? Write the price on the line.
- Circle the coins that match the price.

Answers

1. Apples; 1 dime, 1 nickel, 2 pennies or 3 nickels, 2 pennies
2. 25, 35, 45, 50, 55, 56, 57; 57¢; bananas
3. Oranges or grapes; oranges: 34¢— 1 quarter, 1 nickel, 4 pennies or 2 dimes, 2 nickels, 4 pennies; grapes: 73¢— 2 quarters, 2 dimes, 3 pennies or 2 quarters, 1 dime, 2 nickels, 3 pennies

Scoring Rubric

4	**Full Achievement** The child correctly marks the fruit that costs the least, circles the coins that match the price, counts on to determine the amount of money shown with coins, and identifies the fruit that costs the same amount. The child picks a different fruit, tells the cost, and identifies coins that match the price.
3	**Substantial Achievement** The child completes most of the items correctly, that is, he or she, may mark the fruit that costs the least, circle the coins that match the price, count on to determine the amount of money shown with coins, and identify the fruit that costs the same amount. The child may also have difficulty picking a different fruit, telling the cost, or identifying the coins that match the price.
2	**Partial Achievement** The child may need help to complete some of the items in the activity: marking the fruit that costs the least and circling the coins that match the price, counting on to determine the amount of money shown, or identifying the fruit that costs the same amount. The child may make an attempt but does not correctly give the cost of a different fruit or identify the coins to match the price.
1	**Little Achievement** The child makes an attempt but needs assistance to complete the steps of the activity.
0	**No Achievement** The child does not complete any of the steps of the activity correctly.

Name _____

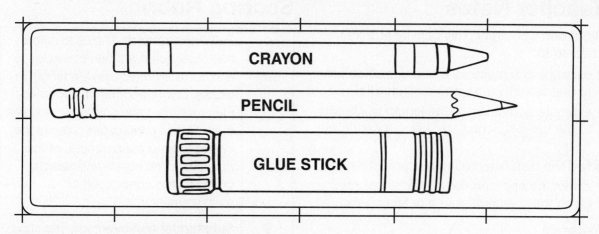

Use the pictures for problems 1–4.

 Color one object in the box orange.

Write the name of the object. _____

Estimate the length in inches. About ____ inches

Use an inch ruler to measure the length. ____ inches

2 Color another object green. Write the name of the object.

_____

Estimate the length in centimeters. About ____ centimeters

Use a centimeter ruler to measure the length.

____ centimeters

3 Count how many inches around the box of school supplies.

____ inches

4 Circle an object in the box.
Would you measure the object in
grams or kilograms? Circle your answer.   grams   kilograms

Chapter 10 Performance Assessment

Teacher Notes

Skills and Concepts This activity requires children to:

- estimate and measure the length of objects to the nearest inch using an inch ruler.
- estimate and measure the length of objects to the nearest centimeter using a centimeter ruler.
- find the distance around a shape in inches.
- select the appropriate unit for measuring, given the choice of grams or kilograms.

Materials

- orange and green crayons
- inch rulers
- centimeter rulers

Guiding the Activity

- Look at the objects in the box of school supplies at the top of the page.
- Color one object orange.
- Estimate the length of the object in inches.
- Write your estimate on the line.
- Use an inch ruler to measure the length of the orange object.
- Write the length on the line.
- Color another object green.
- Estimate the length of the object in centimeters.
- Write your estimate on the line.
- Use a centimeter ruler to measure the length of the green object.
- Write the length on the line.
- Count how many inches around the box.
- Write the number of inches on the line.
- Circle one of the objects in the box.
- Would you measure the object in grams or kilograms?
- Circle your answer.

Answers

Problems 1 and 2: Estimates will vary.
Actual measurements:
glue stick; 3 inches; 7 or 8 centimeters
crayon; 4 inches; 10 or 11 centimeters
pencil; 5 inches; 12 or 13 centimeters

3. 16 inches

4. grams

Scoring Rubric

4	**Full Achievement** The child colors one object orange, then estimates and correctly measures the length in inches; colors another object green, then estimates and correctly measures the length in centimeters; counts the inches around the perimeter of the box, circles an object and selects grams as the correct unit of measurement.
3	**Substantial Achievement** The child completes most of the items correctly, that is, he or she, may color one object orange, then estimate and measure the length in inches; color another object green, then estimate and measure the length in centimeters. The child may have difficulty either counting the inches around the perimeter of the box or circling an object and selecting grams as the correct unit of measure.
2	**Partial Achievement** The child may need help to complete some of the items in the activity, that is, coloring one object orange, then estimating and measuring the length in inches; coloring another object green, then estimating and measuring the length in centimeters. The child may make an attempt, but does not correctly count the inches around the perimeter of the box, nor circle an object and select grams as the correct unit of measure.
1	**Little Achievement** The child makes an attempt but needs assistance to complete the steps of the activity.
0	**No Achievement** The child does not complete any of the steps of the activity correctly.

Name _____

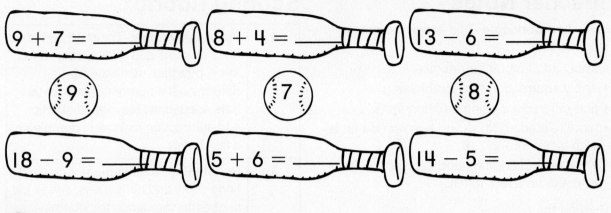

9 + 7 = _____

8 + 4 = _____

13 − 6 = _____

9

7

8

18 − 9 = _____

5 + 6 = _____

14 − 5 = _____

1　Write the sum or difference on each baseball bat.

2　How many bats are there? _____ bats

3　The team has 14 players. How many more bats are needed so each player will have one? Write a subtraction sentence to answer the question.

_____ − _____ = _____ more bats

4　Circle a bat with an addition sentence.
Write a related subtraction sentence.

_____ − _____ = _____

5　Circle 2 of the baseballs.

Write the numbers. _____ and _____
Use your numbers to make a fact family.

6　Write 2 addition facts for the fact family.

_____ + _____ = _____　　_____ + _____ = _____

7　Now write 2 subtraction facts for the fact family.

_____ − _____ = _____　　_____ − _____ = _____

Teacher Notes

Skills and Concepts This activity requires children to:

- apply addition fact strategies.
- apply subtraction fact strategies.
- find differences using addition facts.
- write related addition and subtraction facts with sums through 18.
- write related addition and subtraction facts to make up a fact family.

Guiding the Activity

- Look at the baseball bats at the top of the page.
- Write the sum or difference on each baseball bat.

- Count the baseball bats. Write the number on the line.
- The team has 14 players. How many more bats are needed so each player will have one bat?
- Write a subtraction sentence to show how many more bats are needed.

- Circle one of the bats with an addition sentence.
- Write a related subtraction sentence.

- Circle two of the baseballs. Write the numbers on the lines.
- Use the numbers to make a fact family.
- Write two addition facts for the fact family.
- Write two subtraction facts for the fact family.

Scoring Rubric

4	**Full Achievement** The child correctly finds all sums and differences, writes the subtraction sentence to determine the number of additional bats needed, writes related addition and subtraction facts, and completes a fact family.
3	**Substantial Achievement** The child finds sums and differences, writes the subtraction sentence to determine the number of additional bats needed, writes related addition and subtraction facts, and completes a fact family with minor errors.
2	**Partial Achievement** The child may need help to find the sums and differences, to write the correct subtraction sentence to determine the number of additional bats needed, to write a related subtraction fact, or to complete a fact family.
1	**Little Achievement** The child makes an attempt but needs assistance to complete the steps of the activity.
0	**No Achievement** The child does not complete any of the steps of the activity correctly.

Answers

1. $9 + 7 = 16$; $8 + 4 = 12$; $13 - 6 = 7$; $18 - 9 = 9$; $5 + 6 = 11$; $14 - 5 = 9$

2. 6

3. $14 - 6 = 8$ more bats

4. Answers will vary. Possible answers: $12 - 4 = 8$ and $12 - 8 = 4$; or $16 - 9 = 7$ and $16 - 7 = 9$; or $11 - 5 = 6$ and $11 - 6 = 5$.

5. Answers will vary. Possible answers: 9 and 7; or 9 and 8; or 7 and 8.

6. Possible answers for addition fact families: $9 + 7 = 16$ and $7 + 9 = 16$; or $9 + 8 = 17$ and $8 + 9 = 17$; or $7 + 8 = 15$ and $8 + 7 = 15$.

7. Possible answers for subtraction facts: $16 - 9 = 7$ and $16 - 7 = 9$; or $17 - 9 = 8$ and $17 - 8 = 9$; or $15 - 7 = 8$ and $15 - 8 = 7$.

Name _____

Bags of Marbles

Box 1   22 50 30 67   Box 2   6 8 7 9

1 Look at the bags of marbles in Box 1.

Write the largest number. _____

Write the smallest number. _____

Add the numbers.

Tens	Ones
+	

2 Pick a number from Box 1 that ends in zero.

Write the number. _____

Use the number in these sentences and find the sum or difference.

20 + _____ = _____

49 + _____ = _____

70 – _____ = _____

97 – _____ = _____

3 Color 1 bag in each box yellow.

Write the numbers of the bags.   _____ and _____

Do you need to regroup to add these numbers?

Circle yes or no.   yes   no

Write an addition sentence.   _____ + _____ = _____

4 Color 1 bag in each box blue.

Write the numbers of the bags.   _____ and _____

Do you need to regroup to subtract these numbers?

Circle yes or no.   yes   no

Tens	Ones
–	

Write a subtraction problem. Find the difference.

Teacher Notes

Skills and Concepts This activity requires children to:

- add multiples of 10 for sums to 100.
- add tens to a two-digit number.
- add two-digit numbers without regrouping.
- add a one-digit number and a two-digit number with and without regrouping.
- subtract a multiple of 10 from a multiple of 10, 100 or less.
- subtract a multiple of 10 from a two-digit number.
- subtract a one-digit number from a two-digit number with and without regrouping.

Materials

- yellow and blue crayons
- base 10 blocks (optional)

Guiding the Activity

- Look at the bags of marbles in Box 1 at the top of the page.
- Write the largest number. Write the smallest number.
- Add the numbers to find the sum.

- Pick a number from Box 1 with a zero.
- Write the number.
- Use the number in each sentence and find the sum or difference.

- Color 1 bag of marbles in each box yellow.
- Write the numbers.
- Do you need to regroup to add these numbers?
- Circle yes or no.
- Write an addition sentence and solve.

- Color another bag of marbles in each box blue.
- Write the numbers.
- Do you need to regroup to subtract these numbers?
- Circle yes or no.
- Write the subtraction sentence and solve.

Answers

1. $67 + 22 = 89$ **3.** Answers will vary.

2. Answers will vary.   **4.** Answers will vary.

Scoring Rubric

4	**Full Achievement** The child correctly writes and solves addition and subtraction sentences and regroups when necessary. He or she chooses the correct numbers to write the addition and subtraction sentences.
3	**Substantial Achievement** The child writes and solves addition and subtraction sentences and regroups with minor errors. He or she chooses the correct numbers to write the addition and subtraction sentences.
2	**Partial Achievement** The child may need help to write and solve addition or subtraction sentences. He or she may choose the correct numbers to add and subtract but have difficulty knowing when to regroup.
1	**Little Achievement** The child makes an attempt but needs assistance to complete the steps of the activity.
0	**No Achievement** The child does not complete any of the steps of the activity correctly.

Basic-Facts Timed Tests

Purpose
The purpose of the Basic-Facts Timed Test is to provide students with practice of the basic facts that they may encounter in the corresponding chapter. Rapid recall of basic addition, subtraction, multiplication, and division facts will give students confidence when learning new material. For instance, being proficient in basic addition and multiplication facts will eliminate frustration and increase accuracy as students learn to do addition and multiplication computation.

The Basic-Facts Timed Tests are designed so that they can be given in a variety of formats, and can be used as often as needed.

• Tests can be used as written tests.

• Tests can be given orally and the students respond orally.

• Tests can be given orally and the students record their response.

When giving the test orally, teachers can state the facts in order shown on each test, in reverse order, or in random order.

Time Limit for the Tests
It is important to consider the amount of time that students should be given to complete each test. You may want to consider your students' proficiency when deciding on how much time to allow.

• If a student is proficient, time how long it initially takes the student to complete a timed test and use that time as a goal time.

• If a student struggles with rapid recall, allow the student enough time to complete the test so the student gets practice with out being frustrated.

• As accuracy increases, challenge the student to a new goal time. Be careful not to make the goal time unattainable.

Additional Material Available
The Core Manipulative Kits contain Basic-Facts Flash Cards on key rings that can be used to supplement the Basic-Facts Timed Tests. The Kit for Grade 1 and Grade 2 contains addition, subtraction, and multiplication flash cards. The Kits for Grade 3 through Grade 6 contain multiplication and division flash cards.

Name _____

Give each answer.

1. $7 + 2 =$ _____

2. $3 + 1 =$ _____

3. $2 + 2 =$ _____

4. $4 + 1 =$ _____

5. $8 + 2 =$ _____

6. $5 + 3 =$ _____

7. $6 + 1 =$ _____

8. $3 + 2 =$ _____

9. $4 + 2 =$ _____

10. $8 + 1 =$ _____

11. $6 + 3 =$ _____

12. $5 + 1 =$ _____

13. $7 - 3 =$ _____

14. $6 - 1 =$ _____

15. $9 - 2 =$ _____

16. $8 - 3 =$ _____

17. $6 - 2 =$ _____

18. $10 - 1 =$ _____

19. $7 - 2 =$ _____

20. $9 - 3 =$ _____

21. $4 - 2 =$ _____

22. $11 - 3 =$ _____

23. $10 - 1 =$ _____

24. $11 - 2 =$ _____

25. $8 - 2 =$ _____

Name _____

Give each answer.

1. $2 + 7 =$ _____

2. $6 + 1 =$ _____

3. $2 + 4 =$ _____

4. $4 + 0 =$ _____

5. $8 + 1 =$ _____

6. $7 + 3 =$ _____

7. $6 + 1 =$ _____

8. $3 + 8 =$ _____

9. $10 + 2 =$ _____

10. $6 + 4 =$ _____

11. $9 + 3 =$ _____

12. $0 + 9 =$ _____

13. $7 - 3 =$ _____

14. $9 - 7 =$ _____

15. $12 - 5 =$ _____

16. $8 - 3 =$ _____

17. $7 - 2 =$ _____

18. $11 - 4 =$ _____

19. $7 - 4 =$ _____

20. $9 - 6 =$ _____

21. $10 - 2 =$ _____

22. $11 - 8 =$ _____

23. $10 - 1 =$ _____

24. $5 - 4 =$ _____

25. $10 - 6 =$ _____

Name _____

Give each answer.

1. $12 - 7 =$ _____

2. $10 - 9 =$ _____

3. $5 - 2 =$ _____

4. $7 - 2 =$ _____

5. $11 - 6 =$ _____

6. $8 - 4 =$ _____

7. $12 - 5 =$ _____

8. $7 - 3 =$ _____

9. $11 - 5 =$ _____

10. $10 - 7 =$ _____

11. $9 - 0 =$ _____

12. $7 - 1 =$ _____

13. $10 - 6 =$ _____

14. $6 + 5 =$ _____

15. $5 - 5 =$ _____

16. $8 - 3 =$ _____

17. $8 + 2 =$ _____

18. $11 - 7 =$ _____

19. $6 + 4 =$ _____

20. $9 - 2 =$ _____

21. $8 + 4 =$ _____

22. $11 - 10 =$ _____

23. $7 - 7 =$ _____

24. $6 + 1 =$ _____

25. $9 - 4 =$ _____

Name _____

Give each answer.

1. $7 + 8 =$ _____

2. $3 + 9 =$ _____

3. $8 + 3 =$ _____

4. $9 + 0 =$ _____

5. $8 + 5 =$ _____

6. $11 + 3 =$ _____

7. $6 + 9 =$ _____

8. $7 + 5 =$ _____

9. $11 + 2 =$ _____

10. $12 + 4 =$ _____

11. $6 + 6 =$ _____

12. $15 + 0 =$ _____

13. $12 - 9 =$ _____

14. $6 + 6 =$ _____

15. $14 - 9 =$ _____

16. $13 - 12 =$ _____

17. $16 - 10 =$ _____

18. $10 + 2 =$ _____

19. $13 - 7 =$ _____

20. $8 + 8 =$ _____

21. $14 - 3 =$ _____

22. $15 - 5 =$ _____

23. $8 + 4 =$ _____

24. $14 + 2 =$ _____

25. $13 - 1 =$ _____

Name _____

Give each answer.

1. $12 - 9 =$ _____

2. $10 - 3 =$ _____

3. $15 - 2 =$ _____

4. $7 - 1 =$ _____

5. $13 - 6 =$ _____

6. $16 - 4 =$ _____

7. $15 - 11 =$ _____

8. $9 - 8 =$ _____

9. $13 - 3 =$ _____

10. $8 - 6 =$ _____

11. $11 - 0 =$ _____

12. $14 - 6 =$ _____

13. $10 - 6 =$ _____

14. $7 + 8 =$ _____

15. $15 - 13 =$ _____

16. $12 - 3 =$ _____

17. $8 + 5 =$ _____

18. $11 - 7 =$ _____

19. $3 + 12 =$ _____

20. $16 - 11 =$ _____

21. $8 + 4 =$ _____

22. $11 - 5 =$ _____

23. $16 - 7 =$ _____

24. $10 + 4 =$ _____

25. $15 - 7 =$ _____

Name _____

Give each answer.

1. $8 + 7 =$ _____

2. $6 + 5 =$ _____

3. $9 + 4 =$ _____

4. $16 + 0 =$ _____

5. $8 + 3 =$ _____

6. $9 + 9 =$ _____

7. $6 + 7 =$ _____

8. $4 + 8 =$ _____

9. $11 + 2 =$ _____

10. $6 + 4 =$ _____

11. $3 + 11 =$ _____

12. $17 + 1 =$ _____

13. $16 - 6 =$ _____

14. $15 + 2 =$ _____

15. $18 - 5 =$ _____

16. $16 - 14 =$ _____

17. $6 + 12 =$ _____

18. $11 - 4 =$ _____

19. $5 + 10 =$ _____

20. $15 - 6 =$ _____

21. $17 - 14 =$ _____

22. $15 - 8 =$ _____

23. $18 - 12 =$ _____

24. $10 + 7 =$ _____

25. $11 - 6 =$ _____

Name _____

Give each answer.

1. $12 - 10 =$ _____

2. $18 - 3 =$ _____

3. $15 - 8 =$ _____

4. $17 - 14 =$ _____

5. $13 - 5 =$ _____

6. $16 - 2 =$ _____

7. $17 - 5 =$ _____

8. $18 - 9 =$ _____

9. $14 - 0 =$ _____

10. $16 - 9 =$ _____

11. $17 - 11 =$ _____

12. $18 - 8 =$ _____

13. $15 + 3 =$ _____

14. $11 + 4 =$ _____

15. $17 - 5 =$ _____

16. $12 - 8 =$ _____

17. $7 + 9 =$ _____

18. $11 - 7 =$ _____

19. $5 + 12 =$ _____

20. $16 - 11 =$ _____

21. $11 + 3 =$ _____

22. $11 - 10 =$ _____

23. $17 - 4 =$ _____

24. $12 + 4 =$ _____

25. $18 - 5 =$ _____

Name _____

Give each answer.

1. $10 + 8 =$ _____

2. $15 + 2 =$ _____

3. $4 + 14 =$ _____

4. $10 + 1 =$ _____

5. $8 + 4 =$ _____

6. $9 + 9 =$ _____

7. $5 + 12 =$ _____

8. $11 + 5 =$ _____

9. $3 + 14 =$ _____

10. $17 + 1 =$ _____

11. $3 + 13 =$ _____

12. $14 + 1 =$ _____

13. $16 - 6 =$ _____

14. $11 + 7 =$ _____

15. $18 - 5 =$ _____

16. $17 - 6 =$ _____

17. $9 + 8 =$ _____

18. $12 - 4 =$ _____

19. $15 - 10 =$ _____

20. $4 + 12 =$ _____

21. $18 - 9 =$ _____

22. $15 - 8 =$ _____

23. $18 - 7 =$ _____

24. $11 + 6 =$ _____

25. $13 + 3 =$ _____

Name _____

Give each answer.

1. $17 - 10 =$ _____

2. $10 - 10 =$ _____

3. $18 - 12 =$ _____

4. $16 - 14 =$ _____

5. $8 - 5 =$ _____

6. $16 - 5 =$ _____

7. $18 - 13 =$ _____

8. $17 - 9 =$ _____

9. $14 - 10 =$ _____

10. $16 - 4 =$ _____

11. $17 - 12 =$ _____

12. $18 - 11 =$ _____

13. $12 + 6 =$ _____

14. $11 + 4 =$ _____

15. $17 - 6 =$ _____

16. $18 - 13 =$ _____

17. $14 + 4 =$ _____

18. $16 - 4 =$ _____

19. $4 + 10 =$ _____

20. $16 - 11 =$ _____

21. $2 + 16 =$ _____

22. $16 - 10 =$ _____

23. $15 - 13 =$ _____

24. $12 + 4 =$ _____

25. $18 - 6 =$ _____

Name _____

Give each answer.

1. $9 + 8 =$ _____

2. $11 + 2 =$ _____

3. $4 + 10 =$ _____

4. $10 + 6 =$ _____

5. $8 + 5 =$ _____

6. $6 + 6 =$ _____

7. $5 + 11 =$ _____

8. $9 + 5 =$ _____

9. $3 + 12 =$ _____

10. $16 + 1 =$ _____

11. $4 + 9 =$ _____

12. $14 + 2 =$ _____

13. $15 - 5 =$ _____

14. $11 + 4 =$ _____

15. $16 - 5 =$ _____

16. $15 - 6 =$ _____

17. $9 + 7 =$ _____

18. $12 - 8 =$ _____

19. $14 - 10 =$ _____

20. $5 + 12 =$ _____

21. $16 - 8 =$ _____

22. $15 - 7 =$ _____

23. $13 - 7 =$ _____

24. $8 + 6 =$ _____

25. $12 + 4 =$ _____

Name _____

Give each answer.

1. $16 - 10 =$ _____

2. $8 - 8 =$ _____

3. $16 - 8 =$ _____

4. $17 - 14 =$ _____

5. $14 - 6 =$ _____

6. $13 - 8 =$ _____

7. $12 - 5 =$ _____

8. $17 - 8 =$ _____

9. $14 - 11 =$ _____

10. $16 - 7 =$ _____

11. $17 - 12 =$ _____

12. $13 - 6 =$ _____

13. $9 + 9 =$ _____

14. $8 + 9 =$ _____

15. $16 - 6 =$ _____

16. $18 - 9 =$ _____

17. $5 + 6 =$ _____

18. $16 - 4 =$ _____

19. $7 + 6 =$ _____

20. $15 - 7 =$ _____

21. $4 + 8 =$ _____

22. $16 - 7 =$ _____

23. $15 - 9 =$ _____

24. $7 + 7 =$ _____

25. $12 - 6 =$ _____

Name _____

Give each answer.

1. $8 + 8 =$ _____

2. $11 + 7 =$ _____

3. $4 + 11 =$ _____

4. $10 + 4 =$ _____

5. $8 + 9 =$ _____

6. $6 + 6 =$ _____

7. $5 + 8 =$ _____

8. $9 + 6 =$ _____

9. $2 + 12 =$ _____

10. $7 + 8 =$ _____

11. $4 + 9 =$ _____

12. $11 + 2 =$ _____

13. $14 - 4 =$ _____

14. $8 + 9 =$ _____

15. $11 - 5 =$ _____

16. $14 - 6 =$ _____

17. $9 + 7 =$ _____

18. $13 - 8 =$ _____

19. $15 - 10 =$ _____

20. $4 + 12 =$ _____

21. $16 - 8 =$ _____

22. $15 - 9 =$ _____

23. $16 - 7 =$ _____

24. $8 + 10 =$ _____

25. $7 + 8 =$ _____

Written Tests

Scott Foresman–Addison Wesley Mathematics provides you with written tests for each chapter of your mathematics program. There are two forms of a free-response test and two forms of a multiple-choice test. In addition, cumulative tests and Performance Assessments are provided. You may also want to distribute and discuss **"Tips for Test Taking"** (blackline master) with your students.

Diagnosing Readiness for Grade 1
This multiple-choice test may be used at the beginning of the school year to assess student mastery of the previous grade. The test items address

- Place Value, Numbers, and Money
- Basic Facts and Algebra Concepts
- Computation
- Measurement, Geometry Statistics, and Probability
- Problem Solving

Chapter Test: Free Response and Multiple Choice
Both forms of the Free-Response tests parallel the corresponding test in the Pupil Edition, item for item. See the Chapter Tests in the Teacher Edition for an item analysis. There are more questions for each objective on the Multiple-Choice Tests than on the Chapter Test in the Pupil Edition or on the Free-Response Tests. However, the lesson objectives are tested in the same order on the Multiple-Choice tests as on the Free-Response tests.

Cumulative Tests
There is a Cumulative Test after every three chapters in the Pupil Edition. Each test is a 4-page long multiple-choice test.

Tips for Test Taking

Following Instructions
- Listen carefully as your teacher explains the test.

Budget Your Time
- Do the questions in order if you can.
- If a question seems very hard, skip it and go back to it later.

Read Carefully
- Watch for extra information in a problem.
- Watch for words like *not.*
- Be sure to answer the questions asked.

Make Smart Choices
- Estimate when you can so that you have a better idea what the answer might be.
- Eliminate answer choices that are not reasonable or are clearly wrong.
- Check an answer that you think is correct by working backward.

Mark Answers Carefully
- If you are using a "bubble" response sheet or a gridded response form, be careful to match each question number with the correct number of the answer row.
- If you skip a question, be sure to leave that question's answer space blank.

Name_____

Date_____

1.	Ⓐ Ⓑ Ⓒ Ⓓ		21.	Ⓐ Ⓑ Ⓒ Ⓓ
2.	Ⓐ Ⓑ Ⓒ Ⓓ		22.	Ⓐ Ⓑ Ⓒ Ⓓ
3.	Ⓐ Ⓑ Ⓒ Ⓓ		23.	Ⓐ Ⓑ Ⓒ Ⓓ
4.	Ⓐ Ⓑ Ⓒ Ⓓ		24.	Ⓐ Ⓑ Ⓒ Ⓓ
5.	Ⓐ Ⓑ Ⓒ Ⓓ		25.	Ⓐ Ⓑ Ⓒ Ⓓ
6.	Ⓐ Ⓑ Ⓒ Ⓓ		26.	Ⓐ Ⓑ Ⓒ Ⓓ
7.	Ⓐ Ⓑ Ⓒ Ⓓ		27.	Ⓐ Ⓑ Ⓒ Ⓓ
8.	Ⓐ Ⓑ Ⓒ Ⓓ		28.	Ⓐ Ⓑ Ⓒ Ⓓ
9.	Ⓐ Ⓑ Ⓒ Ⓓ		29.	Ⓐ Ⓑ Ⓒ Ⓓ
10.	Ⓐ Ⓑ Ⓒ Ⓓ		30.	Ⓐ Ⓑ Ⓒ Ⓓ
11.	Ⓐ Ⓑ Ⓒ Ⓓ		31.	Ⓐ Ⓑ Ⓒ Ⓓ
12.	Ⓐ Ⓑ Ⓒ Ⓓ		32.	Ⓐ Ⓑ Ⓒ Ⓓ
13.	Ⓐ Ⓑ Ⓒ Ⓓ		33.	Ⓐ Ⓑ Ⓒ Ⓓ
14.	Ⓐ Ⓑ Ⓒ Ⓓ		34.	Ⓐ Ⓑ Ⓒ Ⓓ
15.	Ⓐ Ⓑ Ⓒ Ⓓ		35.	Ⓐ Ⓑ Ⓒ Ⓓ
16.	Ⓐ Ⓑ Ⓒ Ⓓ		36.	Ⓐ Ⓑ Ⓒ Ⓓ
17.	Ⓐ Ⓑ Ⓒ Ⓓ		37.	Ⓐ Ⓑ Ⓒ Ⓓ
18.	Ⓐ Ⓑ Ⓒ Ⓓ		38.	Ⓐ Ⓑ Ⓒ Ⓓ
19.	Ⓐ Ⓑ Ⓒ Ⓓ		39.	Ⓐ Ⓑ Ⓒ Ⓓ
20.	Ⓐ Ⓑ Ⓒ Ⓓ		40.	Ⓐ Ⓑ Ⓒ Ⓓ

Name _____

Which figures show the sorting rule?

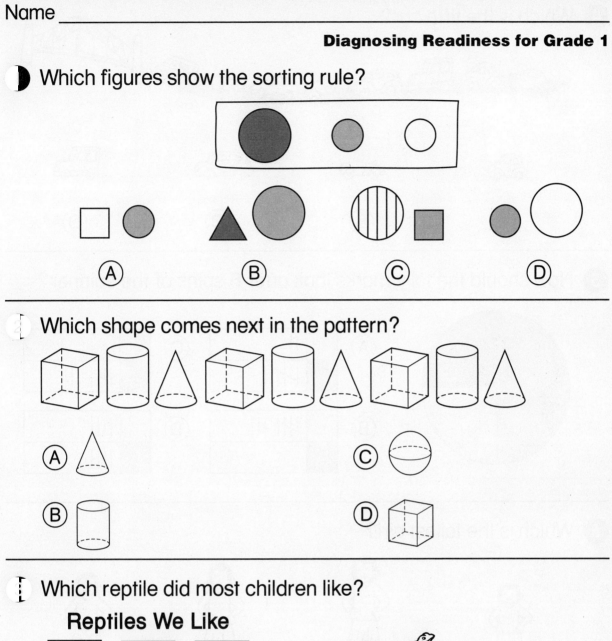

    Ⓐ   Ⓑ   Ⓒ   Ⓓ

Which shape comes next in the pattern?

Ⓐ   Ⓒ

Ⓑ   Ⓓ

Which reptile did most children like?

Reptiles We Like

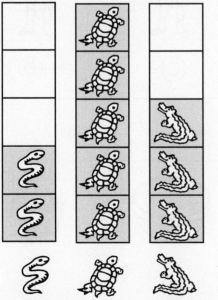

Ⓐ

Ⓑ

Ⓒ

Ⓓ

Which is the fifth car?

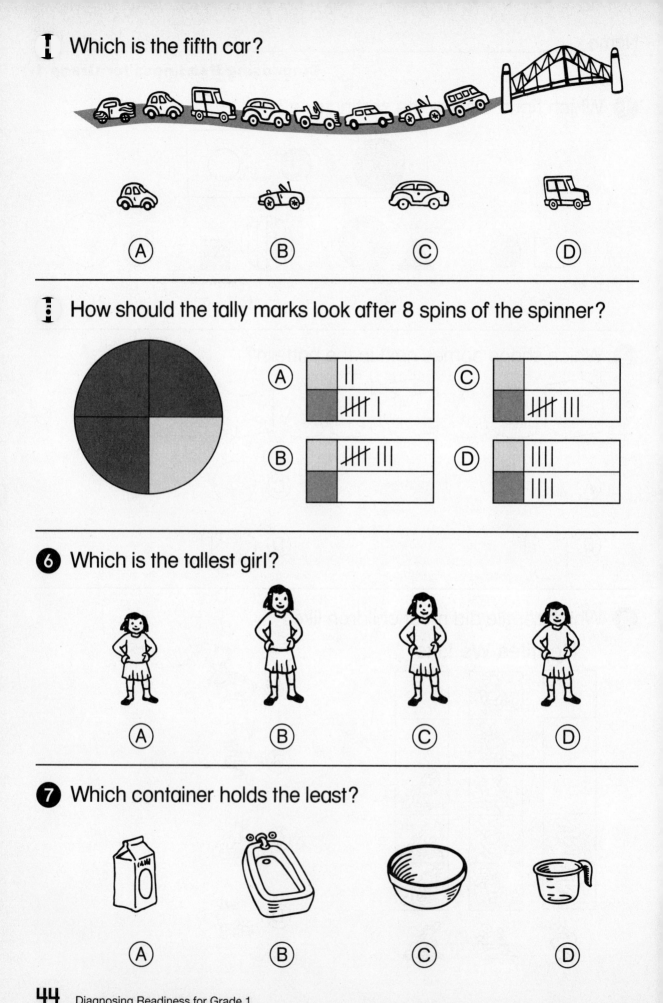

Ⓐ   Ⓑ   Ⓒ   Ⓓ

How should the tally marks look after 8 spins of the spinner?

Ⓐ   Ⓒ

Ⓑ   Ⓓ

6 Which is the tallest girl?

Ⓐ   Ⓑ   Ⓒ   Ⓓ

7 Which container holds the least?

Ⓐ   Ⓑ   Ⓒ   Ⓓ

8 Which is the missing number?

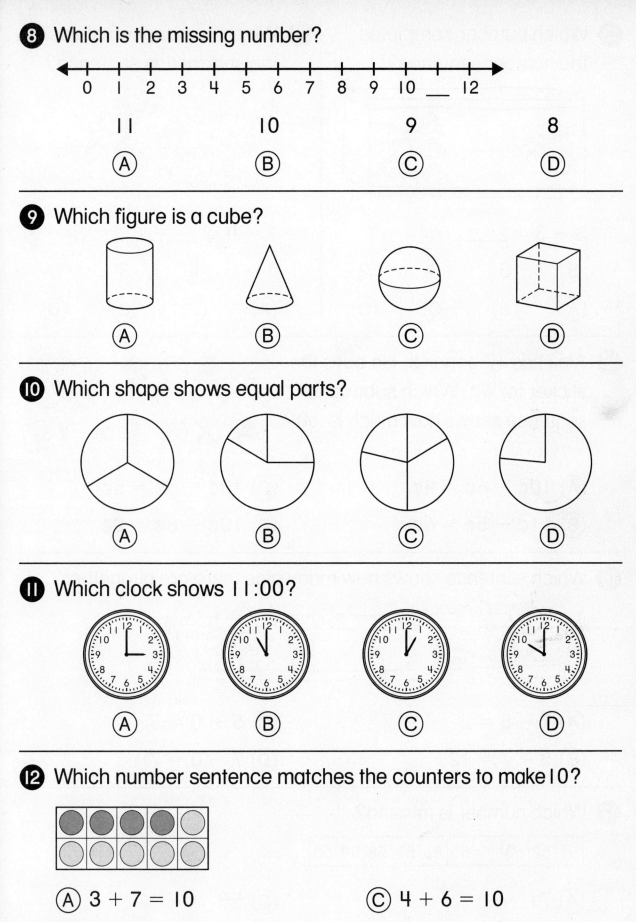

0 1 2 3 4 5 6 7 8 9 10 ___ 12

11	10	9	8
Ⓐ	Ⓑ	Ⓒ	Ⓓ

9 Which figure is a cube?

Ⓐ　　　Ⓑ　　　Ⓒ　　　Ⓓ

10 Which shape shows equal parts?

Ⓐ　　　Ⓑ　　　Ⓒ　　　Ⓓ

11 Which clock shows 11:00?

Ⓐ　　　Ⓑ　　　Ⓒ　　　Ⓓ

12 Which number sentence matches the counters to make 10?

Ⓐ 3 + 7 = 10　　　　　Ⓒ 4 + 6 = 10

Ⓑ 5 + 5 = 10　　　　　Ⓓ 2 + 8 = 10

13 Which number completes the number sentence?

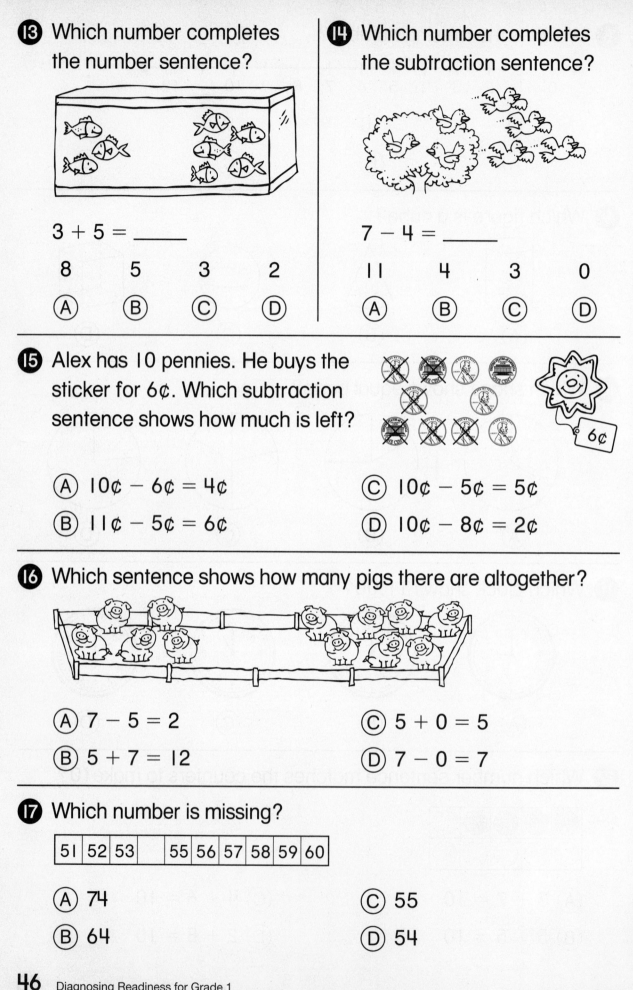

3 + 5 = _____

8	5	3	2
Ⓐ	Ⓑ	Ⓒ	Ⓓ

14 Which number completes the subtraction sentence?

7 − 4 = _____

11	4	3	0
Ⓐ	Ⓑ	Ⓒ	Ⓓ

---

15 Alex has 10 pennies. He buys the sticker for 6¢. Which subtraction sentence shows how much is left?

Ⓐ 10¢ − 6¢ = 4¢   Ⓒ 10¢ − 5¢ = 5¢

Ⓑ 11¢ − 5¢ = 6¢   Ⓓ 10¢ − 8¢ = 2¢

---

16 Which sentence shows how many pigs there are altogether?

Ⓐ 7 − 5 = 2   Ⓒ 5 + 0 = 5

Ⓑ 5 + 7 = 12   Ⓓ 7 − 0 = 7

---

17 Which number is missing?

51	52	53		55	56	57	58	59	60

Ⓐ 74   Ⓒ 55

Ⓑ 64   Ⓓ 54

Name _____

1 Circle the picture that comes next in the pattern.

2 Circle the number that tells how many.

3 Count the animals. Write how many.

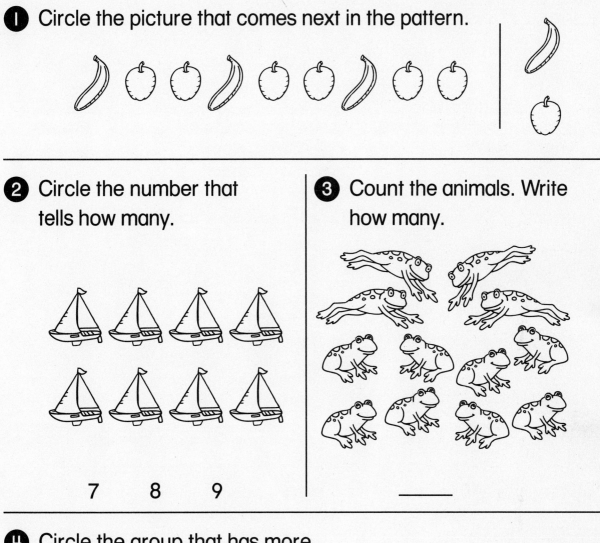

7 8 9

_____

4 Circle the group that has more.

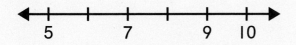

5 Write the missing numbers.

5   7   9 10

____ ____ ____

Name _____

Write the numbers that show ways to make 7.

1

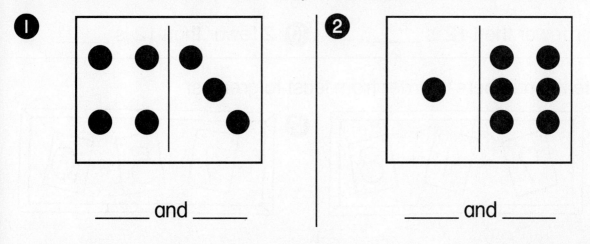

_____ and _____

2

_____ and _____

Write the numbers that show ways to make 10.

3

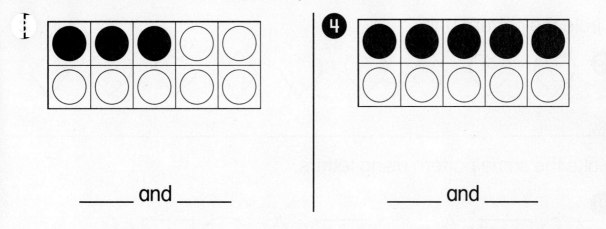

_____ and _____

4

_____ and _____

Write one way to put 6 pennies into 2 piles.

5 _____ and _____

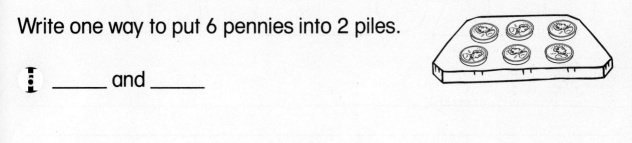

Circle **more** or **fewer.**

6 8 is _____ than 10.   **more**   **fewer**

Write the numbers.

7 8 and 1 more is _____.   **8** 9 and 2 more is _____.

9 1 fewer than 12 is _____.   **10** 2 fewer than 12 is _____.

Write the numbers in order from least to greatest.

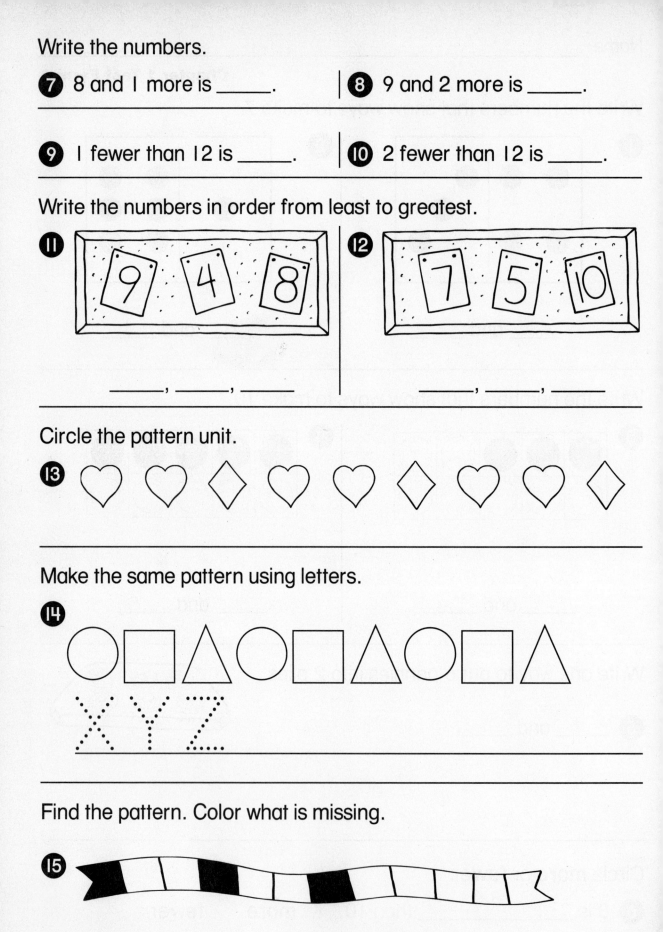

11 9   4   8

12 7   5   10

_____, _____, _____   _____, _____, _____

Circle the pattern unit.

13 ♡ ♡ ◇ ♡ ♡ ◇ ♡ ♡ ◇

Make the same pattern using letters.

14 ○ □ △ ○ □ △ ○ □ △

X Y Z

Find the pattern. Color what is missing.

15

Name _____

Write the numbers that show ways to make 6.

1

_____ and _____

2

_____ and _____

Write the numbers that show ways to make 10.

3

_____ and _____

4

_____ and _____

Write one way to put
11 paper clips into 2 piles.

5 _____ and _____

Circle **more** or **fewer.**

6 9 is _____ than 10.   **more   fewer**

Write the numbers.

7 7 and 1 more is _____. | **8** 7 and 2 more is _____.

9 1 fewer than 10 is _____. | **10** 2 fewer than 10 is _____.

Write the numbers in order from least to greatest.

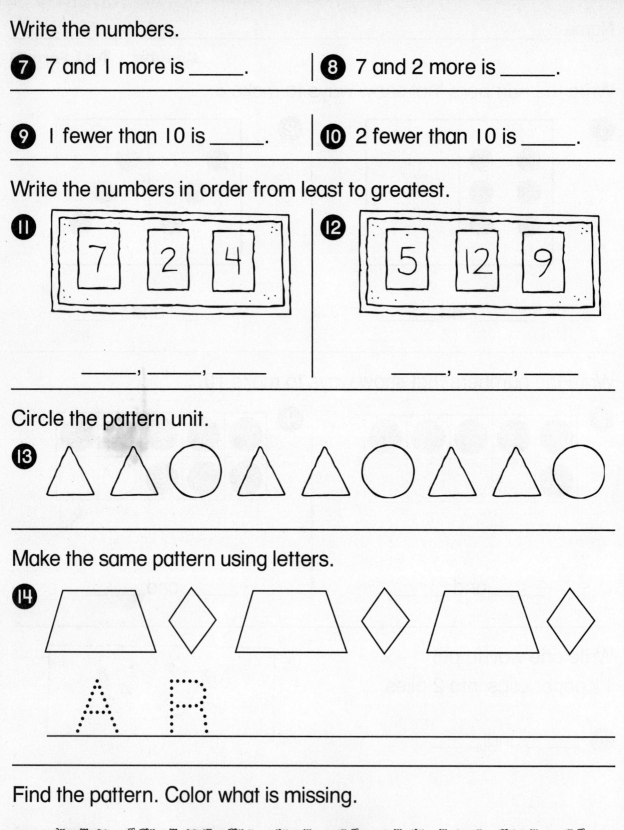

11 7 2 4

12 5 12 9

_____, _____, _____ | _____, _____, _____

Circle the pattern unit.

13

Make the same pattern using letters.

14

A B

Find the pattern. Color what is missing.

15

Name _____

Which numbers show ways to make 6?

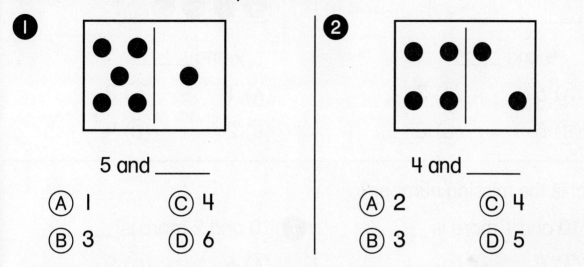

1   5 and _____

Ⓐ I   Ⓒ 4

Ⓑ 3   Ⓓ 6

2   4 and _____

Ⓐ 2   Ⓒ 4

Ⓑ 3   Ⓓ 5

We can show 7 in different ways.

Which of these shows 7?

3

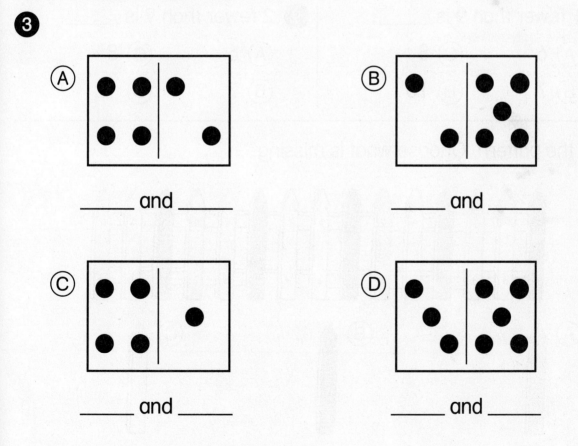

Ⓐ   _____ and _____

Ⓑ   _____ and _____

Ⓒ   _____ and _____

Ⓓ   _____ and _____

Which numbers show ways to make 10?

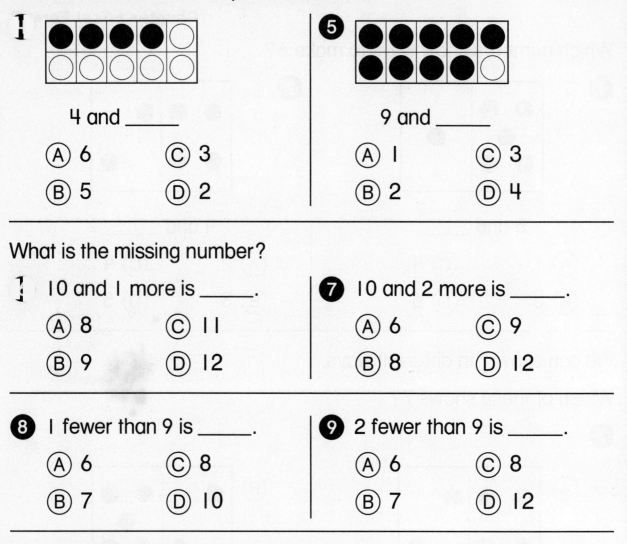

1.

4 and _____

(A) 6   (C) 3

(B) 5   (D) 2

5.

9 and _____

(A) 1   (C) 3

(B) 2   (D) 4

What is the missing number?

6. 10 and 1 more is _____.

(A) 8   (C) 11

(B) 9   (D) 12

7. 10 and 2 more is _____.

(A) 6   (C) 9

(B) 8   (D) 12

---

8. 1 fewer than 9 is _____.

(A) 6   (C) 8

(B) 7   (D) 10

9. 2 fewer than 9 is _____.

(A) 6   (C) 8

(B) 7   (D) 12

Find the pattern. Choose what is missing.

10.

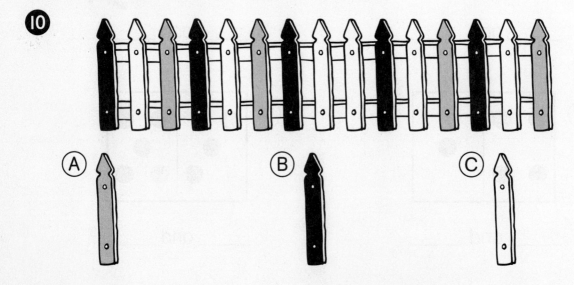

(A)   (B)   (C)

11 Which shows the numbers in order from least to greatest?

| 7 | 6 | 9 |

Ⓐ 6, 9, 7

Ⓑ 7, 9, 6

Ⓒ 6, 7, 9

Ⓓ 9, 6, 7

12 Which shows the numbers in order from greatest to least?

| 11 | 6 | 8 |

Ⓐ 11, 8, 6

Ⓑ 6, 11, 8

Ⓒ 8, 6, 11

Ⓓ 6, 8, 11

13 Which numbers show one way to put 10 peanuts into 2 piles?

____ and ____

Ⓐ 3 and 5

Ⓑ 4 and 6

Ⓒ 4 and 7

Ⓓ 4 and 5

14 Which numbers show one way to put 12 buttons into 2 piles?

____ and ____

Ⓐ 2 and 9

Ⓑ 5 and 6

Ⓒ 5 and 7

Ⓓ 4 and 6

15 Which number is greater than 9?

Ⓐ 10   Ⓒ 8

Ⓑ 9   Ⓓ 7

16 Which number is less than 7?

Ⓐ 9   Ⓒ 7

Ⓑ 8   Ⓓ 6

17 Find the pattern. Mark the pattern unit.

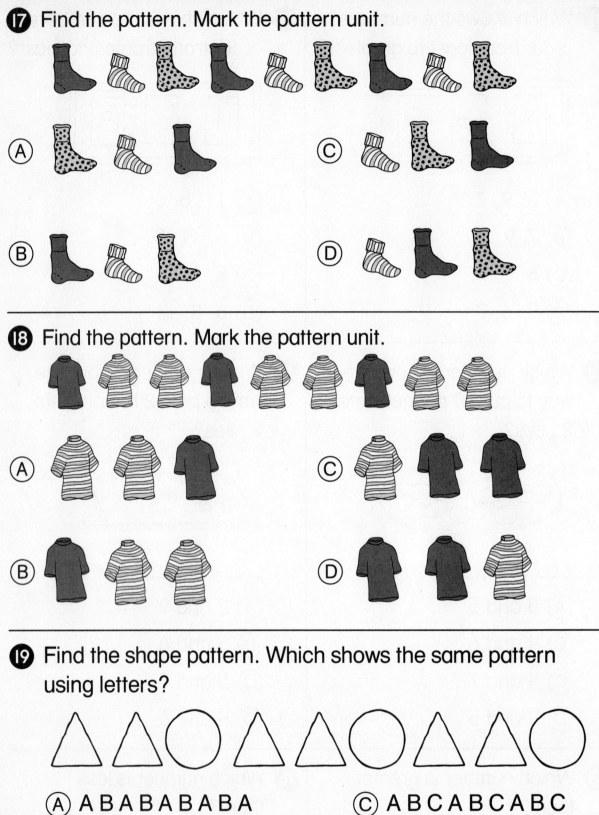

Ⓐ

Ⓑ

Ⓒ

Ⓓ

18 Find the pattern. Mark the pattern unit.

Ⓐ

Ⓑ

Ⓒ

Ⓓ

19 Find the shape pattern. Which shows the same pattern using letters?

Ⓐ A B A B A B A B A

Ⓑ A B B A B B A B B

Ⓒ A B C A B C A B C

Ⓓ A A B A A B A A B

Name _____

Which numbers show ways to make 7?

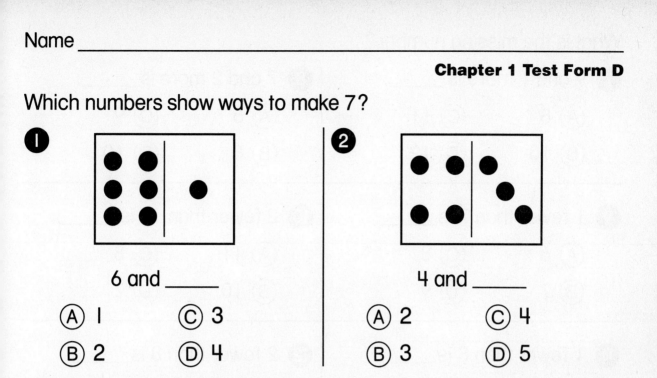

1

6 and _____

(A) 1 (C) 3

(B) 2 (D) 4

2

4 and _____

(A) 2 (C) 4

(B) 3 (D) 5

Which numbers show ways to make 8?

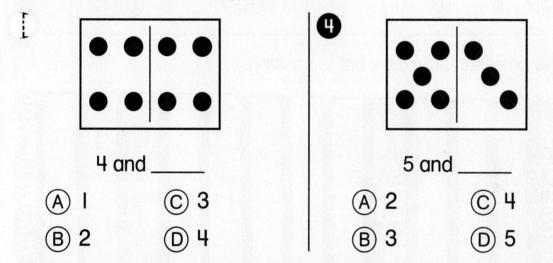

3

4 and _____

(A) 1 (C) 3

(B) 2 (D) 4

4

5 and _____

(A) 2 (C) 4

(B) 3 (D) 5

Which numbers show ways to make 10?

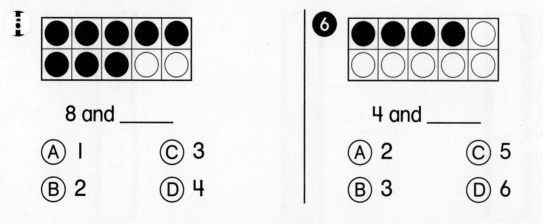

5

8 and _____

(A) 1 (C) 3

(B) 2 (D) 4

6

4 and _____

(A) 2 (C) 5

(B) 3 (D) 6

What is the missing number?

9 and 1 more is _____.

  (A) 8   (C) 11

  (B) 10   (D) 12

8 7 and 2 more is _____.

  (A) 5   (C) 9

  (B) 8   (D) 10

---

9 1 fewer than 7 is _____.

  (A) 6   (C) 8

  (B) 7   (D) 9

10 2 fewer than 10 is _____.

  (A) 11   (C) 8

  (B) 10   (D) 7

---

11 1 fewer than 8 is _____.

  (A) 6   (C) 9

  (B) 7   (D) 10

12 2 fewer than 8 is _____.

  (A) 6   (C) 9

  (B) 7   (D) 12

Find the pattern. Choose what is missing.

13

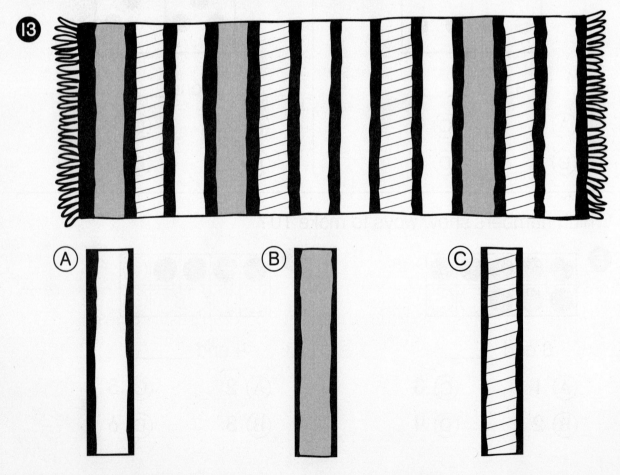

  (A)   (B)   (C)

14 Which shows the numbers in order from least to greatest?

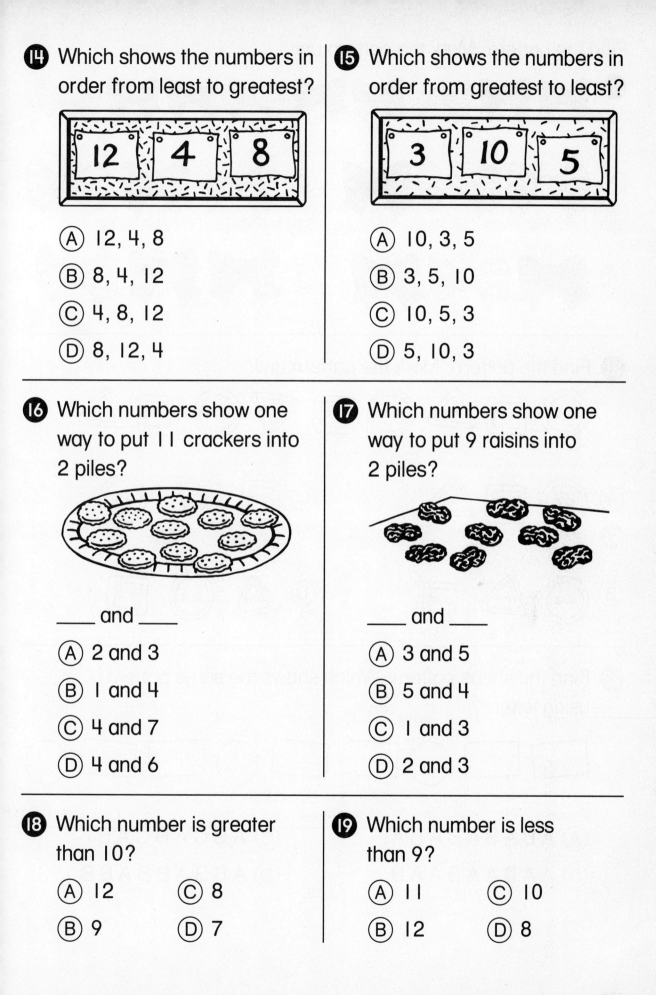

12   4   8

Ⓐ 12, 4, 8

Ⓑ 8, 4, 12

Ⓒ 4, 8, 12

Ⓓ 8, 12, 4

15 Which shows the numbers in order from greatest to least?

3   10   5

Ⓐ 10, 3, 5

Ⓑ 3, 5, 10

Ⓒ 10, 5, 3

Ⓓ 5, 10, 3

16 Which numbers show one way to put 11 crackers into 2 piles?

____ and ____

Ⓐ 2 and 3

Ⓑ 1 and 4

Ⓒ 4 and 7

Ⓓ 4 and 6

17 Which numbers show one way to put 9 raisins into 2 piles?

____ and ____

Ⓐ 3 and 5

Ⓑ 5 and 4

Ⓒ 1 and 3

Ⓓ 2 and 3

18 Which number is greater than 10?

Ⓐ 12   Ⓒ 8

Ⓑ 9   Ⓓ 7

19 Which number is less than 9?

Ⓐ 11   Ⓒ 10

Ⓑ 12   Ⓓ 8

Find the pattern. Mark the pattern unit.

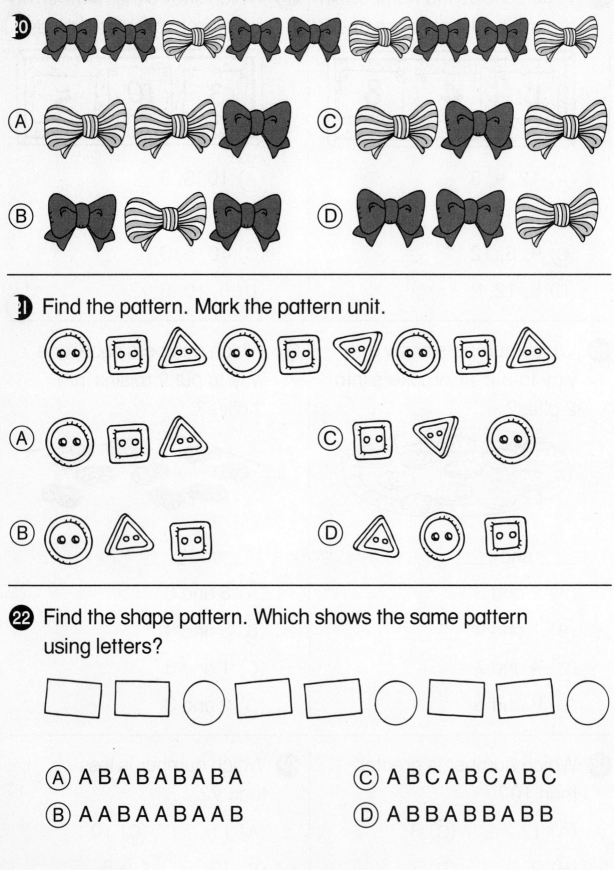

20

Ⓐ

Ⓑ

Ⓒ

Ⓓ

21 Find the pattern. Mark the pattern unit.

Ⓐ

Ⓑ

Ⓒ

Ⓓ

22 Find the shape pattern. Which shows the same pattern using letters?

Ⓐ A B A B A B A B A

Ⓑ A A B A A B A A B

Ⓒ A B C A B C A B C

Ⓓ A B B A B B A B B

Name _____

1 Write the number that tells how many.

★ ★ ★
★ ★ ★

____ | ____

★ ★ ★ ★
★ ★ ★ ★

____

---

2 Jo and Sal played a game.
Jo tossed a 5.
Sal tossed a 3.

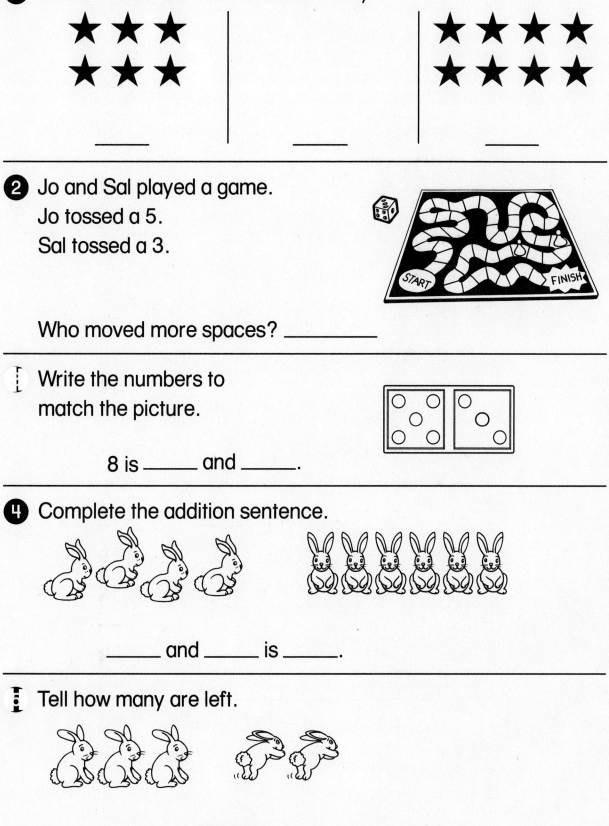

Who moved more spaces? _____

---

3 Write the numbers to
match the picture.

8 is ____ and ____.

---

4 Complete the addition sentence.

____ and ____ is ____.

---

5 Tell how many are left.

____ are left.

Name _____

Write each addition sentence.

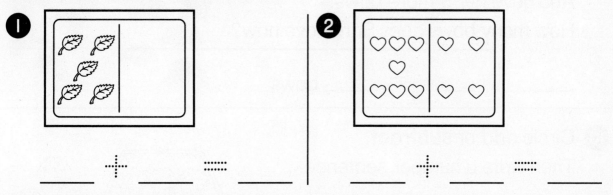

1. ____ + ____ = ____

2. ____ + ____ = ____

Write each subtraction sentence.

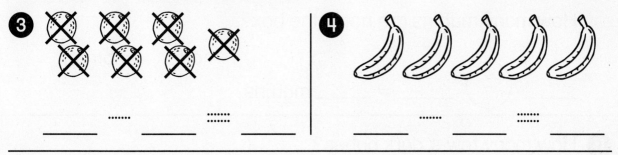

3. ____ − ____ = ____

4. ____ − ____ = ____

Add to find the sum.

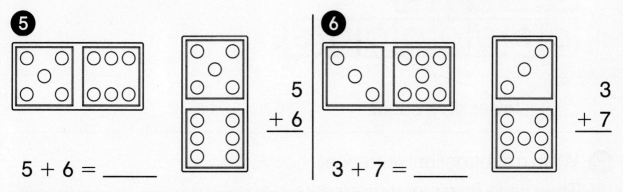

5. 5 + 6 = ____ $\begin{array}{r} 5 \\ + 6 \\ \hline \end{array}$

6. 3 + 7 = ____ $\begin{array}{r} 3 \\ + 7 \\ \hline \end{array}$

Subtract to find the difference.

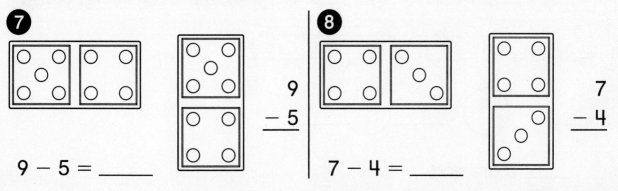

7. 9 − 5 = ____ $\begin{array}{r} 9 \\ - 5 \\ \hline \end{array}$

8. 7 − 4 = ____ $\begin{array}{r} 7 \\ - 4 \\ \hline \end{array}$

9 Write an addition sentence to answer the question.

Sara had 6 bows.
Ana gave her 5 more bows.
How many bows does Sara have now?

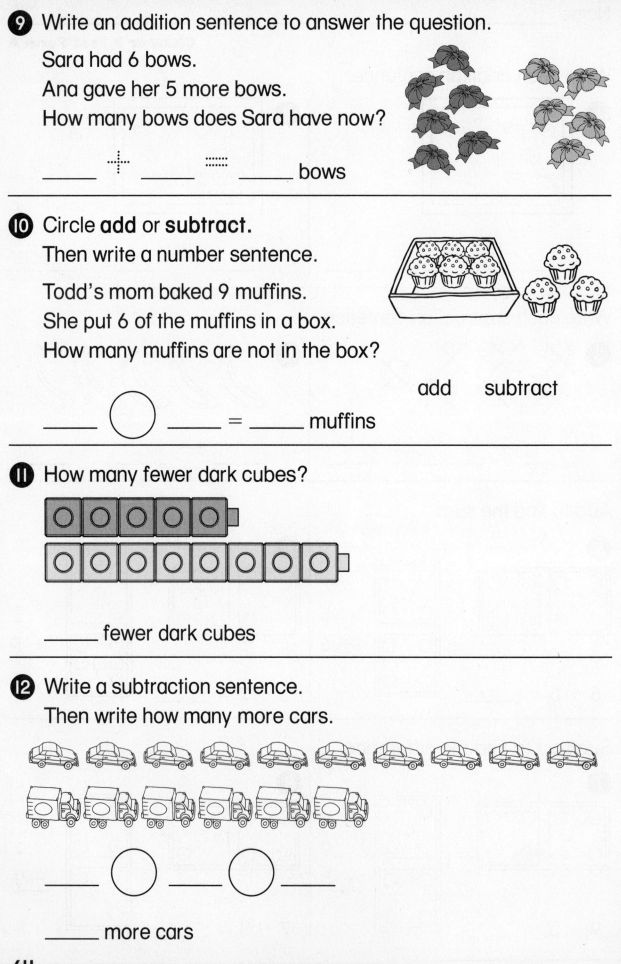

_____ ┼ _____ ┅ _____ bows

---

10 Circle **add** or **subtract**.
Then write a number sentence.

Todd's mom baked 9 muffins.
She put 6 of the muffins in a box.
How many muffins are not in the box?

add   subtract

_____ ◯ _____ = _____ muffins

---

11 How many fewer dark cubes?

_____ fewer dark cubes

---

12 Write a subtraction sentence.
Then write how many more cars.

_____ ◯ _____ ◯ _____

_____ more cars

Name _____

Write each addition sentence.

1

2

___ + ___ = ___   ___ + ___ = ___

Write each subtraction sentence.

3

4

___ − ___ = ___   ___ − ___ = ___

Add to find the sum.

5

$$4 + 8 = \underline{\hspace{1cm}}$$

$$\begin{array}{r} 4 \\ + 8 \\ \hline \end{array}$$

6

$$2 + 9 = \underline{\hspace{1cm}}$$

$$\begin{array}{r} 2 \\ + 9 \\ \hline \end{array}$$

Subtract to find the difference.

7

$$7 - 5 = \underline{\hspace{1cm}}$$

$$\begin{array}{r} 7 \\ - 5 \\ \hline \end{array}$$

8

$$9 - 6 = \underline{\hspace{1cm}}$$

$$\begin{array}{r} 9 \\ - 6 \\ \hline \end{array}$$

Write an addition sentence to answer the question.

9 Tom had 4 kites.
Rick gave him 5 more kites.
How many kites does Tom have now?

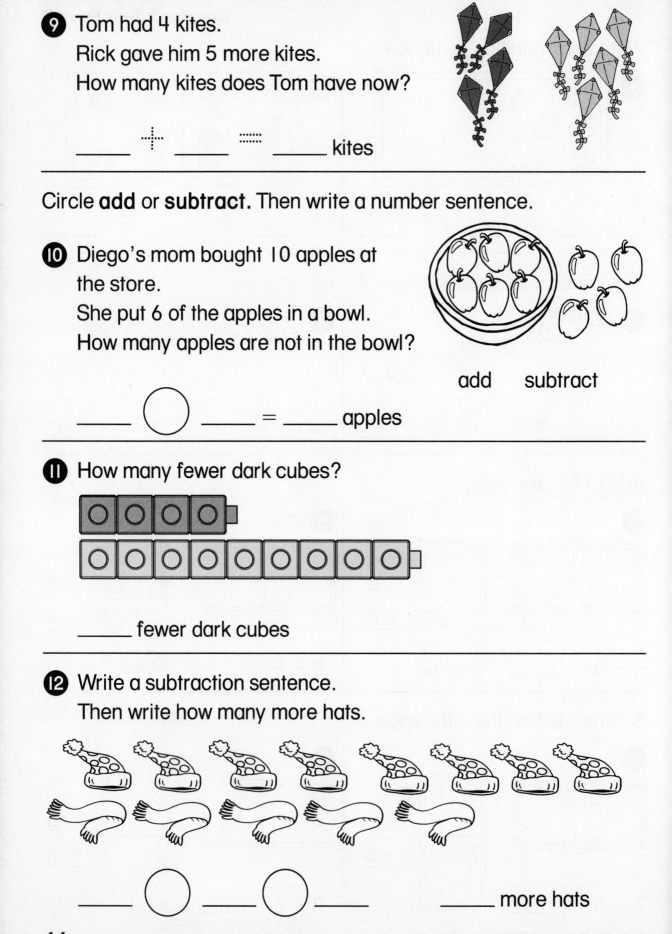

_____ + _____ = _____ kites

Circle **add** or **subtract**. Then write a number sentence.

10 Diego's mom bought 10 apples at
the store.
She put 6 of the apples in a bowl.
How many apples are not in the bowl?

add   subtract

_____ ◯ _____ = _____ apples

---

11 How many fewer dark cubes?

_____ fewer dark cubes

---

12 Write a subtraction sentence.
Then write how many more hats.

_____ ◯ _____ ◯ _____   _____ more hats

Name _____

Mark the best answer.

Which addition sentence matches the picture?

1

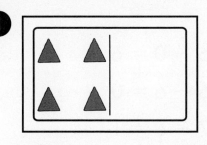

(A) $4 + 2 = 6$ (C) $4 + 4 = 8$

(B) $4 + 0 = 4$ (D) $4 + 1 = 5$

2

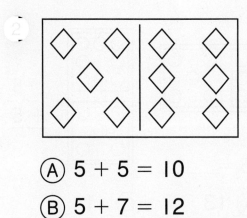

(A) $5 + 5 = 10$ (C) $6 + 6 = 12$

(B) $5 + 7 = 12$ (D) $5 + 6 = 11$

---

3   **4**

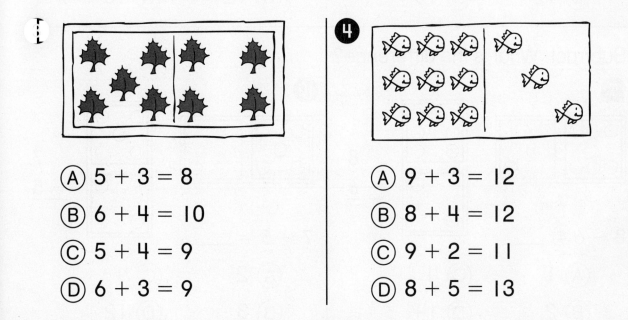

(A) $5 + 3 = 8$ (A) $9 + 3 = 12$

(B) $6 + 4 = 10$ (B) $8 + 4 = 12$

(C) $5 + 4 = 9$ (C) $9 + 2 = 11$

(D) $6 + 3 = 9$ (D) $8 + 5 = 13$

Which subtraction sentence matches the picture?

5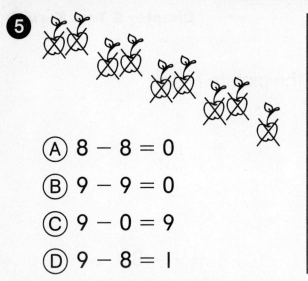

- (A) $8 - 8 = 0$
- (B) $9 - 9 = 0$
- (C) $9 - 0 = 9$
- (D) $9 - 8 = 1$

6

- (A) $6 - 0 = 6$
- (B) $6 - 6 = 0$
- (C) $7 - 6 = 1$
- (D) $7 - 0 = 7$

Add. What is the sum?

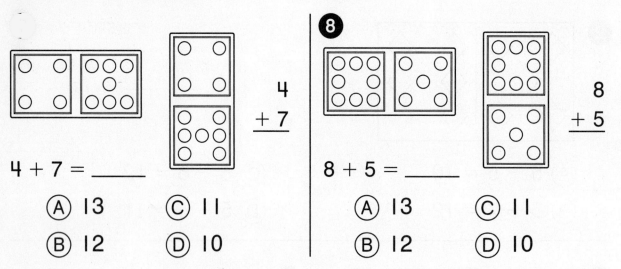

$$4 + 7 = \underline{\qquad}$$

$$\begin{array}{r} 4 \\ + 7 \\ \hline \end{array}$$

- (A) 13
- (B) 12
- (C) 11
- (D) 10

8

$$8 + 5 = \underline{\qquad}$$

$$\begin{array}{r} 8 \\ + 5 \\ \hline \end{array}$$

- (A) 13
- (B) 12
- (C) 11
- (D) 10

Subtract. What is the difference?

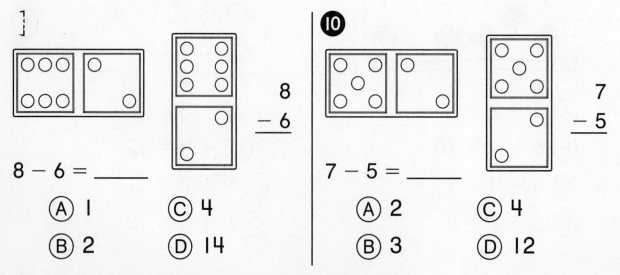

$$8 - 6 = \underline{\qquad}$$

$$\begin{array}{r} 8 \\ - 6 \\ \hline \end{array}$$

- (A) 1
- (B) 2
- (C) 4
- (D) 14

10

$$7 - 5 = \underline{\qquad}$$

$$\begin{array}{r} 7 \\ - 5 \\ \hline \end{array}$$

- (A) 2
- (B) 3
- (C) 4
- (D) 12

What addition sentence answers the question?

11 Dan had 3 books. Tim gave him 7 more books. How many books does Dan have now?

Ⓐ 3 + 6 = 9 books

Ⓑ 3 + 5 = 8 books

Ⓒ 3 + 7 = 10 books

Ⓓ 2 + 7 = 9 books

12 Mom has 2 flowers. Dad gave her 9 more flowers. How many flowers does Mom have now?

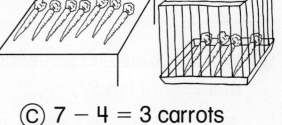

Ⓐ 2 + 8 = 10 flowers

Ⓑ 2 + 9 = 11 flowers

Ⓒ 2 + 7 = 9 flowers

Ⓓ 1 + 9 = 10 flowers

Which number sentence matches the story?

13 Laura has 7 carrots on the table. She put 4 of the carrots in her rabbit's cage. How many carrots are still on the table?

Ⓐ 7 − 3 = 4 carrots

Ⓑ 7 + 3 = 10 carrots

Ⓒ 7 − 4 = 3 carrots

Ⓓ 7 + 4 = 11 carrots

14 Charlie the clown had 6 balls in his hand. Another clown gave him 3 more balls. How many balls does Charlie have now?

Ⓐ 6 + 3 = 9 balls

Ⓑ 6 − 3 = 3 balls

Ⓒ 9 − 3 = 6 balls

Ⓓ 9 + 3 = 12 balls

How many fewer dark cubes?

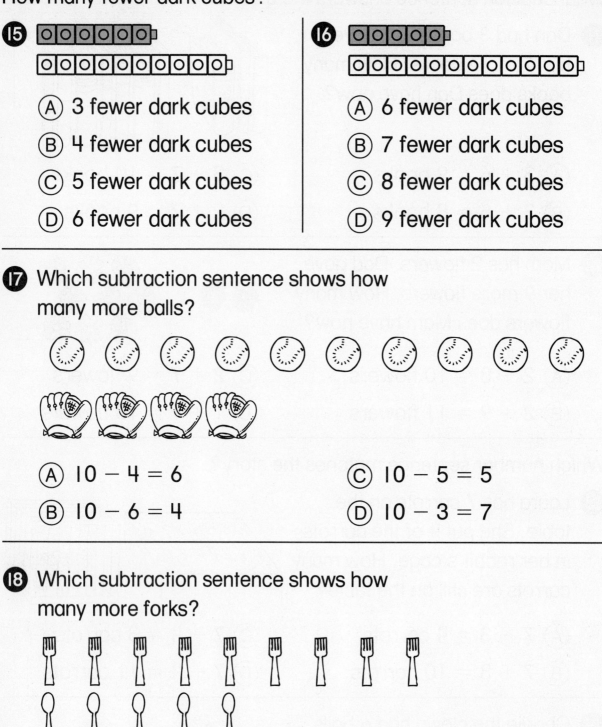

15

Ⓐ 3 fewer dark cubes

Ⓑ 4 fewer dark cubes

Ⓒ 5 fewer dark cubes

Ⓓ 6 fewer dark cubes

16

Ⓐ 6 fewer dark cubes

Ⓑ 7 fewer dark cubes

Ⓒ 8 fewer dark cubes

Ⓓ 9 fewer dark cubes

17 Which subtraction sentence shows how many more balls?

Ⓐ $10 - 4 = 6$

Ⓑ $10 - 6 = 4$

Ⓒ $10 - 5 = 5$

Ⓓ $10 - 3 = 7$

18 Which subtraction sentence shows how many more forks?

Ⓐ $9 - 6 = 3$

Ⓑ $9 - 7 = 2$

Ⓒ $9 - 5 = 4$

Ⓓ $9 - 4 = 5$

Name _____

Mark the best answer.

Which addition sentence matches the picture?

1

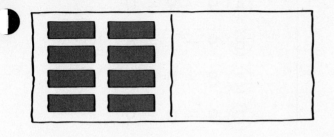

(A) $8 + 0 = 8$ (C) $8 + 2 = 10$

(B) $8 + 1 = 9$ (D) $8 + 3 = 11$

2

(A) $4 + 6 = 10$ (C) $4 + 7 = 11$

(B) $3 + 7 = 10$ (D) $6 + 6 = 12$

3

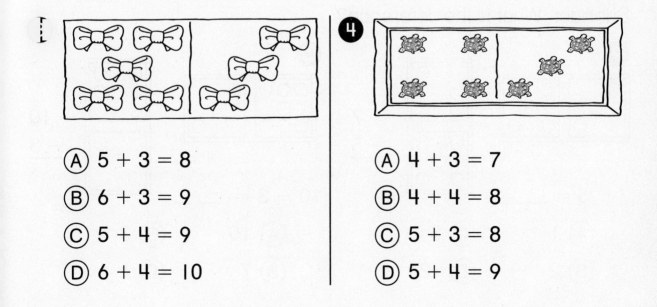

(A) $5 + 3 = 8$ (A) $4 + 3 = 7$

(B) $6 + 3 = 9$ (B) $4 + 4 = 8$

(C) $5 + 4 = 9$ (C) $5 + 3 = 8$

(D) $6 + 4 = 10$ (D) $5 + 4 = 9$

Which subtraction sentence matches the picture?

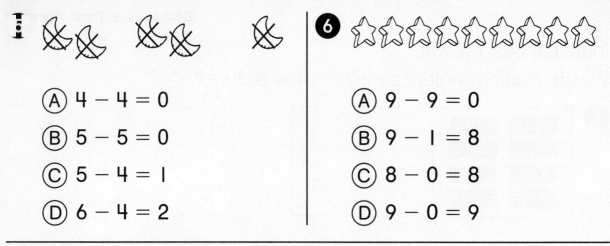

1

- (A) $4 - 4 = 0$
- (B) $5 - 5 = 0$
- (C) $5 - 4 = 1$
- (D) $6 - 4 = 2$

6

- (A) $9 - 9 = 0$
- (B) $9 - 1 = 8$
- (C) $8 - 0 = 8$
- (D) $9 - 0 = 9$

Add. What is the sum?

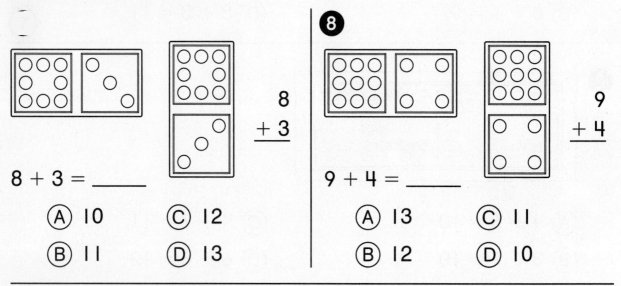

$8 + 3 =$ _____

$$8 \atop +\,3$$

- (A) 10
- (B) 11
- (C) 12
- (D) 13

8

$9 + 4 =$ _____

$$9 \atop +\,4$$

- (A) 13
- (B) 12
- (C) 11
- (D) 10

Subtract. What is the difference?

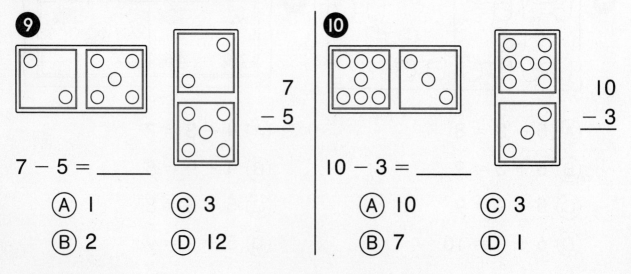

9

$7 - 5 =$ _____

$$7 \atop -\,5$$

- (A) 1
- (B) 2
- (C) 3
- (D) 12

10

$10 - 3 =$ _____

$$10 \atop -\,3$$

- (A) 10
- (B) 7
- (C) 3
- (D) 1

Which addition sentence answers the question?

11 Carla had 8 hearts. Raul gave her 4 hearts. How many hearts does Carla have now?

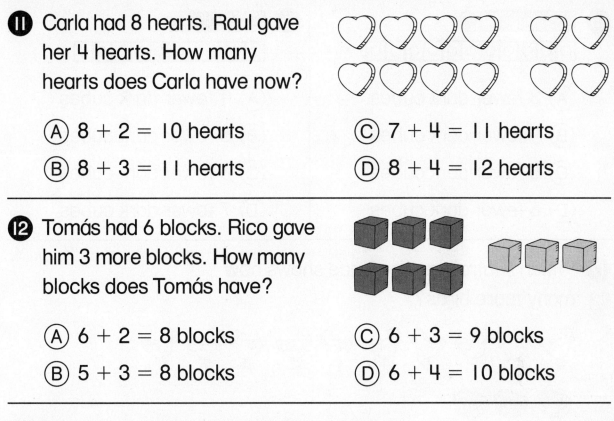

Ⓐ 8 + 2 = 10 hearts

Ⓒ 7 + 4 = 11 hearts

Ⓑ 8 + 3 = 11 hearts

Ⓓ 8 + 4 = 12 hearts

12 Tomás had 6 blocks. Rico gave him 3 more blocks. How many blocks does Tomás have?

Ⓐ 6 + 2 = 8 blocks

Ⓒ 6 + 3 = 9 blocks

Ⓑ 5 + 3 = 8 blocks

Ⓓ 6 + 4 = 10 blocks

Which number sentence matches the story?

13 Rita had 8 dog bones in a bag. She put 4 of the dog bones in her dog's bowl. How many dog bones are still in the bag?

Ⓐ 8 − 4 = 4 dog bones

Ⓒ 8 + 3 = 11 dog bones

Ⓑ 8 − 3 = 5 dog bones

Ⓓ 8 + 4 = 12 dog bones

14 Kathy had 7 charms on her bracelet. Her friend gave her 2 more charms. How many charms does Kathy have now?

Ⓐ 7 − 2 = 5 charms

Ⓒ 7 + 2 = 9 charms

Ⓑ 9 − 2 = 7 charms

Ⓓ 9 + 2 = 11 charms

How many fewer dark cubes?

15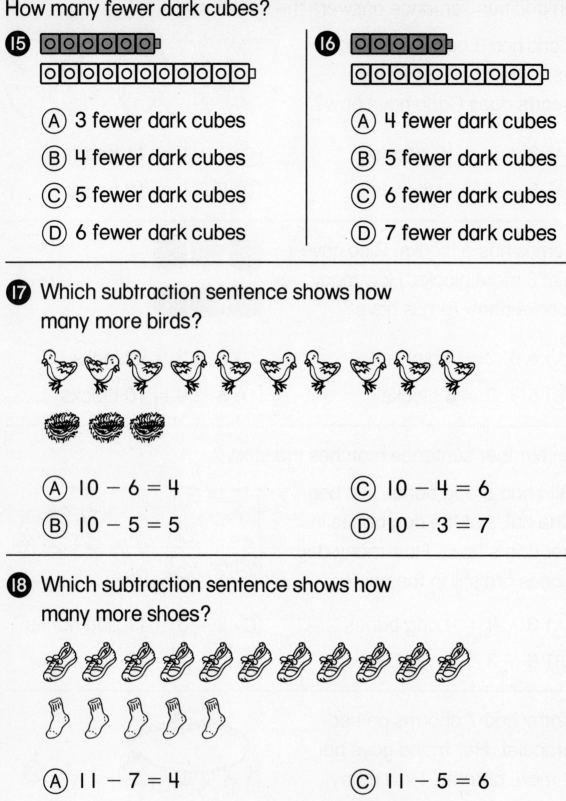

(A) 3 fewer dark cubes

(B) 4 fewer dark cubes

(C) 5 fewer dark cubes

(D) 6 fewer dark cubes

16

(A) 4 fewer dark cubes

(B) 5 fewer dark cubes

(C) 6 fewer dark cubes

(D) 7 fewer dark cubes

17 Which subtraction sentence shows how many more birds?

(A) $10 - 6 = 4$

(B) $10 - 5 = 5$

(C) $10 - 4 = 6$

(D) $10 - 3 = 7$

18 Which subtraction sentence shows how many more shoes?

(A) $11 - 7 = 4$

(B) $11 - 6 = 5$

(C) $11 - 5 = 6$

(D) $11 - 4 = 7$

Name _____

1 Write an addition sentence.

_____ + _____ = _____

---

2 Add to find the sum.

3 + 4 = _____

3
+ 4
____

---

3 Write an addition sentence to answer the question.

There are 7 children sitting in the circle. 4 more children join the circle. How many children are there altogether?

_____ + _____ = _____ children

---

4 4 and 1 more is _____.

---

5 Write the numbers.

10 is _____ and _____.

Name _____

① Count on to find the sum.

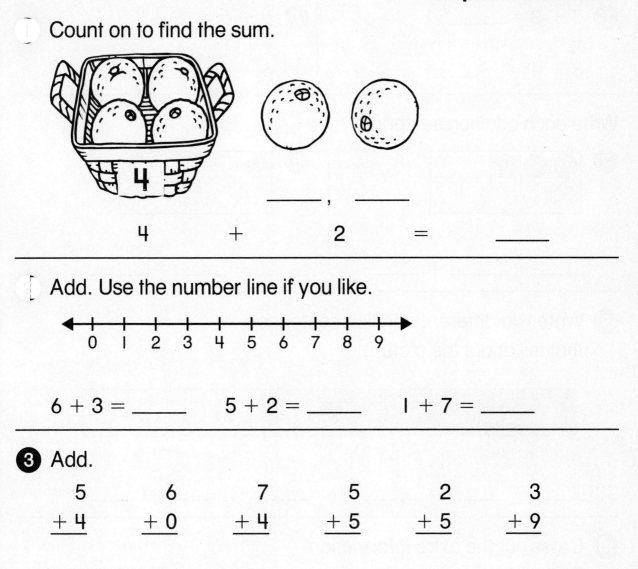

4   +   2   =   _____

_____

② Add. Use the number line if you like.

0 1 2 3 4 5 6 7 8 9

6 + 3 = _____   5 + 2 = _____   1 + 7 = _____

❸ Add.

$$\begin{array}{cc} 5 \\ +4 \\ \hline \end{array}$$ $$\begin{array}{cc} 6 \\ +0 \\ \hline \end{array}$$ $$\begin{array}{cc} 7 \\ +4 \\ \hline \end{array}$$ $$\begin{array}{cc} 5 \\ +5 \\ \hline \end{array}$$ $$\begin{array}{cc} 2 \\ +5 \\ \hline \end{array}$$ $$\begin{array}{cc} 3 \\ +9 \\ \hline \end{array}$$

❹ Draw a picture.
Then write a number sentence.

Tom has 4 cars.
He finds 6 more cars.
How many cars does
Tom have now?

_____ + _____ = _____ cars

Use doubles to add.

1 3 + 3 = _____

3 + 4 = _____

6 6 + 6 = _____

6 + 7 = _____

Write each addition sentence.

7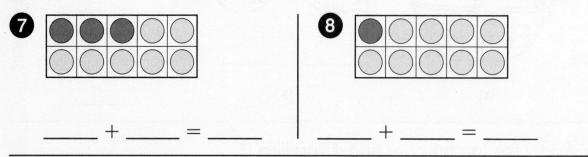

_____ + _____ = _____

8

_____ + _____ = _____

9 Write two different addition sentences that tell about the picture.

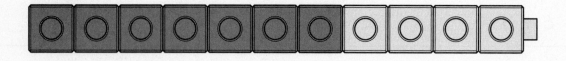

_____ + _____ = _____   _____ + _____ = _____

10 Cross out the extra information. Then write a number sentence to solve the problem.

2 birds are in the tree.
6 more birds fly to the tree.
1 squirrel is in the tree.
How many birds are in the tree now?

_____ + _____ = _____ birds

Name _____

Count on to find the sum.

1

_____ , _____

6 + 2 = _____

_____

2 Add. Use the number line if you like.

0 1 2 3 4 5 6 7 8 9

2 + 6 = _____   4 + 3 = _____   1 + 5 = _____

_____

Add.

3
6	8	7	4	2	3
+ 5	+ 0	+ 2	+ 4	+ 9	+ 7

_____

Draw a picture.

Then write a number sentence.

4 Usha has 3 seashells.
She finds 5 more seashells.
How many seashells does
Usha have now?

_____ + _____ = _____ seashells

Use doubles to add.

5 6 + 6 = _____

6 + 7 = _____

6 7 + 7 = _____

7 + 8 = _____

Write each addition sentence.

7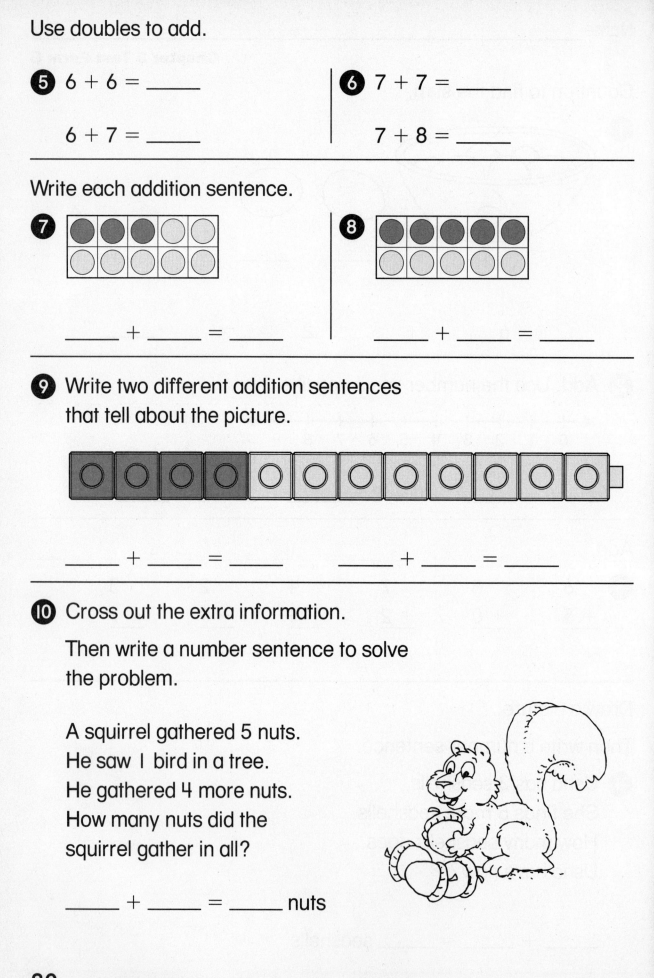

_____ + _____ = _____

8

_____ + _____ = _____

9 Write two different addition sentences that tell about the picture.

_____ + _____ = _____   _____ + _____ = _____

10 Cross out the extra information.

Then write a number sentence to solve the problem.

A squirrel gathered 5 nuts.
He saw 1 bird in a tree.
He gathered 4 more nuts.
How many nuts did the
squirrel gather in all?

_____ + _____ = _____ nuts

Name _____

Mark the best answer.

Count on to find the sum.

1)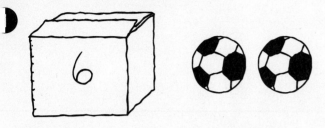

6 + 2 = _____

(A) 4
(B) 7
(C) 8
(D) 9

2

7 + 1 = _____

(A) 6
(B) 8
(C) 9
(D) 10

3

5 + 3 = _____

(A) 4
(B) 5
(C) 7
(D) 8

4 Add. Use the number line if you like.

$$\xleftarrow{\quad} 0 \quad 1 \quad 2 \quad 3 \quad 4 \quad 5 \quad 6 \quad 7 \quad 8 \quad 9 \quad 10 \quad 11 \quad 12 \xrightarrow{\quad}$$

$3 + 6 =$ _____

- (A) 11
- (B) 10
- (C) 9
- (D) 2

5 $7 + 3 =$ _____

- (A) 2
- (B) 9
- (C) 10
- (D) 11

6 $8 + 1 =$ _____

- (A) 12
- (B) 11
- (C) 10
- (D) 9

Add.

$9 + 2 =$ _____

- (A) 6
- (C) 11
- (B) 7
- (D) 12

8 $6 + 0 =$ _____

- (A) 0
- (C) 8
- (B) 6
- (D) 10

9 $2 + 3 =$ _____

- (A) 1
- (C) 4
- (B) 2
- (D) 5

10 $4 + 3 =$ _____

- (A) 7
- (C) 9
- (B) 8
- (D) 10

11 $6 + 2 =$ _____

- (A) 9
- (C) 7
- (B) 8
- (D) 4

12 $9 + 0 =$ _____

- (A) 0
- (C) 10
- (B) 9
- (D) 11

Which number sentence answers the question?

13 Alok has 5 games.
He gets 2 more games.
How many games does Alok have now?

Ⓐ 5 − 2 = 3 games   Ⓒ 5 + 2 = 7 games

Ⓑ 5 − 3 = 2 games   Ⓓ 5 + 3 = 8 games

---

14 Aloya has 4 puzzles.
She gets 3 more puzzles.
How many puzzles does Aloya have now?

Ⓐ 4 − 3 = 1 puzzle   Ⓒ 4 − 1 = 3 puzzles

Ⓑ 4 + 2 = 6 puzzles   Ⓓ 4 + 3 = 7 puzzles

---

15 Which doubles fact will help you add 4 + 5?

Ⓐ 4 + 3

Ⓑ 4 + 4

Ⓒ 6 + 6

Ⓓ 3 + 3

Which addition sentence matches the picture?

16

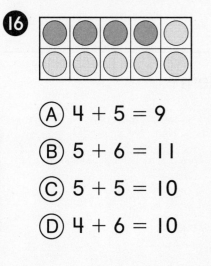

Ⓐ 4 + 5 = 9

Ⓑ 5 + 6 = 11

Ⓒ 5 + 5 = 10

Ⓓ 4 + 6 = 10

Which two addition sentences tell about the picture?

17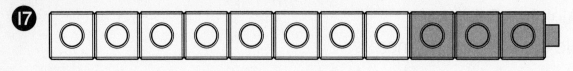

  (A) $3 + 7 = 10; 7 + 3 = 10$

  (B) $8 + 3 = 11; 3 + 8 = 11$

  (C) $7 + 4 = 11; 4 + 7 = 11$

  (D) $8 + 2 = 10; 2 + 8 = 10$

---

18 Which sentence has the extra information?

Mela took 2 books back to the library on Monday.
On Tuesday she took 4 books back to the library.
On Wednesday she read a book about dogs.
How many books did Mela take to the library?

  (A) Mela took 2 books back to the library on Monday.

  (B) On Tuesday she took 4 books back to the library.

  (C) On Wednesday she read a book about dogs.

  (D) No sentence has extra information.

---

19 Which number sentence solves the problem?

  (A) $2 + 5 = 7$ books

  (B) $2 + 4 = 6$ books

  (C) $3 + 4 = 7$ books

  (D) $3 + 3 = 6$ books

Name _____

Mark the best answer.

Count on to find the sum.

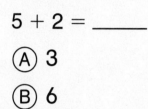

1.

5 + 2 = ____

Ⓐ 3

Ⓑ 6

Ⓒ 7

Ⓓ 8

2.

9 + 1 = ____

Ⓐ 7

Ⓑ 8

Ⓒ 10

Ⓓ 11

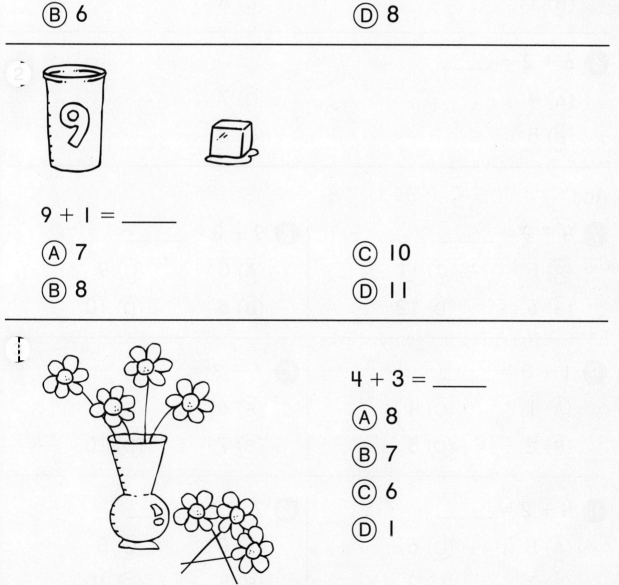

4 + 3 = ____

Ⓐ 8

Ⓑ 7

Ⓒ 6

Ⓓ 1

4 Add. Use the number line if you like.

$$\longleftarrow | \quad | \quad | \quad | \quad | \quad | \quad | \quad | \quad | \quad | \quad | \quad | \quad | \quad \longrightarrow$$
0   1   2   3   4   5   6   7   8   9   10   11   12

5 + 1 = _____

(A) 8   (C) 6

(B) 7   (D) 4

I 9 + 3 = _____

(A) 12   (C) 8

(B) 11   (D) 6

---

6 + 2 = _____

(A) 4   (C) 7

(B) 5   (D) 8

Add.

8 + 3 = _____

(A) 5   (C) 11

(B) 6   (D) 12

8 9 + 0 = _____

(A) 0   (C) 9

(B) 6   (D) 10

---

1 + 3 = _____

(A) 1   (C) 4

(B) 2   (D) 5

10 7 + 3 = _____

(A) 6   (C) 9

(B) 7   (D) 10

---

11 4 + 2 = _____

(A) 8   (C) 6

(B) 7   (D) 2

12 7 + 0 = _____

(A) 0   (C) 8

(B) 7   (D) 10

Which number sentence answers the question?

13 Rita has 8 crayons.
She gets 2 more crayons.
How many crayons does Rita have now?

Ⓐ 8 − 2 = 6 crayons   Ⓒ 8 + 2 = 10 crayons

Ⓑ 8 − 6 = 2 crayons   Ⓓ 8 + 3 = 11 crayons

---

14 Benito has 3 postcards.
He gets 3 more postcards.
How many postcards does Benito have now?

Ⓐ 3 + 3 = 6 postcards   Ⓒ 6 − 3 = 3 postcards

Ⓑ 3 + 2 = 5 postcards   Ⓓ 3 − 3 = 0 postcards

---

15 Which doubles fact will help you add 3 + 4?

Ⓐ 2 + 3

Ⓑ 3 + 3

Ⓒ 6 + 6

Ⓓ 5 + 5

Which addition sentence matches the picture?

16

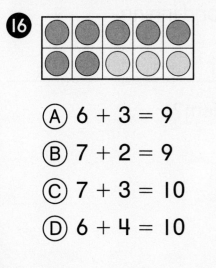

Ⓐ 6 + 3 = 9

Ⓑ 7 + 2 = 9

Ⓒ 7 + 3 = 10

Ⓓ 6 + 4 = 10

17 Which two addition sentences tell about the picture?

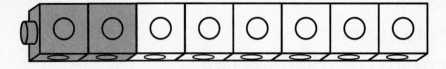

(A) 2 + 5 = 7; 5 + 2 = 7

(B) 2 + 6 = 8; 6 + 2 = 8

(C) 3 + 5 = 8; 5 + 3 = 8

(D) 3 + 6 = 9; 6 + 3 = 9

---

18 Which sentence has the extra information?

Eduardo threw 5 strikes in the first inning.
His team played the Tigers.
He threw 4 more strikes in the second inning.
How many strikes did Eduardo throw?

(A) Eduardo threw 5 strikes in the first inning.

(B) His team played the Tigers.

(C) He threw 4 more strikes in the second inning.

(D) No sentence has extra information.

---

19 Which number sentence solves the problem?

(A) 5 + 4 = 9 strikes

(B) 4 + 4 = 8 strikes

(C) 4 + 3 = 7 strikes

(D) 3 + 3 = 6 strikes

Name _____

Mark the best answer.

1 Which shapes come next in the pattern?

□ □ ○ ○ □ □ ○ ○ □ □ ○ ○

(A) ○ ○   (C) □ ○

(B) ○ □   (D) □ □

---

2 What is the missing number?

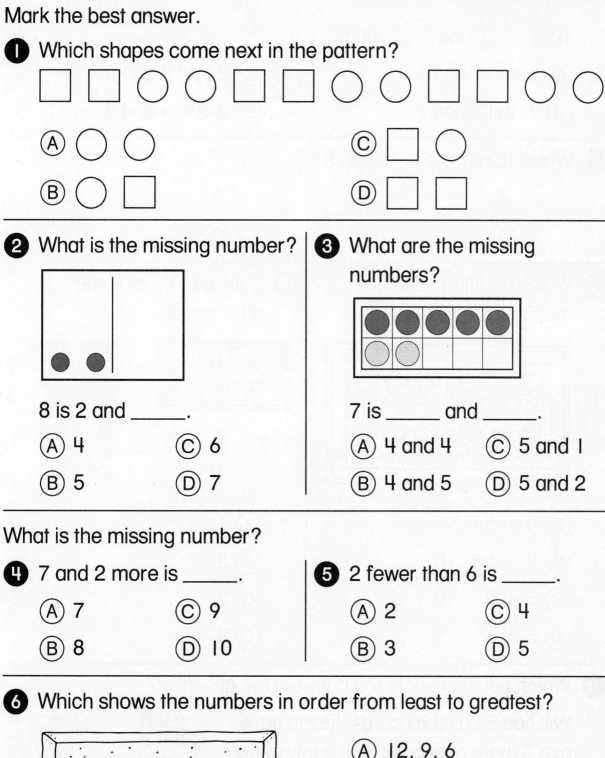

8 is 2 and _____.

(A) 4   (C) 6

(B) 5   (D) 7

3 What are the missing numbers?

7 is _____ and _____.

(A) 4 and 4   (C) 5 and 1

(B) 4 and 5   (D) 5 and 2

What is the missing number?

4 7 and 2 more is _____.

(A) 7   (C) 9

(B) 8   (D) 10

5 2 fewer than 6 is _____.

(A) 2   (C) 4

(B) 3   (D) 5

---

6 Which shows the numbers in order from least to greatest?

(A) 12, 9, 6

(B) 9, 6, 12

(C) 6, 12, 9

(D) 6, 9, 12

7 What is one way to put 12 pencils into 3 piles?

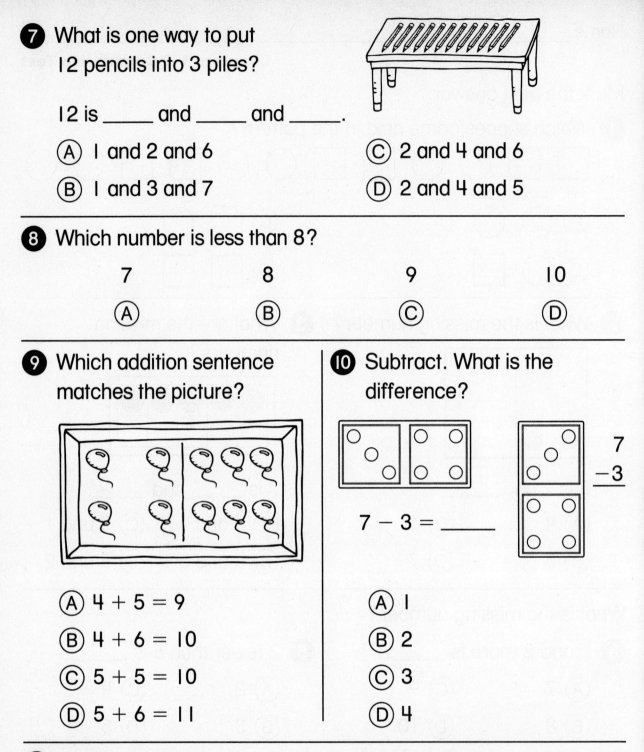

12 is ____ and ____ and ____.

Ⓐ 1 and 2 and 6   Ⓒ 2 and 4 and 6

Ⓑ 1 and 3 and 7   Ⓓ 2 and 4 and 5

---

8 Which number is less than 8?

7   8   9   10

Ⓐ   Ⓑ   Ⓒ   Ⓓ

---

9 Which addition sentence matches the picture?

Ⓐ 4 + 5 = 9

Ⓑ 4 + 6 = 10

Ⓒ 5 + 5 = 10

Ⓓ 5 + 6 = 11

10 Subtract. What is the difference?

7 − 3 = ____

$$\begin{array}{r} 7 \\ -3 \\ \hline \end{array}$$

Ⓐ 1

Ⓑ 2

Ⓒ 3

Ⓓ 4

---

11 Which addition sentence answers the question?

Will had 5 baseball cards. Marta gave him 7 more baseball cards. How many baseball cards does Will have now?

Ⓐ 5 + 6 = 11   Ⓒ 6 + 7 = 13

Ⓑ 5 + 7 = 12   Ⓓ 5 + 8 = 13

12 Which number sentence matches the story? Mica had 10 pennies on the table. She put 5 pennies in the jar. How many pennies are still on the table?

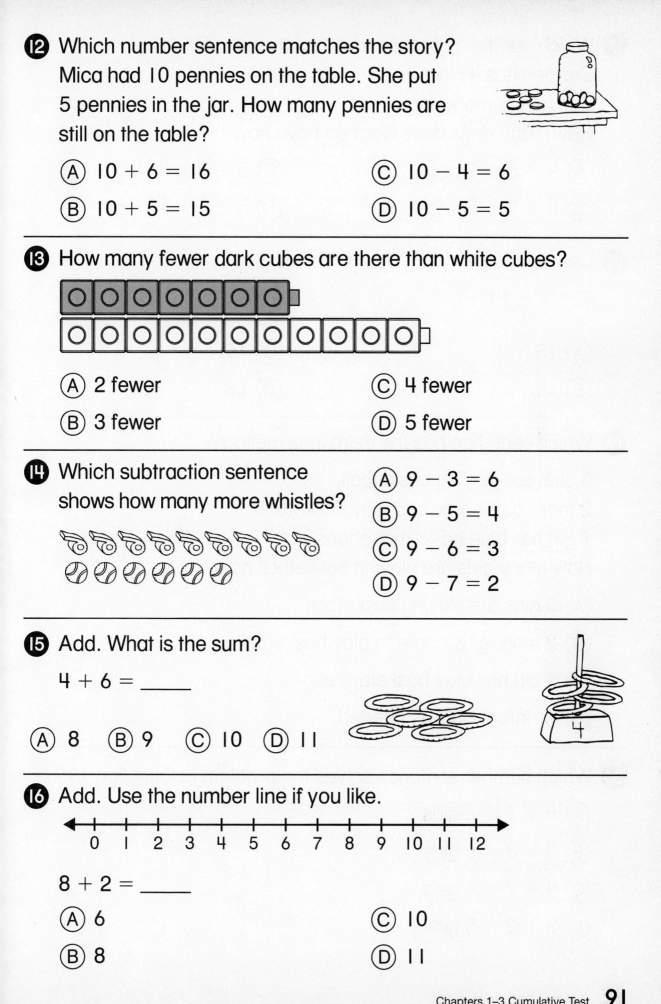

(A) $10 + 6 = 16$

(C) $10 - 4 = 6$

(B) $10 + 5 = 15$

(D) $10 - 5 = 5$

13 How many fewer dark cubes are there than white cubes?

(A) 2 fewer

(C) 4 fewer

(B) 3 fewer

(D) 5 fewer

14 Which subtraction sentence shows how many more whistles?

(A) $9 - 3 = 6$

(B) $9 - 5 = 4$

(C) $9 - 6 = 3$

(D) $9 - 7 = 2$

15 Add. What is the sum?

$4 + 6 =$ _____

(A) 8   (B) 9   (C) 10   (D) 11

16 Add. Use the number line if you like.

$8 + 2 =$ _____

(A) 6

(C) 10

(B) 8

(D) 11

17 Which number sentence matches the story?

Carmen has 4 rings.

She gets 5 more rings.

How many rings does Carmen have now?

(A) $4 + 5 = 9$ rings

(C) $5 - 4 = 1$ ring

(B) $4 + 4 = 8$ rings

(D) $5 - 1 = 4$ rings

---

18 Use doubles to add. What is the sum?

$7 + 7 = 14$ $\qquad$ $7 + 8 = \underline{}$

(A) 13

(C) 15

(B) 14

(D) 16

---

19 Which sentence has the extra information?

3 girls are playing basketball.

2 more girls come and play basketball.

1 girl has blue basketball shoes.

How many girls are playing basketball now?

(A) 3 girls are playing basketball.

(B) 2 more girls come to play basketball.

(C) 1 girl has blue basketball shoes.

(D) All information is needed.

---

20 Which number sentence solves the problem in Question 19?

(A) $5 + 1 = 6$ girls

(B) $3 + 3 = 6$ girls

(C) $4 + 2 = 6$ girls

(D) $3 + 2 = 5$ girls

Name _____

1 Tell how many are left. Then write a subtraction sentence. How many birds are left?

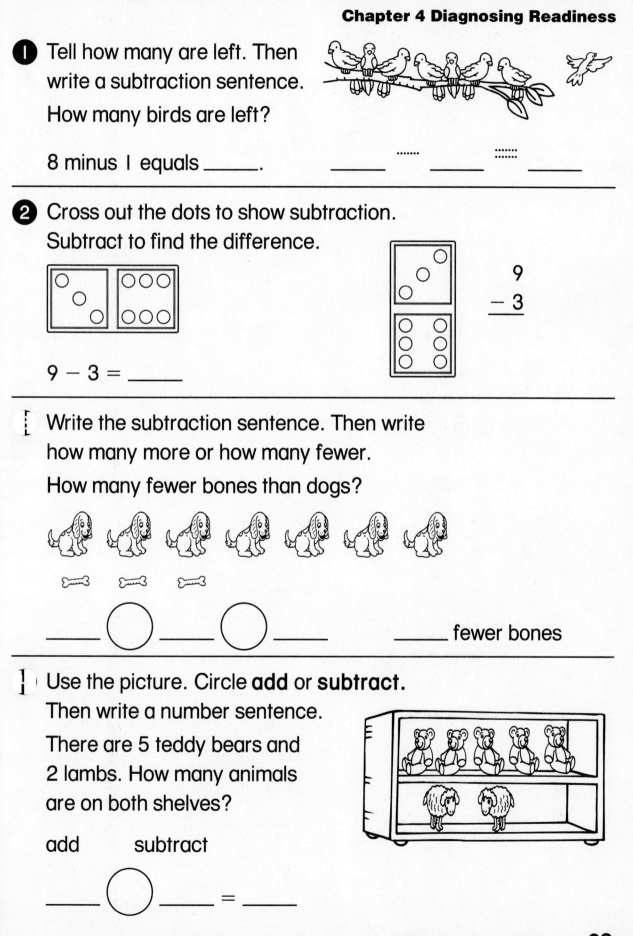

8 minus 1 equals _____.

_____ _____ _____ _____ _____

---

2 Cross out the dots to show subtraction. Subtract to find the difference.

9 − 3 = _____

$$\begin{array}{r} 9 \\ -\ 3 \\ \hline \end{array}$$

---

3 Write the subtraction sentence. Then write how many more or how many fewer. How many fewer bones than dogs?

_____ ◯ _____ ◯ _____   _____ fewer bones

---

4 Use the picture. Circle **add** or **subtract.** Then write a number sentence. There are 5 teddy bears and 2 lambs. How many animals are on both shelves?

add   subtract

_____ ◯ _____ = _____

Name _____

1 Count back to subtract.
Use the number line if you like.

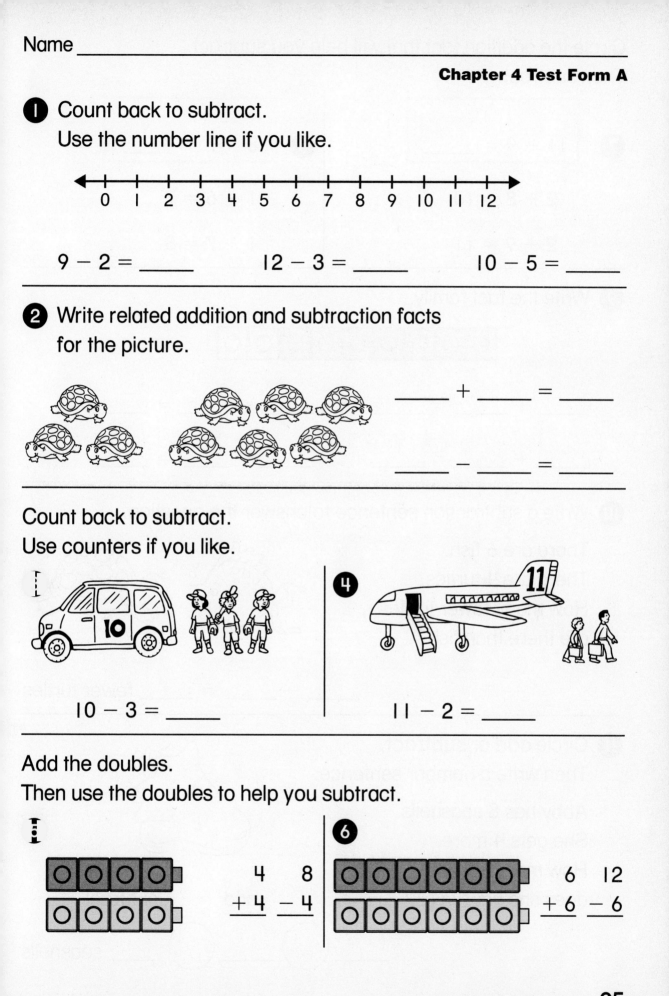

0 1 2 3 4 5 6 7 8 9 10 11 12

9 − 2 = ____   12 − 3 = ____   10 − 5 = ____

2 Write related addition and subtraction facts
for the picture.

____ + ____ = ____

____ − ____ = ____

Count back to subtract.
Use counters if you like.

3

10 − 3 = ____

4

11 − 2 = ____

Add the doubles.
Then use the doubles to help you subtract.

5

4   8
+4   −4

6

6   12
+6   −6

Circle the addition fact that will help you subtract.
Then subtract.

7 | 11 − 9 = _____

2 + 8 = 10

2 + 9 = 11

8 | 8 − 7 = _____

1 + 6 = 7

1 + 7 = 8

9 Write the fact family.

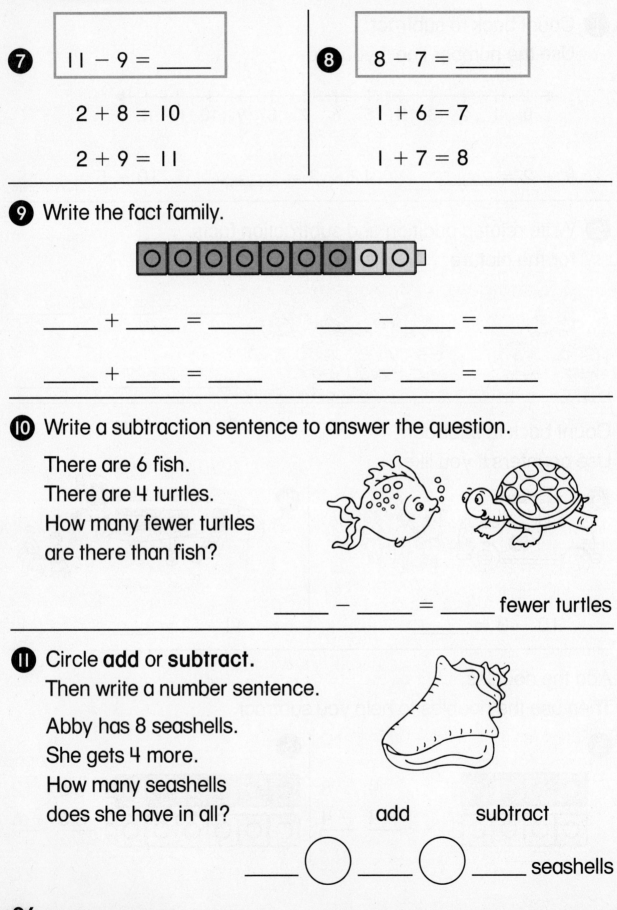

_____ + _____ = _____   _____ − _____ = _____

_____ + _____ = _____   _____ − _____ = _____

10 Write a subtraction sentence to answer the question.

There are 6 fish.
There are 4 turtles.
How many fewer turtles
are there than fish?

_____ − _____ = _____ fewer turtles

11 Circle **add** or **subtract**.
Then write a number sentence.

Abby has 8 seashells.
She gets 4 more.
How many seashells
does she have in all?

add   subtract

_____ ◯ _____ ◯ _____ seashells

1 Count back to subtract.
Use the number line if you like.

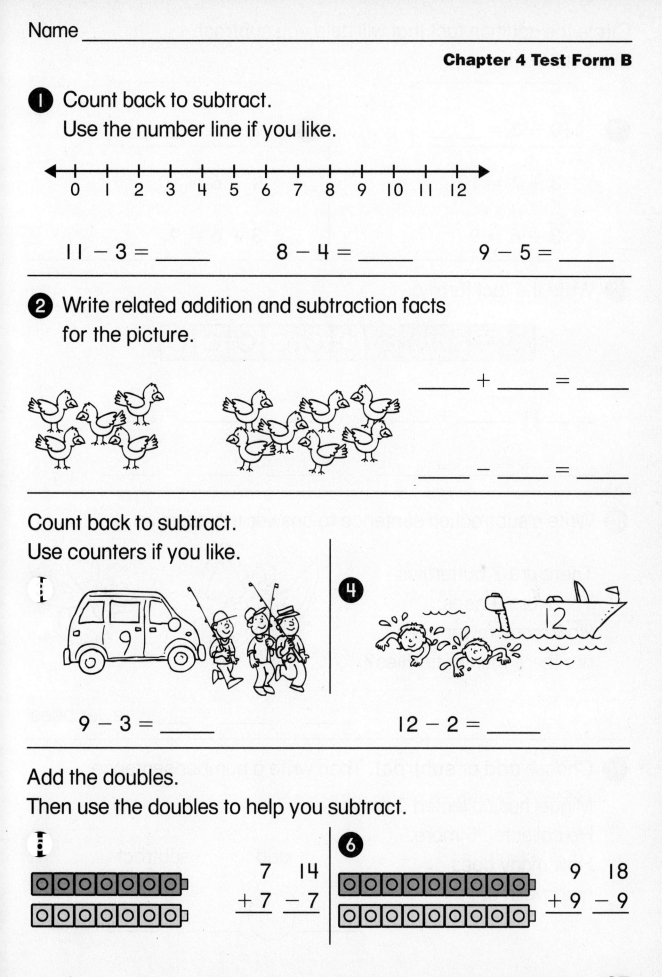

0 1 2 3 4 5 6 7 8 9 10 11 12

$11 - 3 =$ _____ $8 - 4 =$ _____ $9 - 5 =$ _____

2 Write related addition and subtraction facts
for the picture.

_____ $+$ _____ $=$ _____

_____ $-$ _____ $=$ _____

Count back to subtract.
Use counters if you like.

3

$9 - 3 =$ _____

4

$12 - 2 =$ _____

Add the doubles.
Then use the doubles to help you subtract.

5

$\begin{array}{r} 7 \\ +7 \\ \hline \end{array}$ $\begin{array}{r} 14 \\ -7 \\ \hline \end{array}$

6

$\begin{array}{r} 9 \\ +9 \\ \hline \end{array}$ $\begin{array}{r} 18 \\ -9 \\ \hline \end{array}$

Circle the addition fact that will help you subtract.
Then subtract.

7 | $10 - 3 = $ _____

$3 + 7 = 10$

$3 + 6 = 9$

8 | $9 - 6 = $ _____

$4 + 6 = 10$

$3 + 6 = 9$

9 Write the fact family.

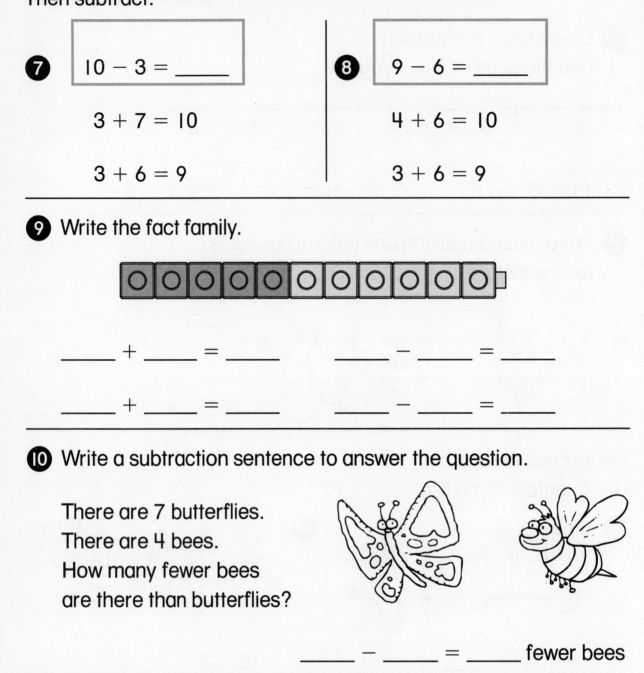

_____ + _____ = _____   _____ − _____ = _____

_____ + _____ = _____   _____ − _____ = _____

10 Write a subtraction sentence to answer the question.

There are 7 butterflies.
There are 4 bees.
How many fewer bees
are there than butterflies?

_____ − _____ = _____ fewer bees

11 Choose **add** or **subtract**. Then write a number sentence.

Miguel has collected 5 rocks.
He collected 5 more.
How many does
he have in all?

add   subtract

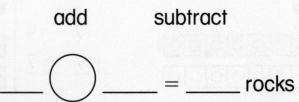

_____ ◯ _____ = _____ rocks

Name _____

Mark the best answer.

1 Use the number line if you like.
What is the difference?

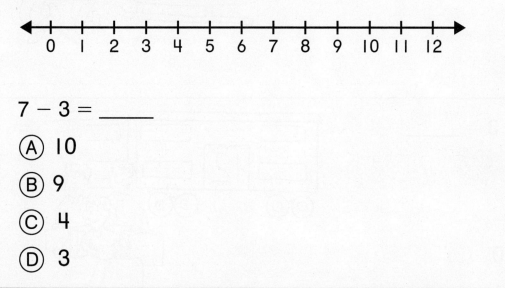

$7 - 3 =$ _____

(A) 10

(B) 9

(C) 4

(D) 3

---

2 What are the related addition and subtraction facts
for the picture?

(A) $6 + 5 = 11; 11 - 5 = 6$

(B) $6 + 4 = 10; 10 - 4 = 6$

(C) $5 + 4 = 9; 9 - 5 = 4$

(D) $5 + 5 = 10; 10 - 5 = 5$

Count back to subtract.
Mark the answer.

3 6 − 2 = _____

(A) 4

(B) 3

(C) 2

(D) 1

4 12 − 3 = _____

(A) 8

(B) 9

(C) 10

(D) 11

Use the picture to answer
questions 5 and 6.

5 Add the doubles.
What is the sum?

$$\begin{array}{r} 2 \\ + 2 \\ \hline \end{array}$$

(A) 0

(B) 2

(C) 4

(D) 8

6 What is the related
subtraction fact?

(A) 4 − 1 = 3

(B) 4 − 2 = 2

(C) 4 − 3 = 1

(D) 4 − 4 = 0

Use the picture to answer
questions 7 and 8.

7 Add the doubles.
What is the sum?

$$7$$
$$+ 7$$

(A) 0

(B) 7

(C) 14

(D) 16

8 What is the related
subtraction fact?

(A) $14 - 6 = 8$

(B) $14 - 14 = 0$

(C) $14 - 8 = 6$

(D) $14 - 7 = 7$

Which addition fact will help you subtract?

9 | $8 - 5 =$ _____ |

(A) $5 + 4 = 9$

(B) $3 + 8 = 11$

(C) $3 + 5 = 8$

(D) $5 + 8 = 13$

10 | $10 - 2 =$ _____ |

(A) $2 + 8 = 10$

(B) $2 + 7 = 9$

(C) $8 + 1 = 9$

(D) $10 + 2 = 12$

11 Which number completes the fact family?

$8 + 4 = 12$ $4 + 8 = 12$

$12 - 8 = 4$ $12 - 4 = $ _____

(A) 4

(B) 6

(C) 8

(D) 12

---

12 Which number sentence completes the fact family?

$7 + 1 = 8$ $1 + 7 = 8$ $8 - 1 = 7$

(A) $8 - 2 = 6$

(B) $8 - 1 = 9$

(C) $7 + 2 = 9$

(D) $8 - 7 = 1$

---

13 Which subtraction sentence answers the question?

There are 9 lizards
There are 8 snakes.
How many fewer snakes
are there than lizards?

(A) $8 - 1 = 7$

(B) $9 - 1 = 8$

(C) $9 - 8 = 1$

(D) $9 - 2 = 7$

14 Which number sentence answers the question?

Maria has 11 beads.
She lost 7 beads.
How many beads does
Maria have now?

(A) $11 + 7 = 18$

(B) $7 + 4 = 11$

(C) $11 - 7 = 4$

(D) $11 - 11 = 0$

Name _____

Mark the best answer.

1. Use the number line if you like.
What is the difference?

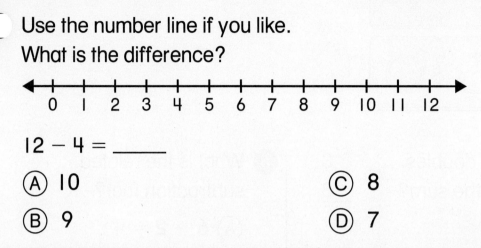

$$12 - 4 = \_\_\_\_$$

(A) 10 (C) 8

(B) 9 (D) 7

2. What are the related addition and subtraction facts
for the picture?

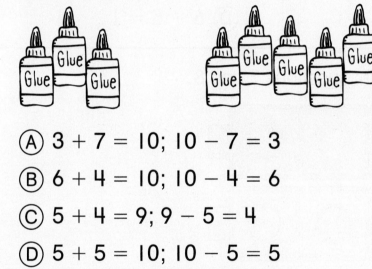

(A) $3 + 7 = 10; 10 - 7 = 3$

(B) $6 + 4 = 10; 10 - 4 = 6$

(C) $5 + 4 = 9; 9 - 5 = 4$

(D) $5 + 5 = 10; 10 - 5 = 5$

Count back to subtract. Mark the answer.

❸ $7 - 2 = \_\_\_\_$

(A) 3

(B) 4

(C) 5

(D) 6

❹ $11 - 3 = \_\_\_\_$

(A) 8

(B) 9

(C) 10

(D) 11

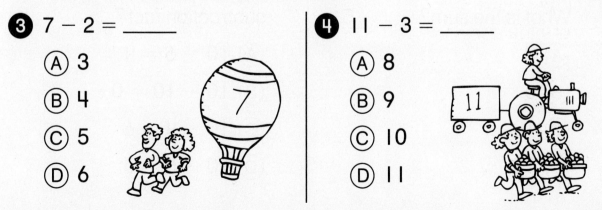

Use the picture to answer questions 5 and 6.

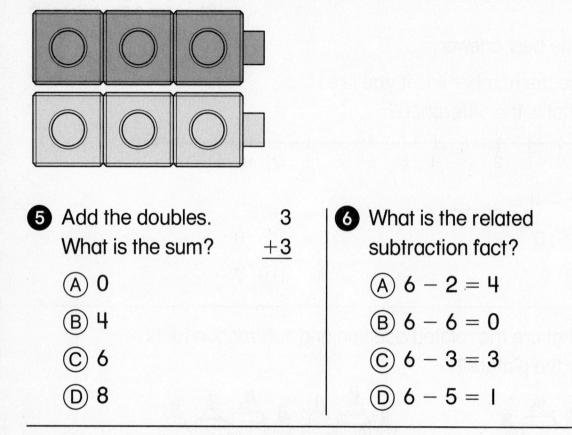

5 Add the doubles.
What is the sum?

3
+3

(A) 0

(B) 4

(C) 6

(D) 8

6 What is the related subtraction fact?

(A) $6 - 2 = 4$

(B) $6 - 6 = 0$

(C) $6 - 3 = 3$

(D) $6 - 5 = 1$

Use the picture to answer questions 7 and 8.

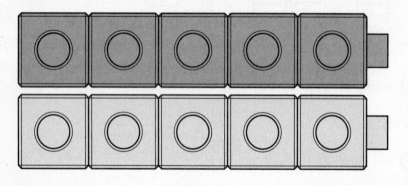

7 Add the doubles.
What is the sum?

5
+5

(A) 0

(B) 5

(C) 10

(D) 12

8 What is the related subtraction fact?

(A) $10 - 6 = 4$

(B) $10 - 10 = 0$

(C) $10 - 4 = 6$

(D) $10 - 5 = 5$

Which addition fact will help you subtract?

9 $9 - 5 =$ _____

   Ⓐ $5 + 4 = 9$

   Ⓑ $4 + 4 = 8$

   Ⓒ $3 + 5 = 8$

   Ⓓ $5 + 6 = 11$

10 $11 - 2 =$ _____

   Ⓐ $2 + 7 = 9$

   Ⓑ $2 + 8 = 10$

   Ⓒ $2 + 9 = 11$

   Ⓓ $10 + 2 = 12$

11 Which number completes the fact family?

$7 + 4 = 11$

$4 + 7 = 11$

$11 - 7 = 4$

$11 - 4 =$ _____

   Ⓐ 4

   Ⓑ 7

   Ⓒ 8

   Ⓓ 11

12 Which number sentence completes the fact family?

$$6 + 4 = 10 \qquad 4 + 6 = 10 \qquad 10 - 4 = 6$$

Ⓐ $6 - 4 = 2$

Ⓑ $6 - 2 = 4$

Ⓒ $6 + 2 = 8$

Ⓓ $10 - 6 = 4$

---

13 Which subtraction sentence answers the question?

There are 6 frogs.
There are 8 crickets.
How many fewer frogs
are there than crickets?

Ⓐ $8 - 1 = 7$

Ⓑ $8 - 2 = 6$

Ⓒ $8 - 4 = 4$

Ⓓ $8 - 6 = 2$

---

14 Which number sentence answers the question?

Gina had 12 crackers.
She ate 7 crackers.
How many crackers
does Gina have now?

Ⓐ $12 - 5 = 7$

Ⓑ $7 + 5 = 12$

Ⓒ $12 - 7 = 5$

Ⓓ $12 - 12 = 0$

Name _____

1 Circle the objects that have the same shape as the cube.

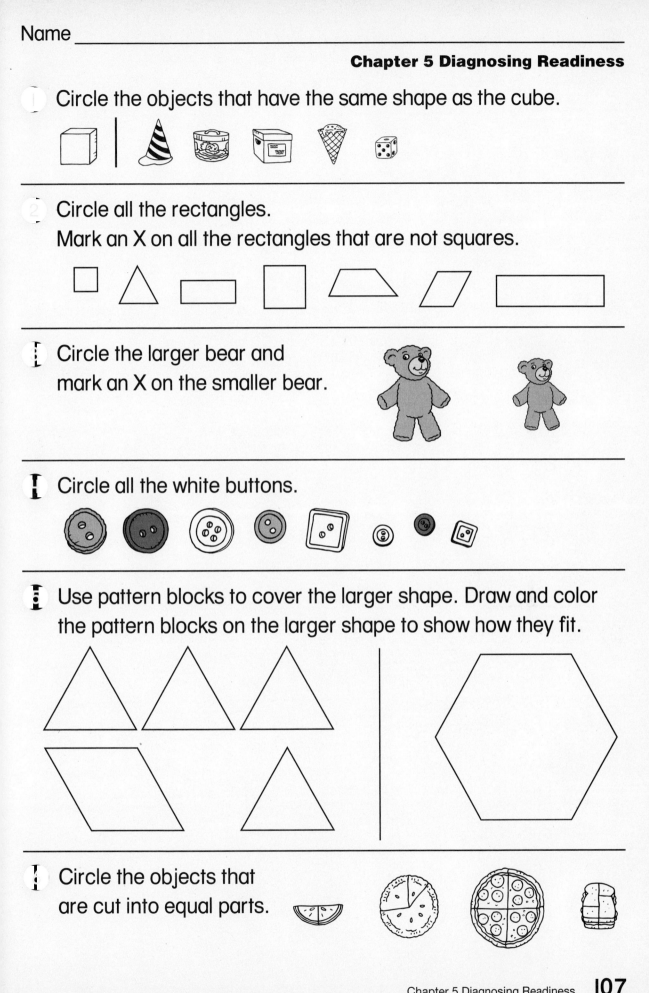

2 Circle all the rectangles.
   Mark an X on all the rectangles that are not squares.

3 Circle the larger bear and
   mark an X on the smaller bear.

4 Circle all the white buttons.

5 Use pattern blocks to cover the larger shape. Draw and color
   the pattern blocks on the larger shape to show how they fit.

6 Circle the objects that
   are cut into equal parts.

Name _____

1 Circle the cylinder.

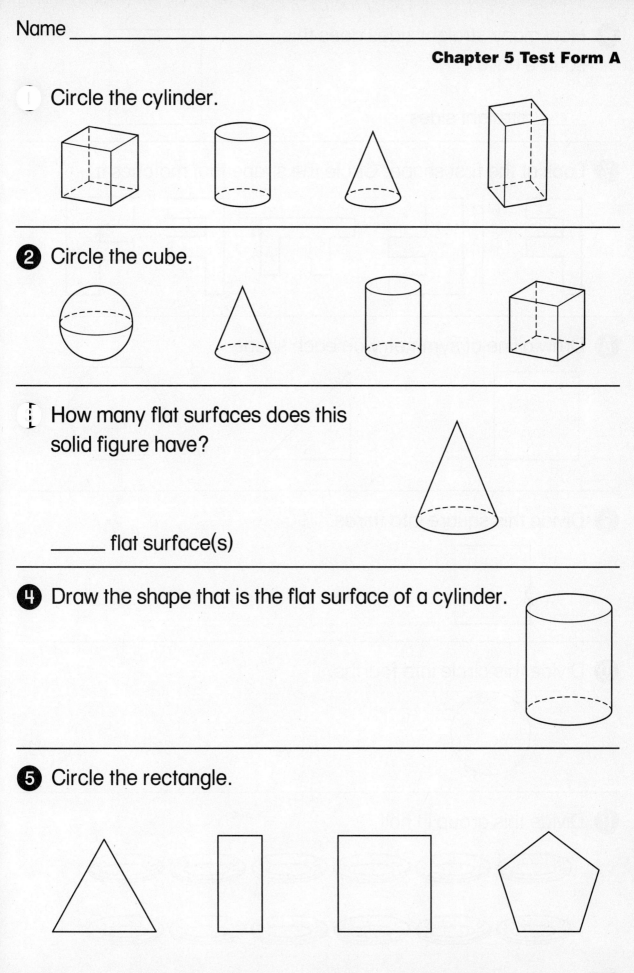

2 Circle the cube.

3 How many flat surfaces does this solid figure have?

_____ flat surface(s)

4 Draw the shape that is the flat surface of a cylinder.

5 Circle the rectangle.

How many straight sides does this square have?

_____ straight sides

7 Look at the first shape. Circle the shape that matches it.

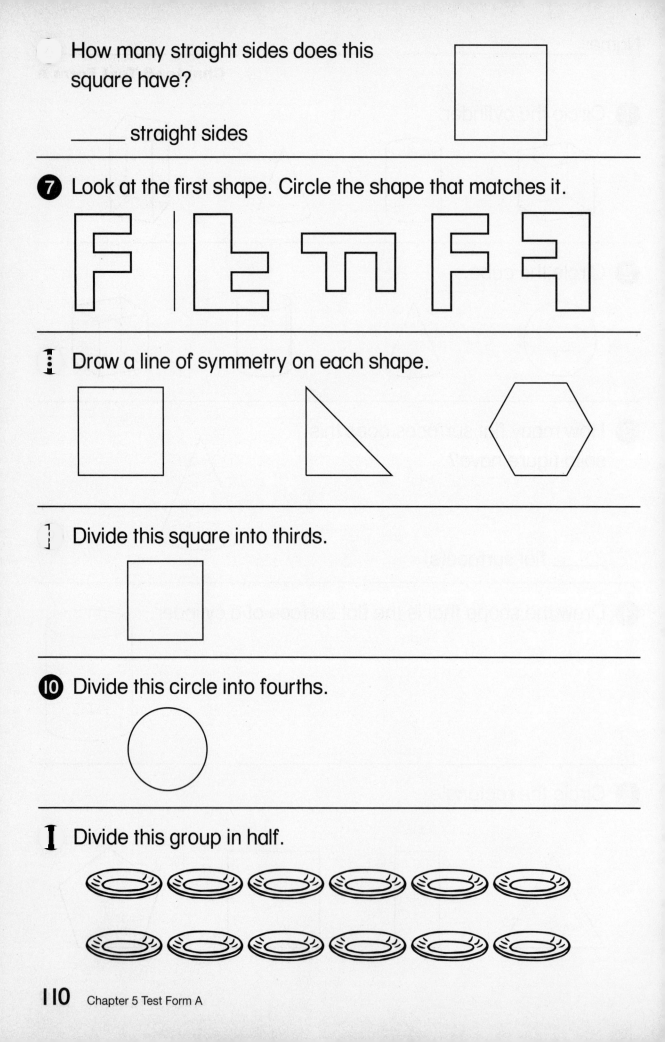

Draw a line of symmetry on each shape.

Divide this square into thirds.

10 Divide this circle into fourths.

Divide this group in half.

Name _____

1 Circle the cylinder.

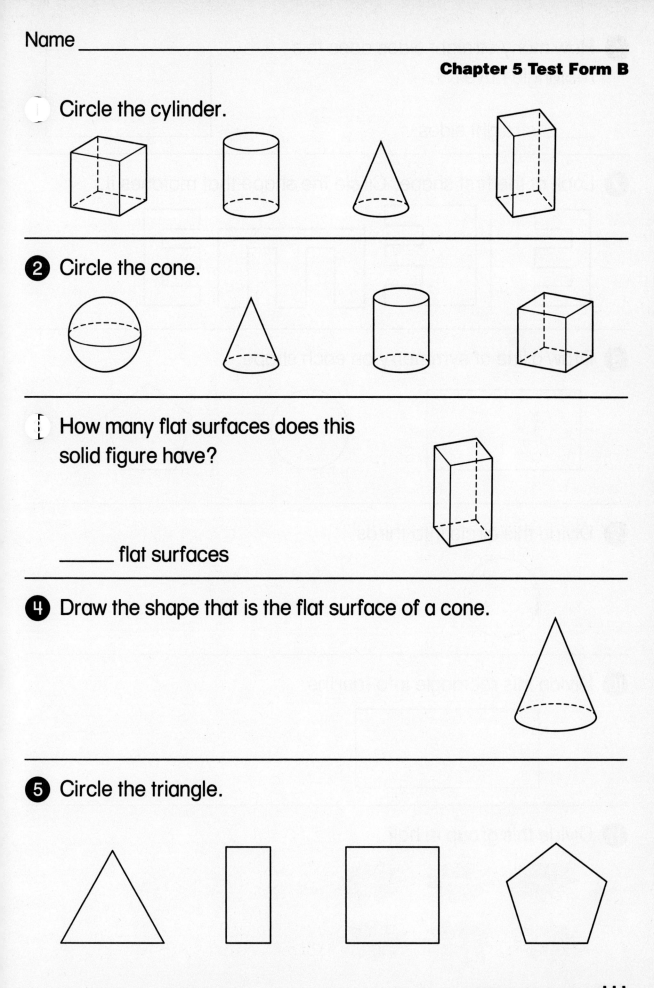

2 Circle the cone.

3 How many flat surfaces does this solid figure have?

_____ flat surfaces

4 Draw the shape that is the flat surface of a cone.

5 Circle the triangle.

6 How many straight sides does this rectangle have?

_____ straight sides

---

7 Look at the first shape. Circle the shape that matches it.

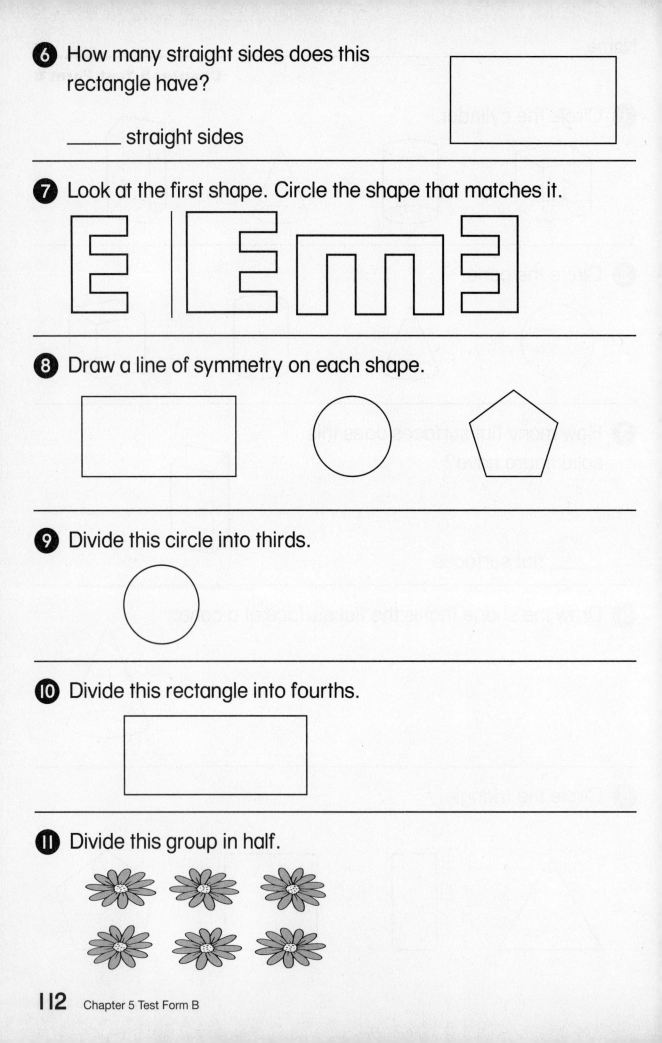

---

8 Draw a line of symmetry on each shape.

---

9 Divide this circle into thirds.

---

10 Divide this rectangle into fourths.

---

11 Divide this group in half.

Name _____

Mark the best answer.

1 Which solid is a cone?

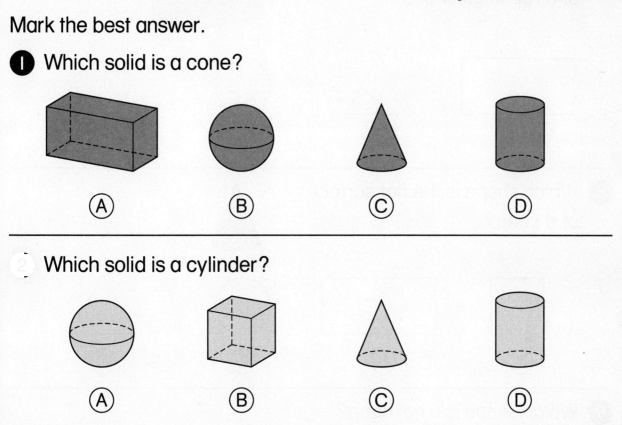

    Ⓐ   Ⓑ   Ⓒ   Ⓓ

---

2 Which solid is a cylinder?

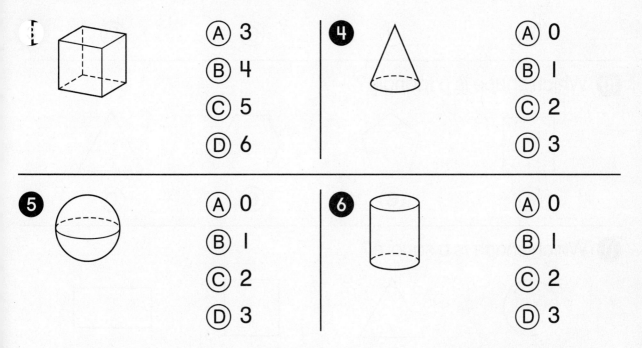

    Ⓐ   Ⓑ   Ⓒ   Ⓓ

Look at the solid figures.
How many flat surfaces does each solid figure have?

3
Ⓐ 3
Ⓑ 4
Ⓒ 5
Ⓓ 6

4
Ⓐ 0
Ⓑ 1
Ⓒ 2
Ⓓ 3

5
Ⓐ 0
Ⓑ 1
Ⓒ 2
Ⓓ 3

6
Ⓐ 0
Ⓑ 1
Ⓒ 2
Ⓓ 3

7 Which shape is the flat surface of a rectangular prism?

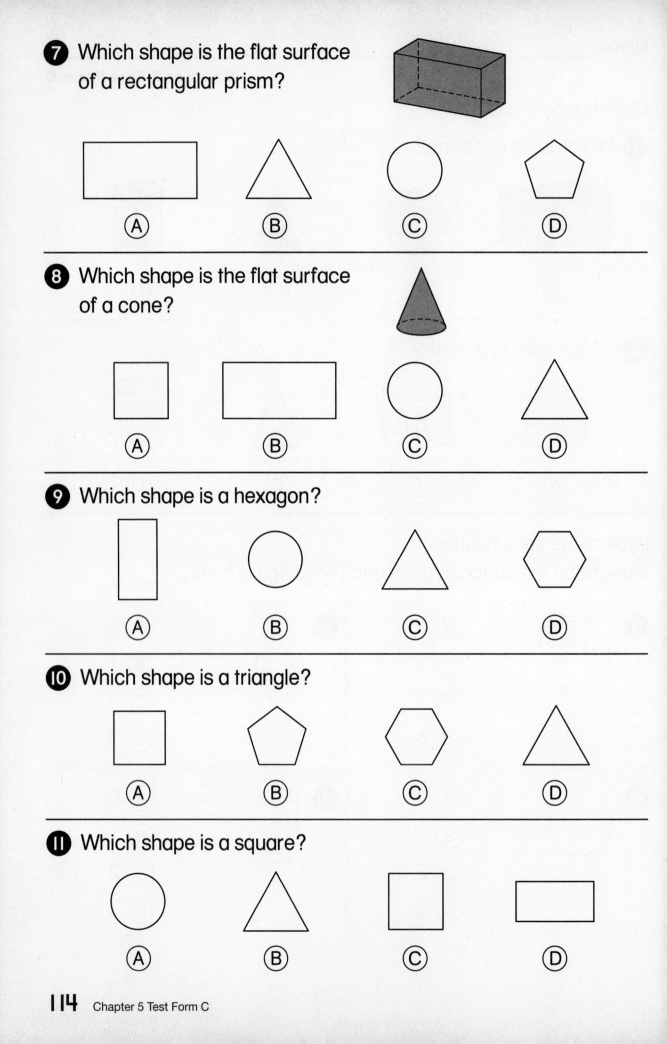

Ⓐ   Ⓑ   Ⓒ   Ⓓ

8 Which shape is the flat surface of a cone?

Ⓐ   Ⓑ   Ⓒ   Ⓓ

9 Which shape is a hexagon?

Ⓐ   Ⓑ   Ⓒ   Ⓓ

10 Which shape is a triangle?

Ⓐ   Ⓑ   Ⓒ   Ⓓ

11 Which shape is a square?

Ⓐ   Ⓑ   Ⓒ   Ⓓ

12 How many straight sides does this rectangle have?

Ⓐ 2   Ⓒ 6

Ⓑ 4   Ⓓ 8

13 How many straight sides does this hexagon have?

Ⓐ 3   Ⓒ 5

Ⓑ 4   Ⓓ 6

14 How many straight sides does this circle have?

Ⓐ 0   Ⓒ 2

Ⓑ 1   Ⓓ 3

15 Which shape matches this shape?

Ⓐ   Ⓑ   Ⓒ   Ⓓ

16 Which shape matches this shape?

Ⓐ   Ⓑ   Ⓒ   Ⓓ

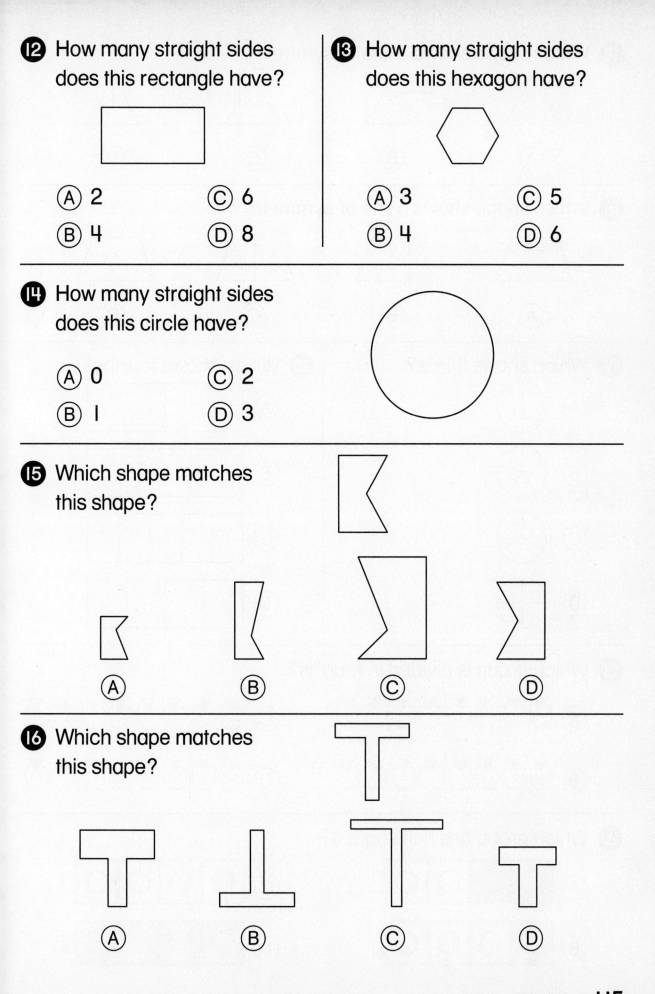

17 Which shape shows a line of symmetry?

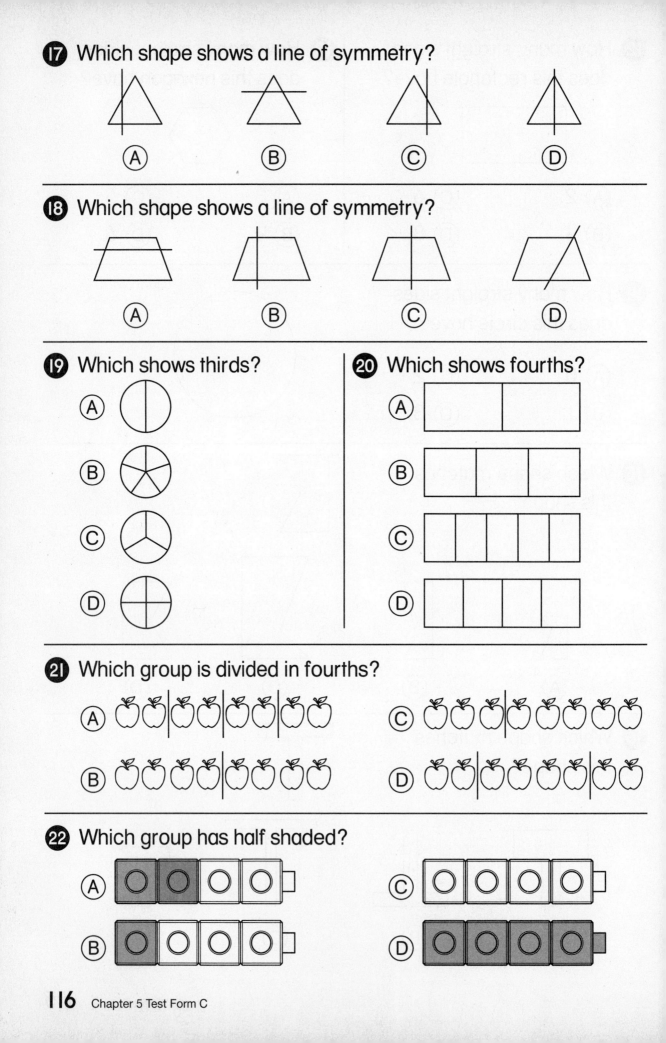

Ⓐ   Ⓑ   Ⓒ   Ⓓ

18 Which shape shows a line of symmetry?

Ⓐ   Ⓑ   Ⓒ   Ⓓ

19 Which shows thirds?

Ⓐ
Ⓑ
Ⓒ
Ⓓ

20 Which shows fourths?

Ⓐ
Ⓑ
Ⓒ
Ⓓ

21 Which group is divided in fourths?

Ⓐ   Ⓒ

Ⓑ   Ⓓ

22 Which group has half shaded?

Ⓐ   Ⓒ

Ⓑ   Ⓓ

Name _____

Mark the best answer.

1 Which solid is a sphere?

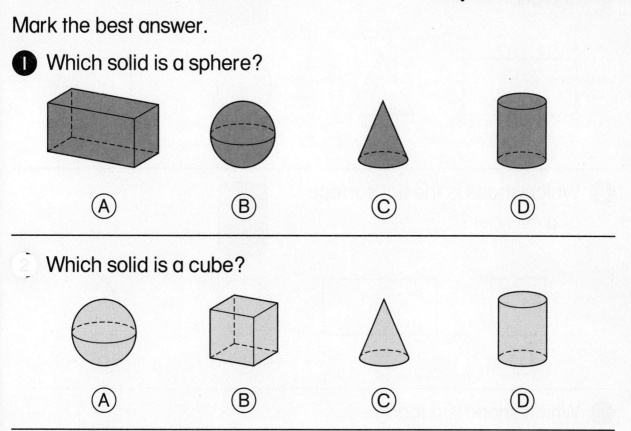

    Ⓐ   Ⓑ   Ⓒ   Ⓓ

2 Which solid is a cube?

    Ⓐ   Ⓑ   Ⓒ   Ⓓ

Look at the solid figures.
How many flat surfaces does each solid figure have?

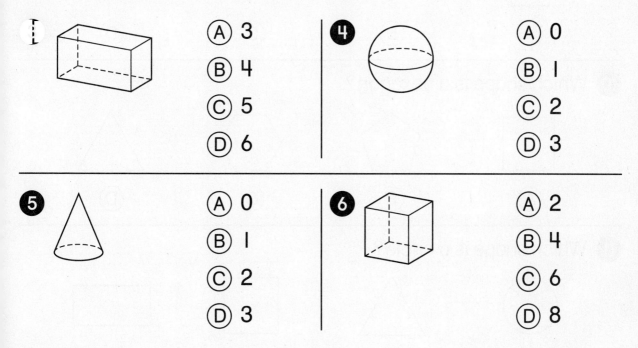

3
Ⓐ 3
Ⓑ 4
Ⓒ 5
Ⓓ 6

4
Ⓐ 0
Ⓑ 1
Ⓒ 2
Ⓓ 3

5
Ⓐ 0
Ⓑ 1
Ⓒ 2
Ⓓ 3

6
Ⓐ 2
Ⓑ 4
Ⓒ 6
Ⓓ 8

7 Which shape is the flat surface of a cube?

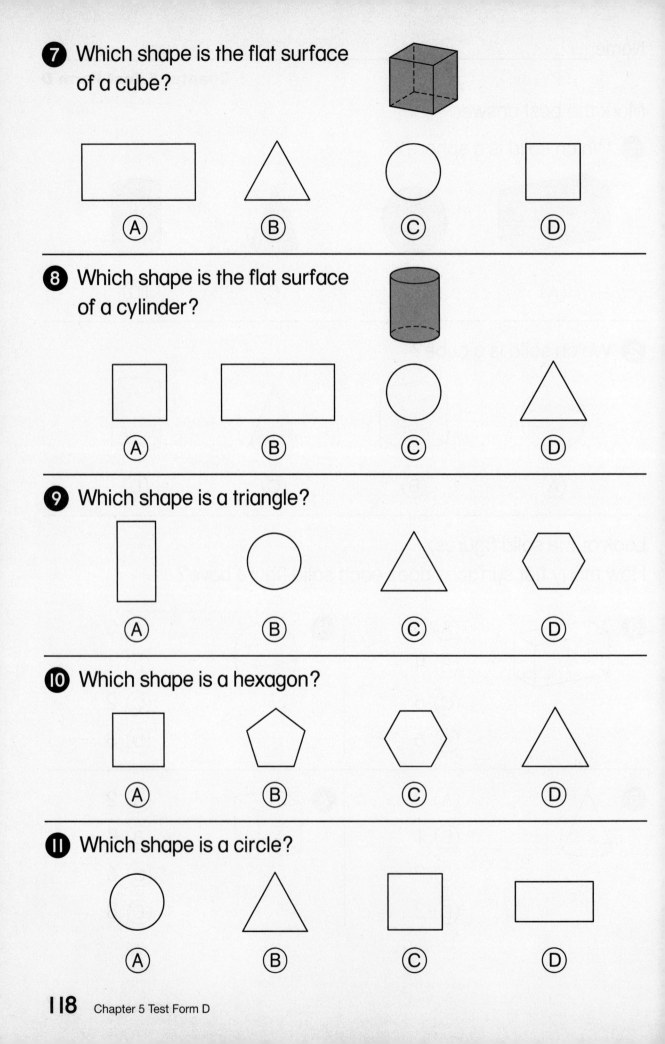

(A) (B) (C) (D)

8 Which shape is the flat surface of a cylinder?

(A) (B) (C) (D)

9 Which shape is a triangle?

(A) (B) (C) (D)

10 Which shape is a hexagon?

(A) (B) (C) (D)

11 Which shape is a circle?

(A) (B) (C) (D)

12 How many straight sides does this square have?

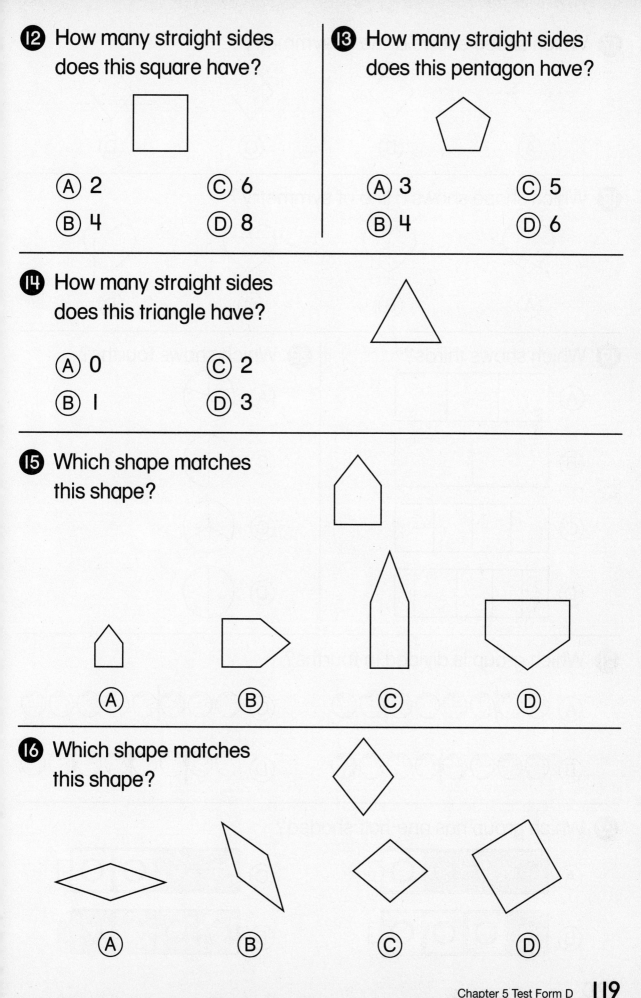

Ⓐ 2   Ⓒ 6

Ⓑ 4   Ⓓ 8

13 How many straight sides does this pentagon have?

Ⓐ 3   Ⓒ 5

Ⓑ 4   Ⓓ 6

14 How many straight sides does this triangle have?

Ⓐ 0   Ⓒ 2

Ⓑ 1   Ⓓ 3

15 Which shape matches this shape?

Ⓐ   Ⓑ   Ⓒ   Ⓓ

16 Which shape matches this shape?

Ⓐ   Ⓑ   Ⓒ   Ⓓ

17 Which shape shows a line of symmetry?

Ⓐ   Ⓑ   Ⓒ   Ⓓ

18 Which shape shows a line of symmetry?

Ⓐ   Ⓑ   Ⓒ   Ⓓ

19 Which shows thirds?

Ⓐ
Ⓑ
Ⓒ
Ⓓ

20 Which shows fourths?

Ⓐ
Ⓑ
Ⓒ
Ⓓ

21 Which group is divided in fourths?

Ⓐ   Ⓒ

Ⓑ   Ⓓ

22 Which group has one-half shaded?

Ⓐ   Ⓒ

Ⓑ   Ⓓ

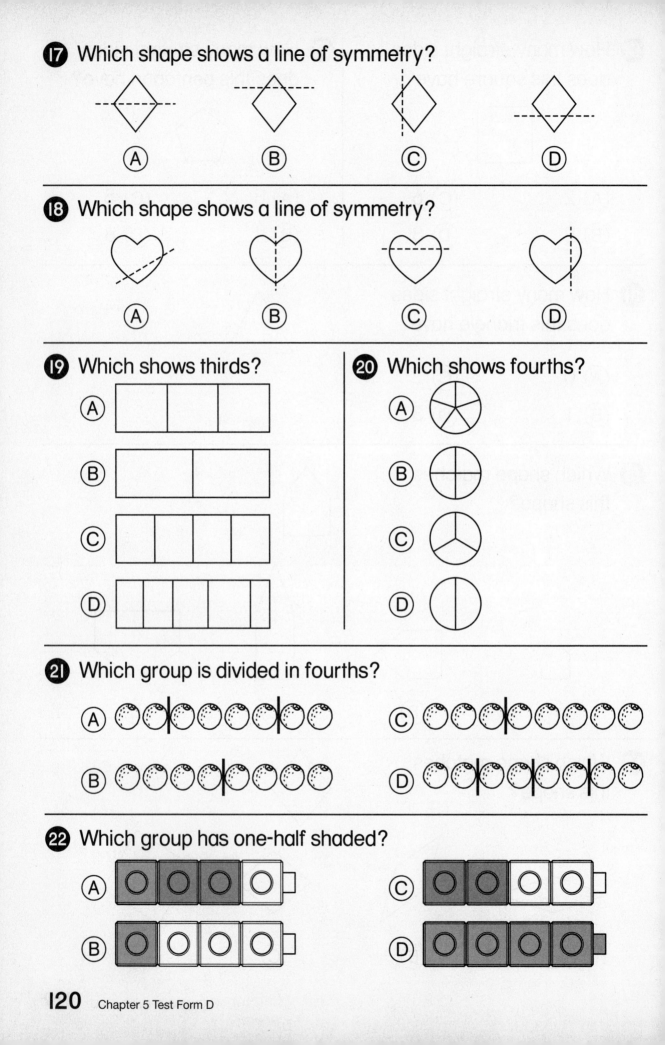

Name _____

1 Circle the event that takes more time.

 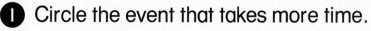

2 Write the time shown on the clock.

_____ o'clock

3 Show 9 o'clock by writing the time on the digital clock and drawing the hour hand on the analog clock.

9 o'clock

4 Match the pictures with the symbols for morning, afternoon, and evening.

morning

afternoon

evening

November						
Sun	Mon	Tue	Wed	Thur	Fri	Sat
					1	2
3		5	6	7	8	9
	11	12	13	14		16
17	18	19	20	21		23
24	25	26		28	29	30

5 Write the missing dates.

6 Color November 13 red.

Name _____

1 How long does this activity take? Circle the correct answer.

less than 1 minute

more than 1 minute

Draw the hands on each clock face.
Then write the time on the other clock.

2 7 o'clock

3 3 o'clock

Write the same time.

4

5

Answer the questions.

6 What day comes after
Thursday?

Tuesday, Wednesday,
Thursday

7 What month comes after
September?

April	May	June
July	August	September

_____   _____

8 When did this activity happen? Draw a line to match.

· morning

· afternoon

· night

9 About how long does each activity take? Draw lines to match.

about 2 minutes   about 2 hours   about 2 days

10 Use the schedule to answer the question.

At what time does Sue go to
see Aunt Leona?

_____

Sue's Schedule	
4:00	Dance Class
6:00	Visit Aunt Leona

11 Write the starting time and the ending time.
Then draw the hands on the clock to show
the ending time.

____ o'clock ➡ I hour ➡ ____ o'clock

Name _____

1 How long does this activity take? Circle the correct answer.

less than 1 minute

more than 1 minute

Draw the hands on each clock face.
Then write the time on the other clock.

2   8 o'clock   **3**   6 o'clock

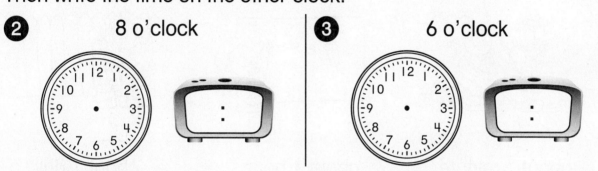

Write the same time.

4   **5**

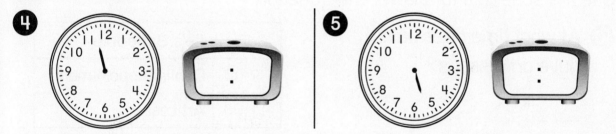

Answer the questions.

6 What day comes after
Monday?

Saturday, Sunday, Monday

7 What month comes after
March?

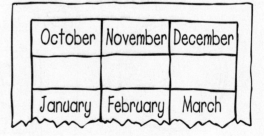

October	November	December
January	February	March

_____   _____

8 When did this activity happen? Draw a line to match.

· morning

· afternoon

· night

9 About how long does each activity take? Draw lines to match.

·   ·   ·

about 1 minute   about 1 hour   about 1 day

Use the schedule to answer the question.

10 At what time does Julie have art lessons?

_____

Julie's Schedule	
9:00	Dentist Appointment
11:00	Art Lesson

11 Write the starting time and the ending time.
Then draw the hands on the clock to show
the ending time.

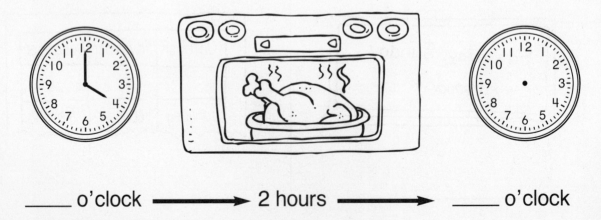

_____ o'clock ⟶ 2 hours ⟶ _____ o'clock

Mark the best answer.

How long does this activity take?

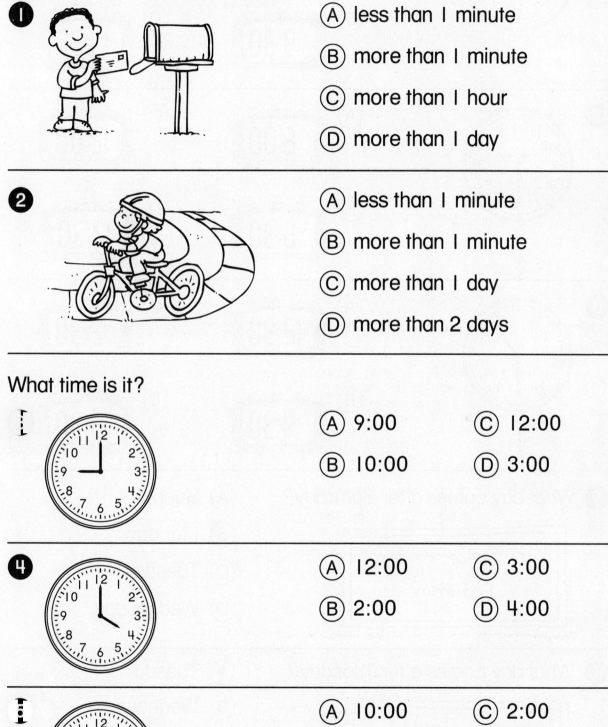

1

- Ⓐ less than 1 minute
- Ⓑ more than 1 minute
- Ⓒ more than 1 hour
- Ⓓ more than 1 day

2

- Ⓐ less than 1 minute
- Ⓑ more than 1 minute
- Ⓒ more than 1 day
- Ⓓ more than 2 days

What time is it?

3

- Ⓐ 9:00
- Ⓒ 12:00
- Ⓑ 10:00
- Ⓓ 3:00

4

- Ⓐ 12:00
- Ⓒ 3:00
- Ⓑ 2:00
- Ⓓ 4:00

5

- Ⓐ 10:00
- Ⓒ 2:00
- Ⓑ 12:00
- Ⓓ 3:00

Which clock shows the same time?

6

A 8:30

B 9:30

C 10:30

D 11:30

7

A 6:00

B 6:30

C 12:00

D 12:30

8

A 12:30

B 1:30

C 2:30

D 3:30

9 What day comes after Saturday?

Thursday, Friday, Saturday

A Sunday

B Monday

C Tuesday

D Wednesday

10 What day comes after Tuesday?

Sunday, Monday, Tuesday

A Tuesday

B Wednesday

C Friday

D Saturday

11 Which month comes after January?

August	September	October
November	December	January

- (A) February
- (B) March
- (C) June
- (D) December

12 Which month comes after April?

November	December	January
February	March	April

- (A) March
- (B) May
- (C) June
- (D) July

When did this activity happen?

13

- (A) morning
- (B) afternoon
- (C) night

14

- (A) morning
- (B) afternoon
- (C) night

About how long does each activity take?

15

- (A) about 1 minute
- (B) about 1 hour
- (C) about 1 day

16

- (A) about 2 minutes
- (B) about 2 hours
- (C) about 2 days

Use the schedule to answer Questions 17–18.

Carla's Saturday Schedule	
8:00	Pancake Breakfast
9:00	Haircut
9:30	Library
10:00	Swimming Lesson
10:30	Dog Walking Job

17 At what time does Carla have swimming lessons?

Ⓐ 9:00   Ⓒ 10:00

Ⓑ 9:30   Ⓓ 10:30

18 At what time does Carla get her hair cut?

Ⓐ 9:00   Ⓒ 10:00

Ⓑ 9:30   Ⓓ 10:30

What is the ending time?

19

1:00 ———→ 2 hours ———————→ _____ o'clock

2:00   3:00   4:00   5:00

Ⓐ   Ⓑ   Ⓒ   Ⓓ

20

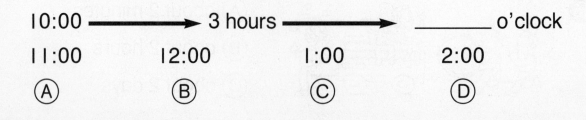

10:00 ———→ 3 hours ———————→ _____ o'clock

11:00   12:00   1:00   2:00

Ⓐ   Ⓑ   Ⓒ   Ⓓ

Name _____

Mark the best answer.

How long does this activity take?

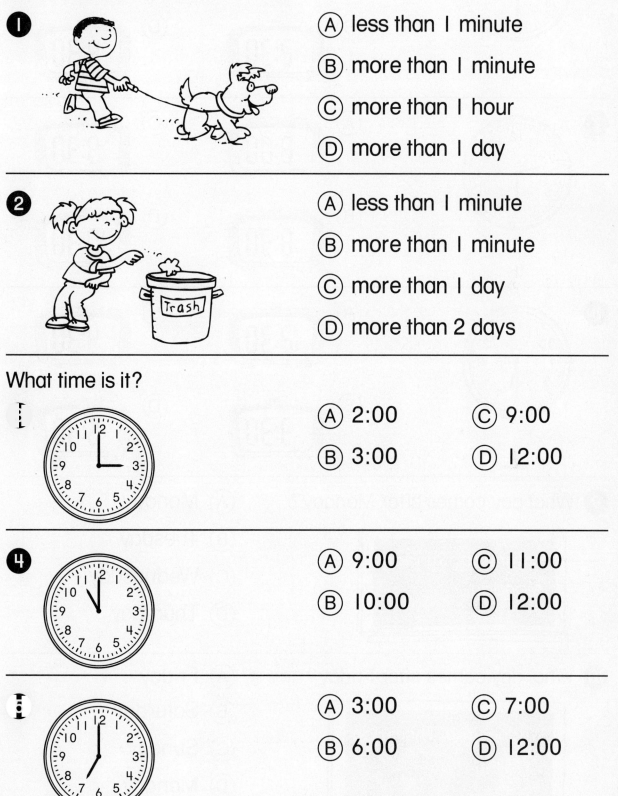

1

(A) less than 1 minute

(B) more than 1 minute

(C) more than 1 hour

(D) more than 1 day

2

(A) less than 1 minute

(B) more than 1 minute

(C) more than 1 day

(D) more than 2 days

What time is it?

3

(A) 2:00   (C) 9:00

(B) 3:00   (D) 12:00

4

(A) 9:00   (C) 11:00

(B) 10:00   (D) 12:00

5

(A) 3:00   (C) 7:00

(B) 6:00   (D) 12:00

Which clock shows the same time?

6

(A) 1:30

(B) 2:30

(C) 3:30

(D) 4:30

7

(A) 8:00

(B) 8:30

(C) 9:30

(D) 10:30

8

(A) 12:30

(B) 3:30

(C) 4:30

(D) 5:30

9 What day comes after Monday?

Saturday, Sunday
Monday

(A) Monday
(B) Tuesday
(C) Wednesday
(D) Thursday

10 What day comes after Friday?

Wednesday, Thursday
Friday

(A) Friday
(B) Saturday
(C) Sunday
(D) Monday

11 Which month comes after September?

April	May	June
July	August	September

- (A) October
- (B) December
- (C) February
- (D) August

---

12 Which month comes after February?

September	October	November
December	January	February

- (A) July
- (B) August
- (C) March
- (D) May

When did this activity happen?

13

- (A) morning
- (B) afternoon
- (C) night

14

- (A) morning
- (B) afternoon
- (C) night

About how long does each activity take?

15

- (A) about 1 minute
- (B) about 1 hour
- (C) about 1 day

16

- (A) about 3 minutes
- (B) about 3 hours
- (C) about 3 days

Use the schedule to answer Questions 17–18.

Diego's After-School Schedule	
3:00	After-School Care
5:00	Dinner
5:30	Scout Meeting
6:00	Soccer Practice
7:30	Homework

17 At what time does Diego have his Scout meeting?

(A) 3:00 (C) 5:30

(B) 5:00 (D) 6:00

18 At what time does Diego do his homework?

(A) 5:00 (C) 6:00

(B) 5:30 (D) 7:30

What is the ending time?

19

9:00 ⟶ 2 hours ⟶ _____ o'clock

10:00   11:00   12:00   1:00

(A)   (B)   (C)   (D)

20

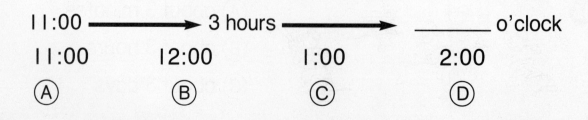

11:00 ⟶ 3 hours ⟶ _____ o'clock

11:00   12:00   1:00   2:00

(A)   (B)   (C)   (D)

Name _____

Mark the best answer.

1 Find the pattern. Mark the pattern unit.

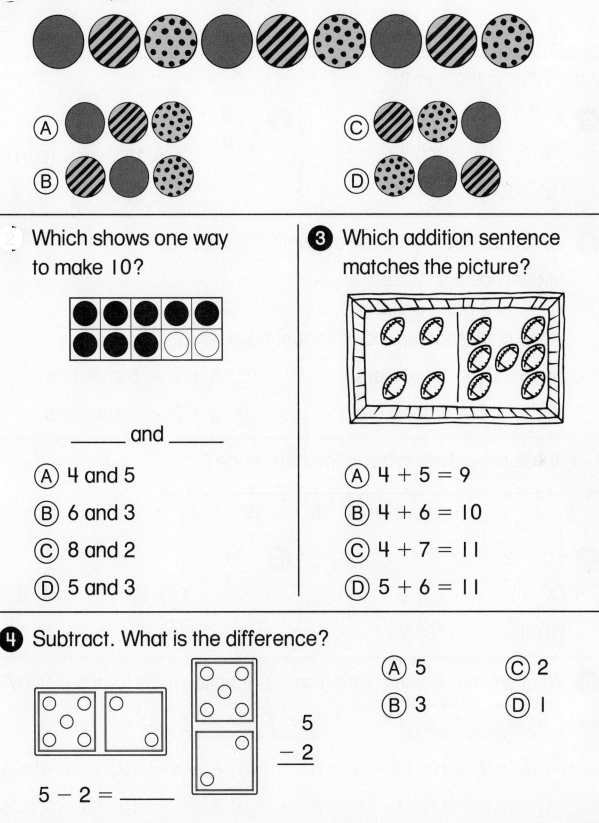

Ⓐ

Ⓑ

Ⓒ

Ⓓ

2 Which shows one way to make 10?

_____ and _____

Ⓐ 4 and 5

Ⓑ 6 and 3

Ⓒ 8 and 2

Ⓓ 5 and 3

3 Which addition sentence matches the picture?

Ⓐ 4 + 5 = 9

Ⓑ 4 + 6 = 10

Ⓒ 4 + 7 = 11

Ⓓ 5 + 6 = 11

4 Subtract. What is the difference?

5 − 2 = _____

$$\begin{array}{r} 5 \\ -\ 2 \\ \hline \end{array}$$

Ⓐ 5   Ⓒ 2

Ⓑ 3   Ⓓ 1

5 Which subtraction sentence shows how many more pails?

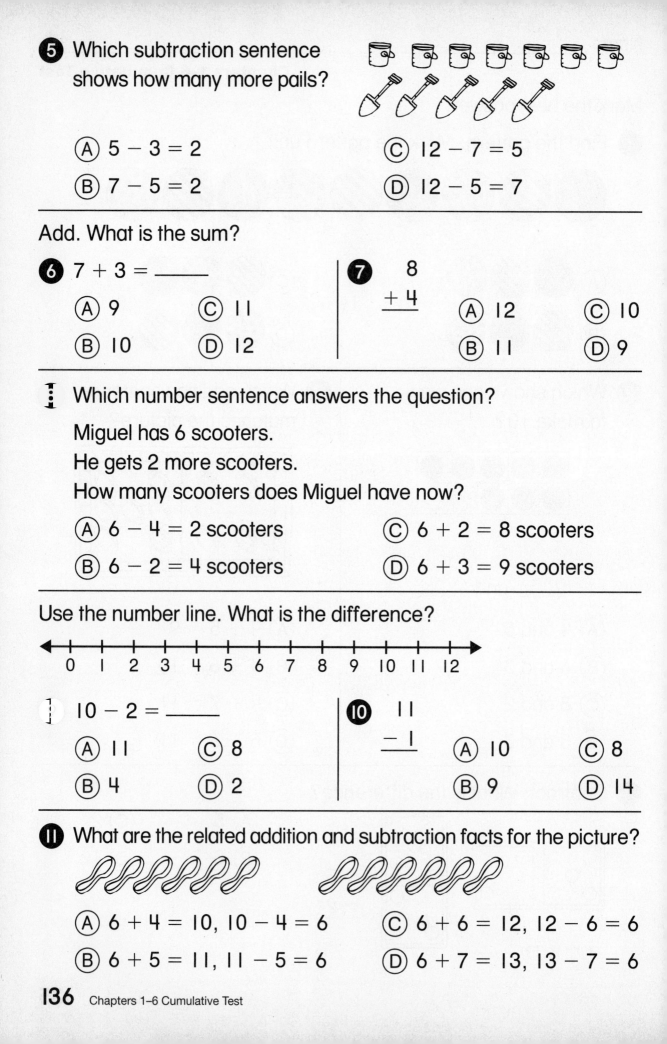

Ⓐ 5 − 3 = 2   Ⓒ 12 − 7 = 5

Ⓑ 7 − 5 = 2   Ⓓ 12 − 5 = 7

Add. What is the sum?

6 7 + 3 = _____

Ⓐ 9   Ⓒ 11

Ⓑ 10   Ⓓ 12

7   8
      + 4
      ____

Ⓐ 12   Ⓒ 10

Ⓑ 11   Ⓓ 9

---

8 Which number sentence answers the question?

Miguel has 6 scooters.
He gets 2 more scooters.
How many scooters does Miguel have now?

Ⓐ 6 − 4 = 2 scooters   Ⓒ 6 + 2 = 8 scooters

Ⓑ 6 − 2 = 4 scooters   Ⓓ 6 + 3 = 9 scooters

Use the number line. What is the difference?

0 1 2 3 4 5 6 7 8 9 10 11 12

9 10 − 2 = _____

Ⓐ 11   Ⓒ 8

Ⓑ 4   Ⓓ 2

10 11
      − 1
      ____

Ⓐ 10   Ⓒ 8

Ⓑ 9   Ⓓ 14

---

11 What are the related addition and subtraction facts for the picture?

Ⓐ 6 + 4 = 10, 10 − 4 = 6   Ⓒ 6 + 6 = 12, 12 − 6 = 6

Ⓑ 6 + 5 = 11, 11 − 5 = 6   Ⓓ 6 + 7 = 13, 13 − 7 = 6

12 Which addition fact will help you subtract?

$$12 - 8 = \underline{\qquad}$$

Ⓐ $4 + 8 = 12$

Ⓒ $8 + 12 = 20$

Ⓑ $8 + 5 = 13$

Ⓓ $12 + 4 = 16$

13 Which subtraction sentence answers the question?

There are 6 birds.
There are 5 worms.
How many fewer worms are there than birds?

Ⓐ $5 - 5 = 0$

Ⓒ $5 - 1 = 4$

Ⓑ $6 - 5 = 1$

Ⓓ $6 - 1 = 5$

14 Which solid is a cone?

Ⓐ   Ⓑ   Ⓒ   Ⓓ

15 How many flat surfaces does this solid figure have?

Ⓐ 0   Ⓒ 2

Ⓑ 1   Ⓓ 4

16 Which shape is the flat surface of a cube?

Ⓐ   Ⓑ   Ⓒ   Ⓓ

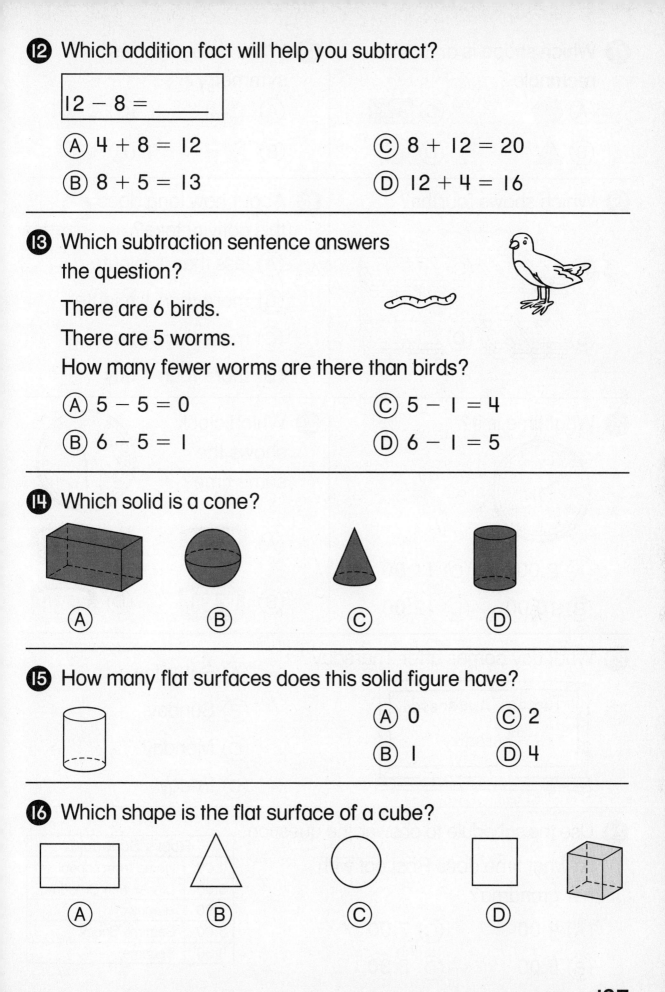

17 Which shape is a rectangle?

Ⓐ 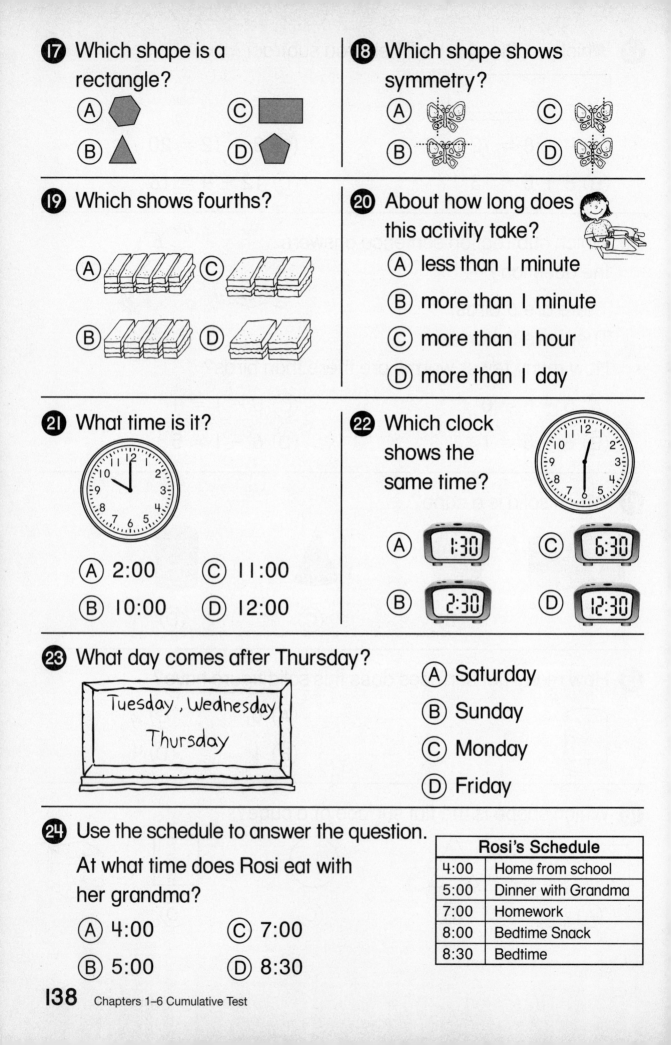   Ⓒ

Ⓑ   Ⓓ

18 Which shape shows symmetry?

Ⓐ   Ⓒ

Ⓑ   Ⓓ

19 Which shows fourths?

Ⓐ   Ⓒ

Ⓑ   Ⓓ

20 About how long does this activity take?

Ⓐ less than 1 minute

Ⓑ more than 1 minute

Ⓒ more than 1 hour

Ⓓ more than 1 day

21 What time is it?

Ⓐ 2:00   Ⓒ 11:00

Ⓑ 10:00   Ⓓ 12:00

22 Which clock shows the same time?

Ⓐ 1:30   Ⓒ 6:30

Ⓑ 2:30   Ⓓ 12:30

23 What day comes after Thursday?

Tuesday, Wednesday
Thursday

Ⓐ Saturday

Ⓑ Sunday

Ⓒ Monday

Ⓓ Friday

24 Use the schedule to answer the question.

At what time does Rosi eat with her grandma?

Ⓐ 4:00   Ⓒ 7:00

Ⓑ 5:00   Ⓓ 8:30

Rosi's Schedule	
4:00	Home from school
5:00	Dinner with Grandma
7:00	Homework
8:00	Bedtime Snack
8:30	Bedtime

Name _____

Count the objects. Write the number.

1 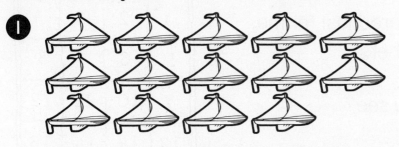 _____

Count the groups of 10 beads. Count on the beads
that are left. Write how many beads there are.

2 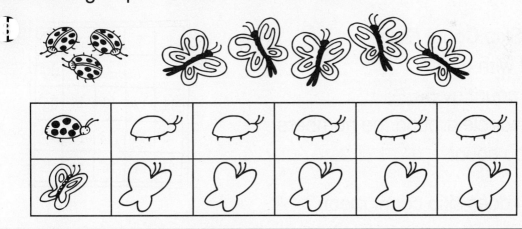 _____

Color a picture on the graph for each insect.
Circle the group of insects that has more.

3

🐞					
🦋					

Count by 5s. Write how many.

4 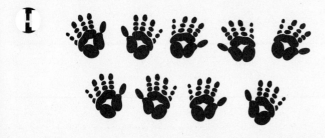 _____

Name _____

1 Grandma made a quilt 1, 2, 3.
With 16 parts numbered just for me.
Color the even numbers.

What pattern do you see?

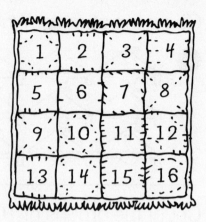

_____

_____

_____

_____

2 The Skip Count Quilt
Start with 5.
Skip count by 5s.
Put a circle around the numbers
as you count.

What does skip count mean?

_____

_____

_____

Name _____

Write each number as 10 and some left over.

1 15 is 10 and _____.   **2** 18 is 10 and _____.

3 Count by 10s. Then write the numbers.

_____ groups of 10

_____

Count on or count back by 1s. Use a hundred chart if you like.

4 71, 72, 73, _____, _____, _____, _____, _____, _____

5 41, 40, 39, _____, _____, _____, _____, _____, _____

6 Circle groups of 10. Then write the numbers.

_____ groups of 10

_____ left over

_____ in all

7 Use the graph to answer the question.

Of which color toy car are there the most? _____

My Toy Car Collection	
Red	
Silver	
White	

8 Color the numbers you say when you count by 5s.

51	52	53	54	55	56	57	58	59	60
61	62	63	64	65	66	67	68	69	70
71	72	73	74	75	76	77	78	79	80

9 How many mittens are there? Count by 2s.

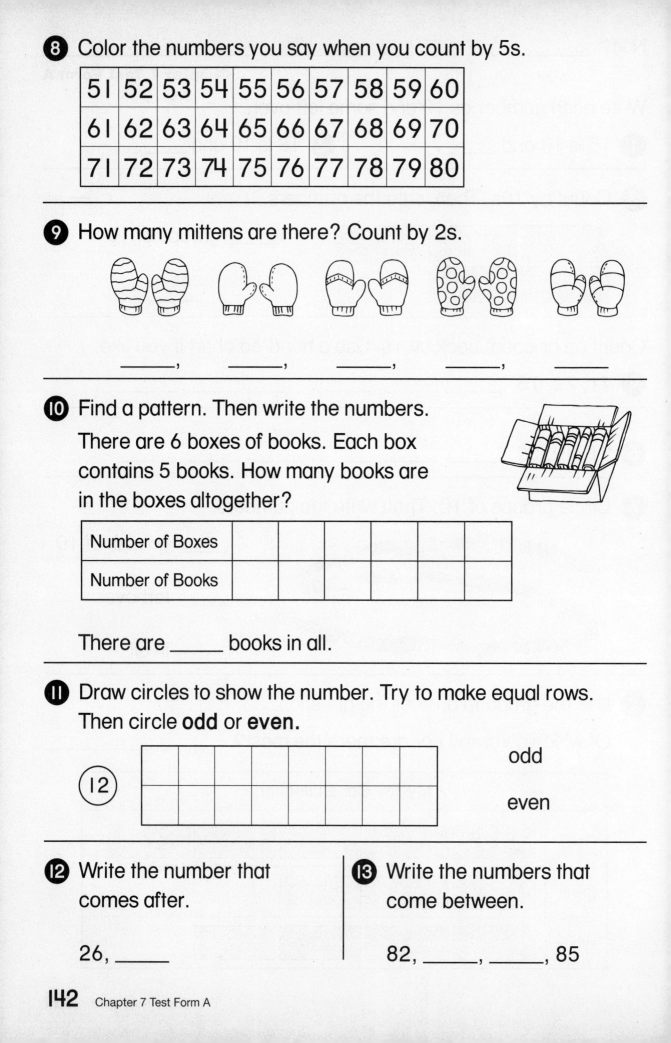

_____, _____, _____, _____, _____

10 Find a pattern. Then write the numbers.

There are 6 boxes of books. Each box contains 5 books. How many books are in the boxes altogether?

Number of Boxes						
Number of Books						

There are _____ books in all.

11 Draw circles to show the number. Try to make equal rows. Then circle **odd** or **even**.

(12)

odd

even

12 Write the number that comes after.

26, _____

13 Write the numbers that come between.

82, _____, _____, 85

Name _____

Write each number as 10 and some left over.

1 13 is 10 and _____.   **2** 16 is 10 and _____.

3 Count by 10s. Then write the numbers.

_____ groups of 10

_____

Count on or count back by 1s. Use a hundred chart if you like.

4 31, 30, 29, _____, _____, _____, _____, _____, _____

5 51, 52, 53, _____, _____, _____, _____, _____, _____

6 Circle groups of 10. Then write the numbers.

_____ groups of 10

_____ left over

_____ in all

7 Use the graph to answer the question.

Of which color rocks are there the most? _____

My Rock Collection	
Brown	
Gray	
Clear	

8 Color the numbers you say when you count by 5s.

1	2	3	4	5	6	7	8	9	10
11	12	13	14	15	16	17	18	19	20
21	22	23	24	25	26	27	28	29	30

9 How many shoes are there? Count by 2s.

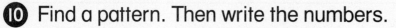

_____, _____, _____, _____, _____, _____, _____

10 Find a pattern. Then write the numbers.

There are 7 baskets with apples.

Each basket contains 10 apples.

How many apples are in the baskets altogether?

Number of Baskets							
Number of Apples							

There are _____ apples in all the baskets.

11 Draw circles to show the number. Try to make equal rows.
Then circle **odd** or **even.**

7

odd

even

12 Write the number that comes after.

15, _____

13 Write the numbers that come between.

19, _____, _____, 22

Name _____

Mark the best answer.

1 Which number is 10 and 7 left over?

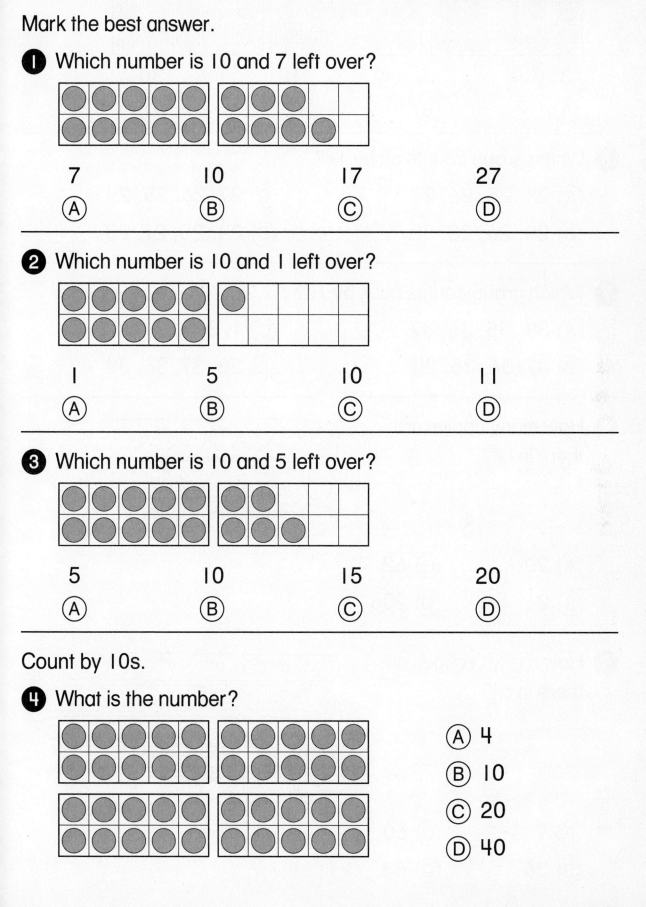

7	10	17	27
Ⓐ	Ⓑ	Ⓒ	Ⓓ

2 Which number is 10 and 1 left over?

1	5	10	11
Ⓐ	Ⓑ	Ⓒ	Ⓓ

3 Which number is 10 and 5 left over?

5	10	15	20
Ⓐ	Ⓑ	Ⓒ	Ⓓ

Count by 10s.

4 What is the number?

Ⓐ 4

Ⓑ 10

Ⓒ 20

Ⓓ 40

5 What is the number?

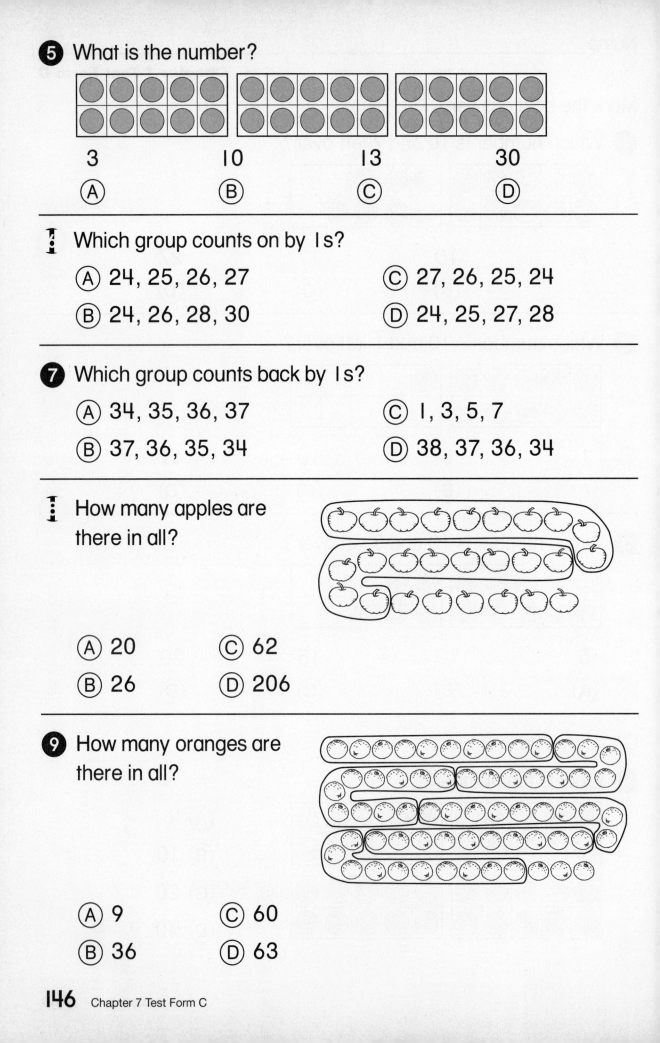

3	10	13	30
Ⓐ	Ⓑ	Ⓒ	Ⓓ

---

6 Which group counts on by 1s?

Ⓐ 24, 25, 26, 27   Ⓒ 27, 26, 25, 24

Ⓑ 24, 26, 28, 30   Ⓓ 24, 25, 27, 28

---

7 Which group counts back by 1s?

Ⓐ 34, 35, 36, 37   Ⓒ 1, 3, 5, 7

Ⓑ 37, 36, 35, 34   Ⓓ 38, 37, 36, 34

---

8 How many apples are there in all?

Ⓐ 20   Ⓒ 62

Ⓑ 26   Ⓓ 206

---

9 How many oranges are there in all?

Ⓐ 9   Ⓒ 60

Ⓑ 36   Ⓓ 63

Use the graph to answer the following questions.

My Leaf Collection

Yellow	⬡⬡⬡⬡⬡ ⬡⬡⬡⬡⬡
Red	⬡⬡⬡⬡⬡
Green	⬡⬡⬡⬡⬡ ⬡⬡⬡⬡⬡ ⬡⬡⬡⬡⬡ ⬡⬡⬡⬡⬡
Orange	⬡⬡⬡⬡⬡ ⬡⬡⬡⬡⬡ ⬡⬡⬡⬡⬡

10 Of which color leaf are there the most?

Ⓐ Yellow   Ⓒ Green

Ⓑ Red   Ⓓ Orange

---

11 Of which color leaf are there the fewest?

Ⓐ Yellow   Ⓒ Green

Ⓑ Red   Ⓓ Orange

---

12 Which numbers do you say when you count by 5s?

| 80 | 81 | 82 | 83 | 84 | 85 | 86 | 87 | 88 | 89 | 90 |

Ⓐ 80, 82, 84, 86, 88, 90   Ⓒ 80, 85, 90

Ⓑ 80, 81, 82, 83, 84, 85   Ⓓ 83, 86, 89

---

13 Which numbers do you say when you count by 5s?

| 21 | 22 | 23 | 24 | 25 | 26 | 27 | 28 | 29 | 30 | 31 |

Ⓐ 25   Ⓒ 25, 30

Ⓑ 21, 30   Ⓓ 21, 22, 23, 24, 25

14 How many mittens are there?
Count by 2s.

1	2	3	6
Ⓐ	Ⓑ	Ⓒ	Ⓓ

15 How many hats are there?
Count by 5s.

4	5	10	20
Ⓐ	Ⓑ	Ⓒ	Ⓓ

16 There are 4 shelves in a bookshelf
with 10 books on each shelf.
How many books are there in all?

Number of Shelves	1	2	3	4
Number of Books	10	20	30	40

Ⓐ 4
Ⓑ 10
Ⓒ 40
Ⓓ 44

17 Which number is odd?

Ⓐ 16   Ⓒ 18
Ⓑ 17   Ⓓ 20

18 Which number is even?

Ⓐ 3   Ⓒ 15
Ⓑ 9   Ⓓ 20

19 Which number comes after?

17, _____

Ⓐ 15   Ⓒ 18
Ⓑ 16   Ⓓ 19

20 Which number comes before?

_____, 53

Ⓐ 45   Ⓒ 52
Ⓑ 50   Ⓓ 54

21 Which numbers come between?

32, _____, _____, 35

36, 37	34, 35	33, 34	30, 31
Ⓐ	Ⓑ	Ⓒ	Ⓓ

Name _____

Mark the best answer.

1 Which number is 10 and 2 left over?

2	10	12	22
Ⓐ	Ⓑ	Ⓒ	Ⓓ

2 Which number is 10 and 9 left over?

9	10	19	20
Ⓐ	Ⓑ	Ⓒ	Ⓓ

3 Which number is 10 and 3 left over?

23	13	10	3
Ⓐ	Ⓑ	Ⓒ	Ⓓ

Count by 10s.

4 What is the number?

2	12	20	40
Ⓐ	Ⓑ	Ⓒ	Ⓓ

5 What is the number?

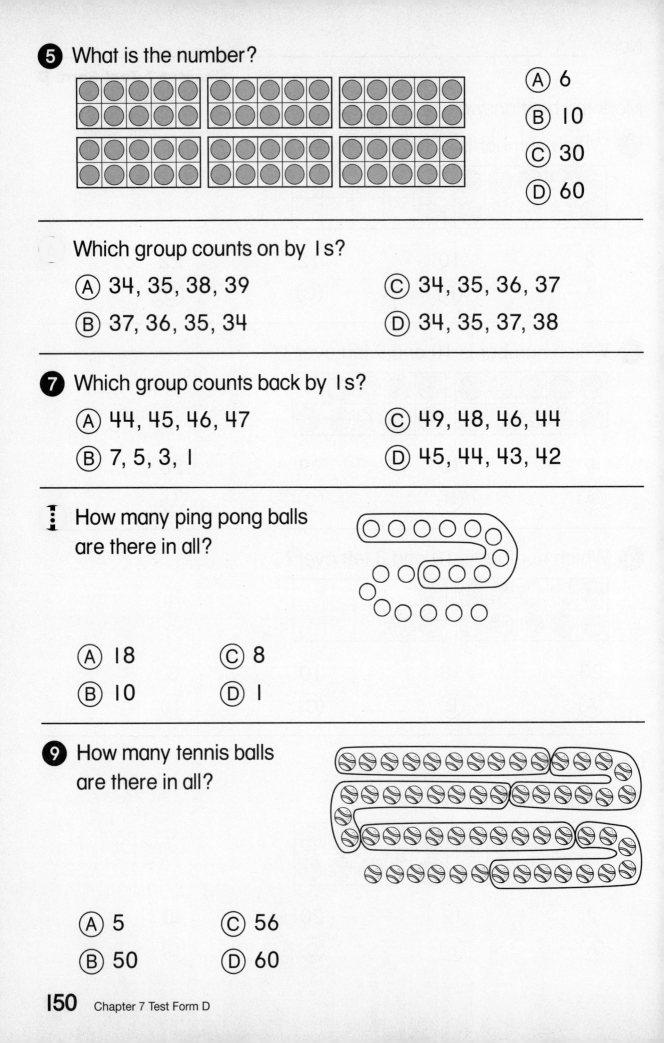

(A) 6

(B) 10

(C) 30

(D) 60

Which group counts on by 1s?

(A) 34, 35, 38, 39

(C) 34, 35, 36, 37

(B) 37, 36, 35, 34

(D) 34, 35, 37, 38

---

7 Which group counts back by 1s?

(A) 44, 45, 46, 47

(C) 49, 48, 46, 44

(B) 7, 5, 3, 1

(D) 45, 44, 43, 42

How many ping pong balls are there in all?

(A) 18   (C) 8

(B) 10   (D) 1

---

9 How many tennis balls are there in all?

(A) 5   (C) 56

(B) 50   (D) 60

Use the graph to answer the following questions.

Fruit Orders

Apples	
Oranges	
Bananas	
Pineapples	

10 Of which kind of fruit order are there the most?

(A) Apples   (C) Bananas

(B) Oranges   (D) Pineapples

11 Of which kind of fruit order are there the fewest?

(A) Pineapples   (C) Oranges

(B) Bananas   (D) Apples

12 Which numbers do you say when you count by 5s?

| 30 | 31 | 32 | 33 | 34 | 35 | 36 | 37 | 38 | 39 | 40 |

(A) 30, 32, 34, 36, 38, 40   (C) 35

(B) 31, 32, 33, 34, 35   (D) 30, 35, 40

13 Which numbers do you say when you count by 5s?

| 71 | 72 | 73 | 74 | 75 | 76 | 77 | 78 | 79 | 80 | 81 |

(A) 75   (C) 72, 73, 74, 75, 76

(B) 75, 80   (D) 72, 74, 76, 78, 80

14 How many paper dolls are there?
Count by 2s.

⿹⿹ ⿹⿹ ⿹⿹
⿹⿹ ⿹⿹

10	8	5	2
Ⓐ	Ⓑ	Ⓒ	Ⓓ

---

15 How many soccer balls are there?
Count by 5s.

5	6	11	30
Ⓐ	Ⓑ	Ⓒ	Ⓓ

---

16 There are 5 plates with 10 muffins on each plate. How many muffins are there in all?

Ⓐ 5
Ⓑ 10
Ⓒ 15
Ⓓ 50

Number of Plates	1	2	3	4	5
Number of Muffins	10	20	30	40	50

---

17 Which number is odd?

Ⓐ 11   Ⓒ 14

Ⓑ 12   Ⓓ 20

18 Which number is even?

Ⓐ 4   Ⓒ 15

Ⓑ 11   Ⓓ 21

---

19 Which number comes after?

23, _____

Ⓐ 22   Ⓒ 25

Ⓑ 24   Ⓓ 26

20 Which number comes before?

_____, 18

Ⓐ 8   Ⓒ 19

Ⓑ 17   Ⓓ 20

---

21 Which numbers come between?

50, _____, _____, 53

49, 50	51, 52	52, 53	53, 54
Ⓐ	Ⓑ	Ⓒ	Ⓓ

Name _____

Circle groups of 10. Then write the numbers.

1

_____ groups of 10

_____ left over

_____ in all

Write the numbers in order from least to greatest.

2

| 4 | 12 | 9 |

_____, _____, _____

least   between   greatest

Circle all the white shapes.

3

Circle all the cubes.

4

Write an addition sentence to answer the question.

5 There are 2 bears in the toy chest.
There are 5 more bears on the floor.
How many bears are there altogether?

____ ⊕ ____ ⊜ ____

Name

1 Write how many hundreds, tens, and ones.
Then write the number.

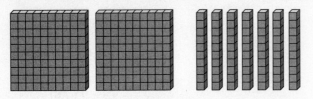

_____

Add 3 more tens. Write the number sentence.

_____

Tell or draw what the picture of the number would look like.

_____

_____

2 Vote for your favorite lunch.

Favorite Lunch					
Chicken bits	✔	✔	✔	✔	✔	
Macaroni and cheese	✔	✔	✔	✔	✔	
Hot dog	✔	✔	✔	✔	✔	

Tell why your vote decided the favorite lunch.

_____

_____

Name _____

Count the tens. Then write the numbers.

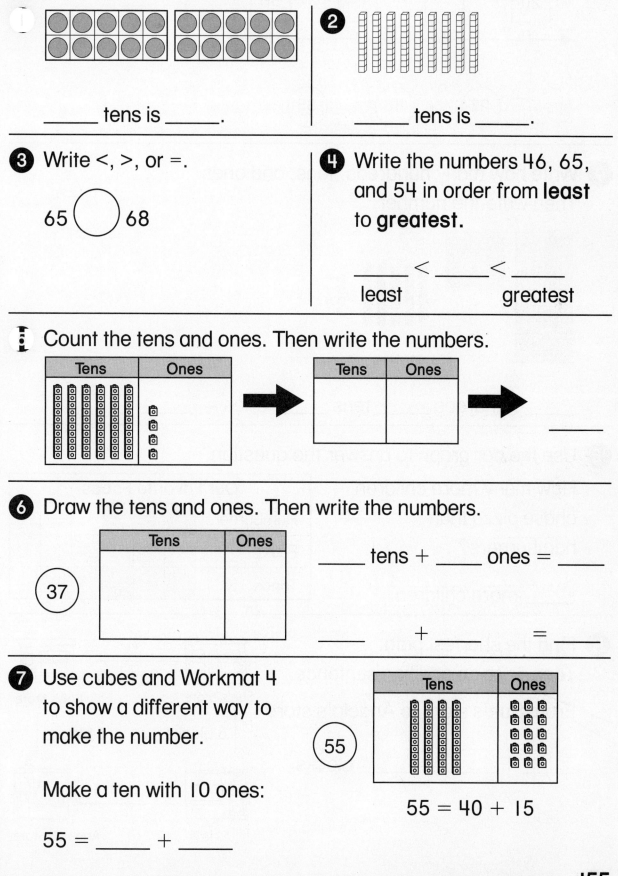

1 _____ tens is _____.

2 _____ tens is _____.

3 Write <, >, or =.

65 ◯ 68

4 Write the numbers 46, 65, and 54 in order from **least** to **greatest**.

_____ < _____ < _____
least   greatest

5 Count the tens and ones. Then write the numbers.

Tens	Ones

➡

Tens	Ones

➡ _____

6 Draw the tens and ones. Then write the numbers.

(37)

Tens	Ones

_____ tens + _____ ones = _____

_____ + _____ = _____

7 Use cubes and Workmat 4 to show a different way to make the number.

(55)

Tens	Ones

Make a ten with 10 ones:

55 = 40 + 15

55 = _____ + _____

8 Complete the number line.
Then draw lines to show where the numbers go.

| 20 | | | 50 |

27   43   35

---

9 Write how many hundreds, tens, and ones.
Then write the number.

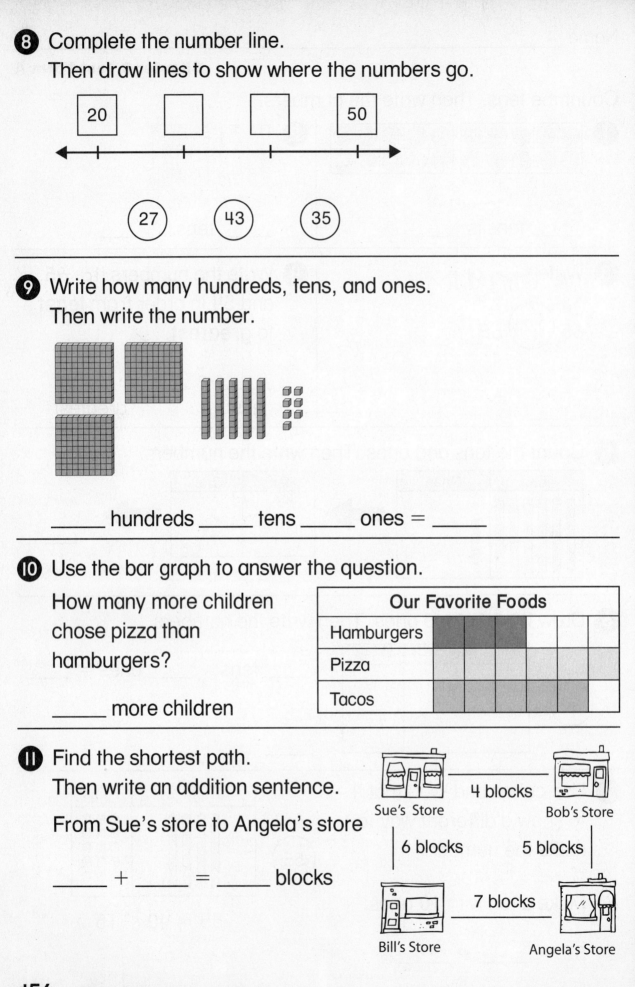

_____ hundreds _____ tens _____ ones = _____

---

10 Use the bar graph to answer the question.

How many more children chose pizza than hamburgers?

_____ more children

Our Favorite Foods					
Hamburgers					
Pizza					
Tacos					

---

11 Find the shortest path.
Then write an addition sentence.

From Sue's store to Angela's store

_____ + _____ = _____ blocks

Sue's Store   4 blocks   Bob's Store

6 blocks   5 blocks

Bill's Store   7 blocks   Angela's Store

Name _____

Count the tens. Then write the numbers.

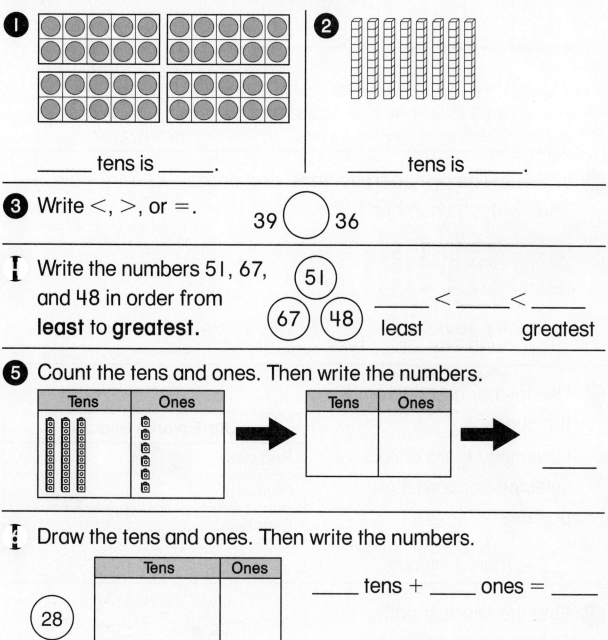

1 _____ tens is _____.

2 _____ tens is _____.

3 Write <, >, or =.   39 ◯ 36

I Write the numbers 51, 67, and 48 in order from **least** to **greatest**.

⑤¹ ⑥⁷ ⑷⁸

_____ < _____ < _____
least   greatest

5 Count the tens and ones. Then write the numbers.

Tens	Ones

➡️

Tens	Ones

➡️ _____

6 Draw the tens and ones. Then write the numbers.

Tens	Ones

㉘

_____ tens + _____ ones = _____

_____ + _____ = _____

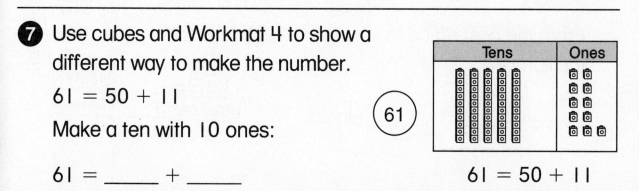

7 Use cubes and Workmat 4 to show a different way to make the number.

61 = 50 + 11

Make a ten with 10 ones:

61 = _____ + _____

㊶

Tens	Ones

61 = 50 + 11

8 Complete the number line.
Then draw lines to show where the numbers go.

30			60

52   46   33

---

9 Write how many hundreds, tens, and ones.
Then write the number.

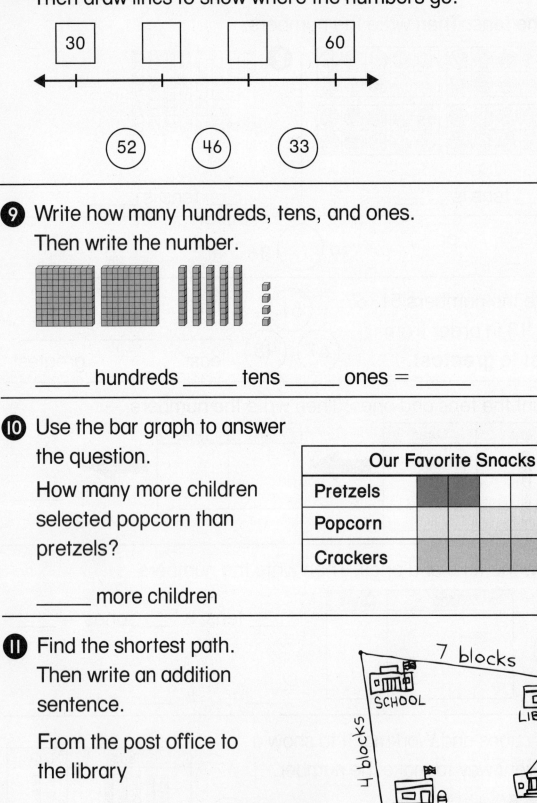

_____ hundreds _____ tens _____ ones = _____

---

10 Use the bar graph to answer the question.

How many more children selected popcorn than pretzels?

Our Favorite Snacks					
Pretzels					
Popcorn					
Crackers					

_____ more children

---

11 Find the shortest path. Then write an addition sentence.

From the post office to the library

_____ + _____ = _____ blocks

7 blocks

SCHOOL   LIBRARY

4 blocks   3 blocks

POST OFFICE   BANK

5 blocks

Name _____

Mark the best answer.

1 What is the missing number?

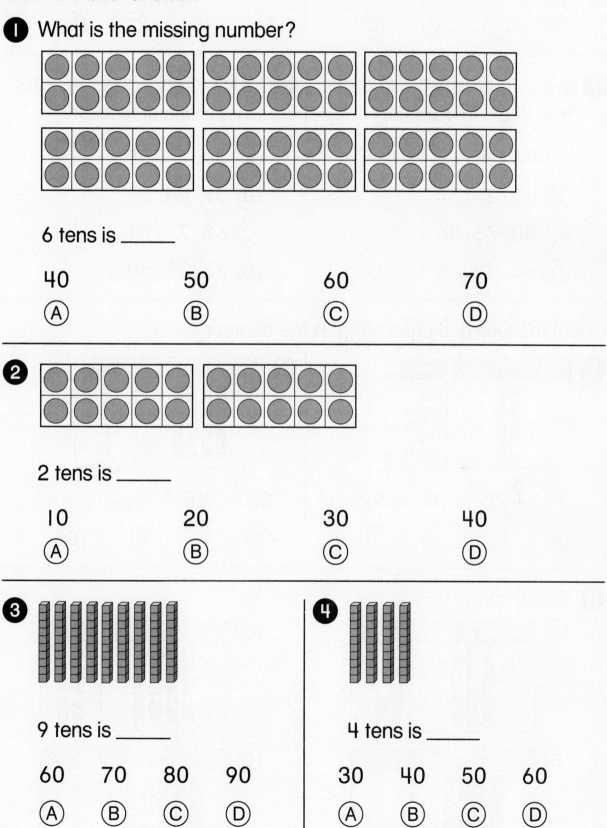

6 tens is _____

40	50	60	70
Ⓐ	Ⓑ	Ⓒ	Ⓓ

2

2 tens is _____

10	20	30	40
Ⓐ	Ⓑ	Ⓒ	Ⓓ

3

9 tens is _____

60	70	80	90
Ⓐ	Ⓑ	Ⓒ	Ⓓ

4

4 tens is _____

30	40	50	60
Ⓐ	Ⓑ	Ⓒ	Ⓓ

5 36 < _____

18	28	35	47
Ⓐ	Ⓑ	Ⓒ	Ⓓ

6 51 > _____

48	55	60	65
Ⓐ	Ⓑ	Ⓒ	Ⓓ

7 Which numbers are in order from least to greatest?

Ⓐ 96, 24, 63

Ⓑ 46, 21, 37

Ⓒ 50, 73, 86

Ⓓ 66, 43, 36

8 Which numbers are in order from greatest to least?

Ⓐ 89, 76, 65

Ⓑ 31, 28, 57

Ⓒ 63, 79, 81

Ⓓ 21, 39, 30

Count the tens and ones. What is the number?

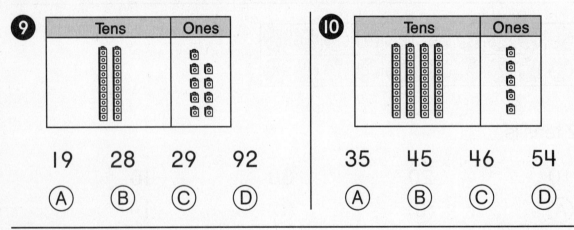

9

Tens	Ones

19	28	29	92
Ⓐ	Ⓑ	Ⓒ	Ⓓ

10

Tens	Ones

35	45	46	54
Ⓐ	Ⓑ	Ⓒ	Ⓓ

11 Which shows 48?

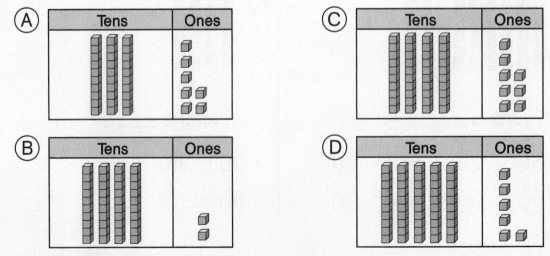

Ⓐ

Tens	Ones

Ⓒ

Tens	Ones

Ⓑ

Tens	Ones

Ⓓ

Tens	Ones

12 Which shows 63?

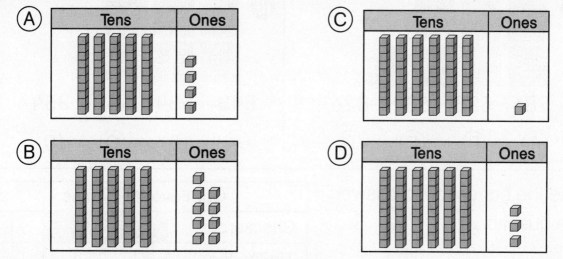

A | Tens | Ones
B | Tens | Ones
C | Tens | Ones
D | Tens | Ones

Which shows a different way to make the number?

13

Tens	Ones

$$43 = 30 + 13$$

- (A) 30 + 2
- (B) 30 + 3
- (C) 40 + 3
- (D) 40 + 13

14

Tens	Ones

$$77 = 60 + 17$$

- (A) 50 + 7
- (B) 60 + 7
- (C) 70 + 7
- (D) 70 + 17

---

15 Which number is between 70 and 80?

67	76	81	88
(A)	(B)	(C)	(D)

16 Which number is between 20 and 30?

12	19	23	32
(A)	(B)	(C)	(D)

Which number shows how many hundreds, tens, and ones?

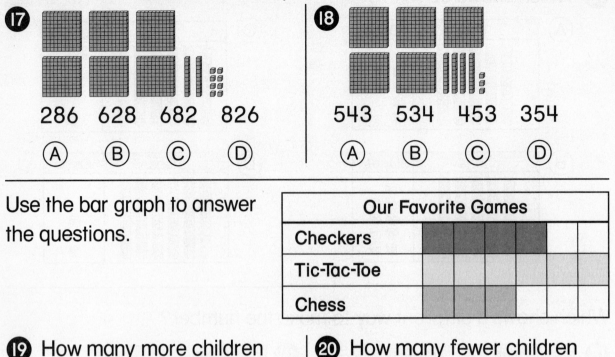

17

286   628   682   826

Ⓐ   Ⓑ   Ⓒ   Ⓓ

18

543   534   453   354

Ⓐ   Ⓑ   Ⓒ   Ⓓ

Use the bar graph to answer the questions.

Our Favorite Games					
Checkers					
Tic-Tac-Toe					
Chess					

19 How many more children selected tic-tac-toe than checkers?

1   2   3   4

Ⓐ   Ⓑ   Ⓒ   Ⓓ

20 How many fewer children selected chess than checkers?

1   2   3   4

Ⓐ   Ⓑ   Ⓒ   Ⓓ

Use the map to answer the questions.

Park   3 blocks   Carla's House

7 blocks   6 blocks

Ice Cream Shop   1 block   Lake

21 What is the shortest path from the park to the lake?

Ⓐ 6 + 1 = 7 blocks

Ⓑ 7 + 1 = 8 blocks

Ⓒ 3 + 6 = 9 blocks

Ⓓ 7 + 3 = 10 blocks

22 What is the shortest path from Carla's house to the ice cream shop?

Ⓐ 6 + 1 = 7 blocks

Ⓑ 7 + 1 = 8 blocks

Ⓒ 3 + 6 = 9 blocks

Ⓓ 7 + 3 = 10 blocks

Name _____

Mark the best answer.

1 What is the missing number?

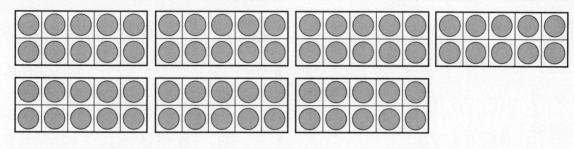
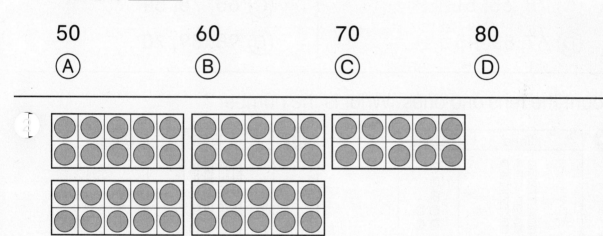

7 tens is _____

50	60	70	80
Ⓐ	Ⓑ	Ⓒ	Ⓓ

2

5 tens is _____

20	30	40	50
Ⓐ	Ⓑ	Ⓒ	Ⓓ

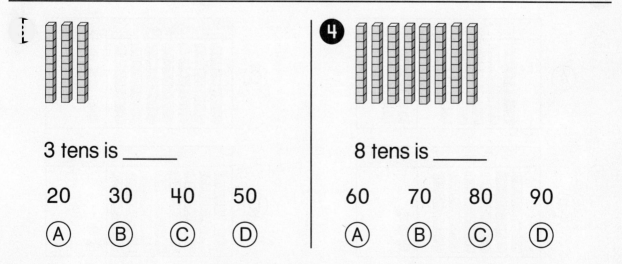

3

3 tens is _____

20	30	40	50
Ⓐ	Ⓑ	Ⓒ	Ⓓ

4

8 tens is _____

60	70	80	90
Ⓐ	Ⓑ	Ⓒ	Ⓓ

5 42 < _____

24	37	40	47
Ⓐ	Ⓑ	Ⓒ	Ⓓ

6 78 > _____

72	80	87	98
Ⓐ	Ⓑ	Ⓒ	Ⓓ

7 Which numbers are in order from least to greatest?

Ⓐ 42, 25, 50

Ⓑ 36, 51, 75

Ⓒ 78, 65, 51

Ⓓ 67, 85, 45

8 Which numbers are in order from greatest to least?

Ⓐ 26, 45, 39

Ⓑ 18, 30, 51

Ⓒ 65, 78, 54

Ⓓ 98, 89, 70

Count the tens and ones. What is the number?

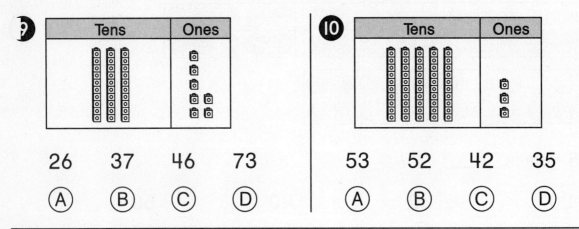

9

26	37	46	73
Ⓐ	Ⓑ	Ⓒ	Ⓓ

10

53	52	42	35
Ⓐ	Ⓑ	Ⓒ	Ⓓ

11 Which shows 75?

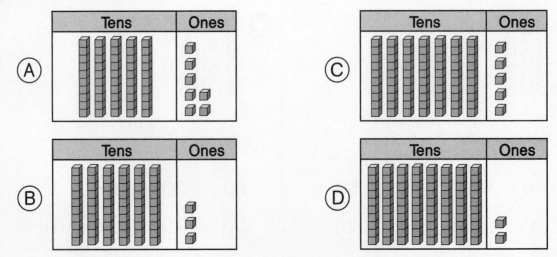

12 Which shows 28?

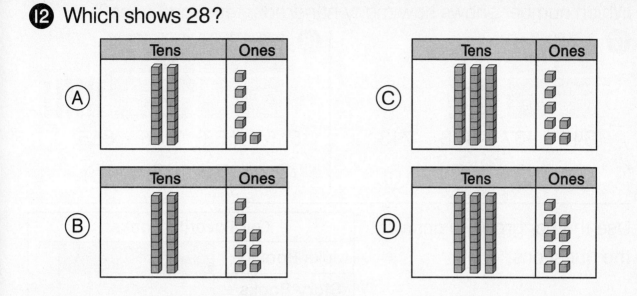

Which shows a different way to make the number?

13

Tens	Ones

$$72 = 60 + 12$$

Ⓐ $60 + 2$

Ⓑ $60 + 3$

Ⓒ $70 + 2$

Ⓓ $70 + 13$

14

Tens	Ones

$$58 = 40 + 18$$

Ⓐ $40 + 8$

Ⓑ $50 + 8$

Ⓒ $50 + 18$

Ⓓ $60 + 8$

---

15 Which number is between 40 and 50?

38	46	52	56
Ⓐ	Ⓑ	Ⓒ	Ⓓ

16 Which number is between 80 and 90?

71	78	87	98
Ⓐ	Ⓑ	Ⓒ	Ⓓ

Which number shows how many hundreds, tens, and ones?

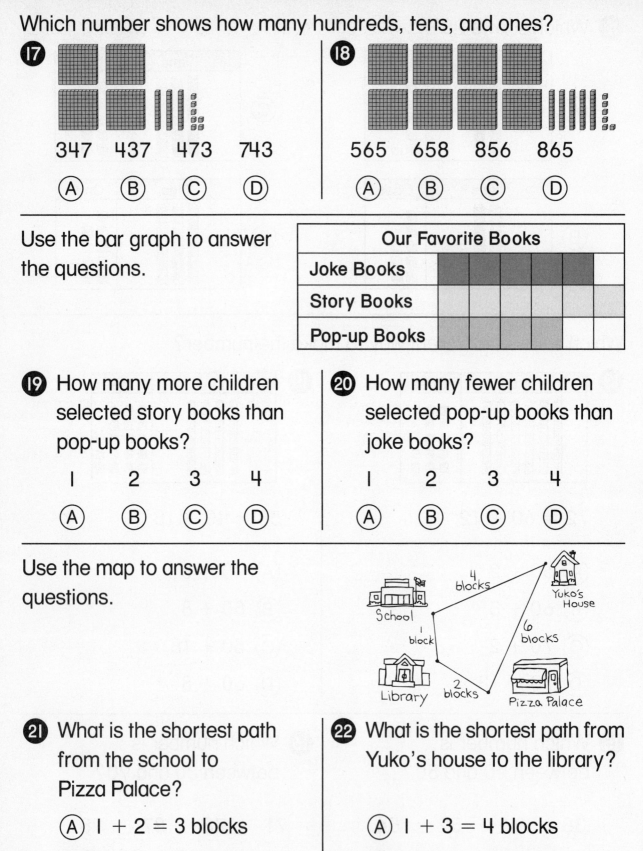

17

347   437   473   743

(A)   (B)   (C)   (D)

18

565   658   856   865

(A)   (B)   (C)   (D)

Use the bar graph to answer the questions.

Our Favorite Books					
Joke Books					
Story Books					
Pop-up Books					

19 How many more children selected story books than pop-up books?

1   2   3   4

(A)   (B)   (C)   (D)

20 How many fewer children selected pop-up books than joke books?

1   2   3   4

(A)   (B)   (C)   (D)

Use the map to answer the questions.

21 What is the shortest path from the school to Pizza Palace?

    (A) $1 + 2 = 3$ blocks

    (B) $4 + 1 = 5$ blocks

    (C) $2 + 6 = 8$ blocks

    (D) $4 + 6 = 10$ blocks

22 What is the shortest path from Yuko's house to the library?

    (A) $1 + 3 = 4$ blocks

    (B) $4 + 1 = 5$ blocks

    (C) $2 + 6 = 8$ blocks

    (D) $4 + 6 = 10$ blocks

Name _____

1 How many sides are there? Count by 5s.

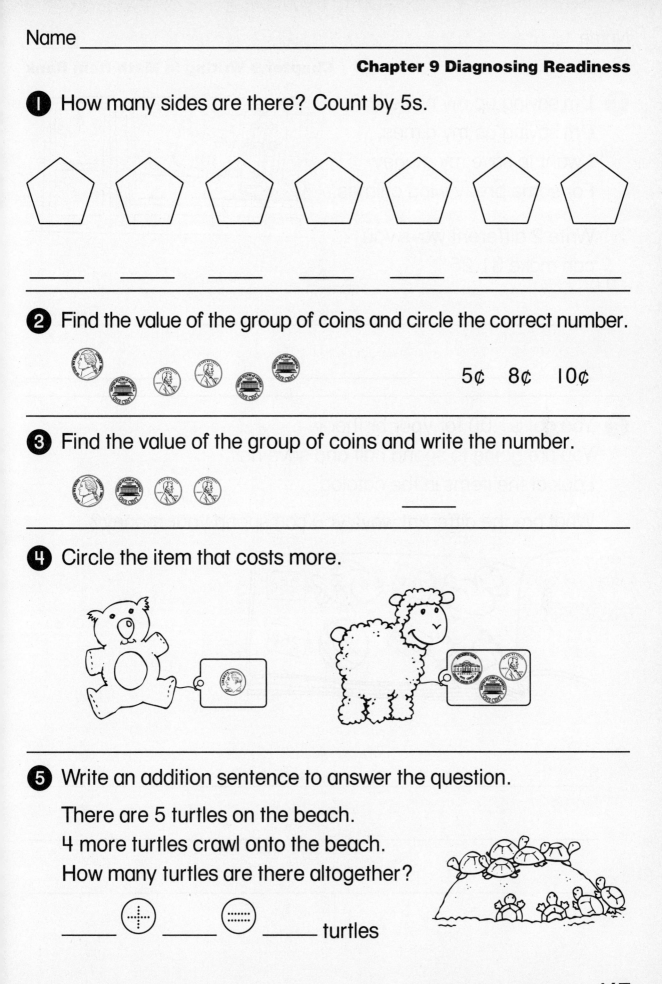

___ ___ ___ ___ ___ ___ ___

2 Find the value of the group of coins and circle the correct number.

5¢   8¢   10¢

3 Find the value of the group of coins and write the number.

_____

4 Circle the item that costs more.

5 Write an addition sentence to answer the question.

There are 5 turtles on the beach.
4 more turtles crawl onto the beach.
How many turtles are there altogether?

____ ⊕ ____ ⊜ ____ turtles

1 I'm saving up my nickels,
I'm saving up my dimes,
I want to save my money,
For some pretty wind chimes.

Write 2 different ways you
can make $1.25.

_____

_____

2 You got $1.00 for your birthday.
You are going to spend half and save half.
Look at the items in the catalog.

What are the different ways you can spend your money?

_____

_____

_____

Name _____

1 Circle the coins that match the price.

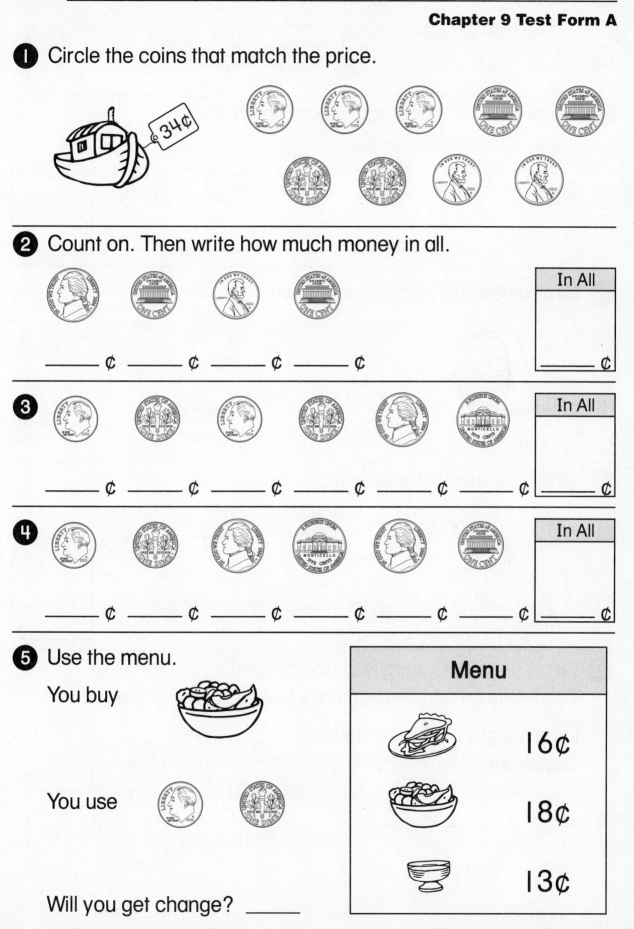

2 Count on. Then write how much money in all.

_____ ¢ _____ ¢ _____ ¢ _____ ¢

In All

_____ ¢

3

_____ ¢ _____ ¢ _____ ¢ _____ ¢ _____ ¢ _____ ¢

In All

_____ ¢

4

_____ ¢ _____ ¢ _____ ¢ _____ ¢ _____ ¢ _____ ¢

In All

_____ ¢

5 Use the menu.

You buy

You use

Will you get change? _____

Menu

16¢

18¢

13¢

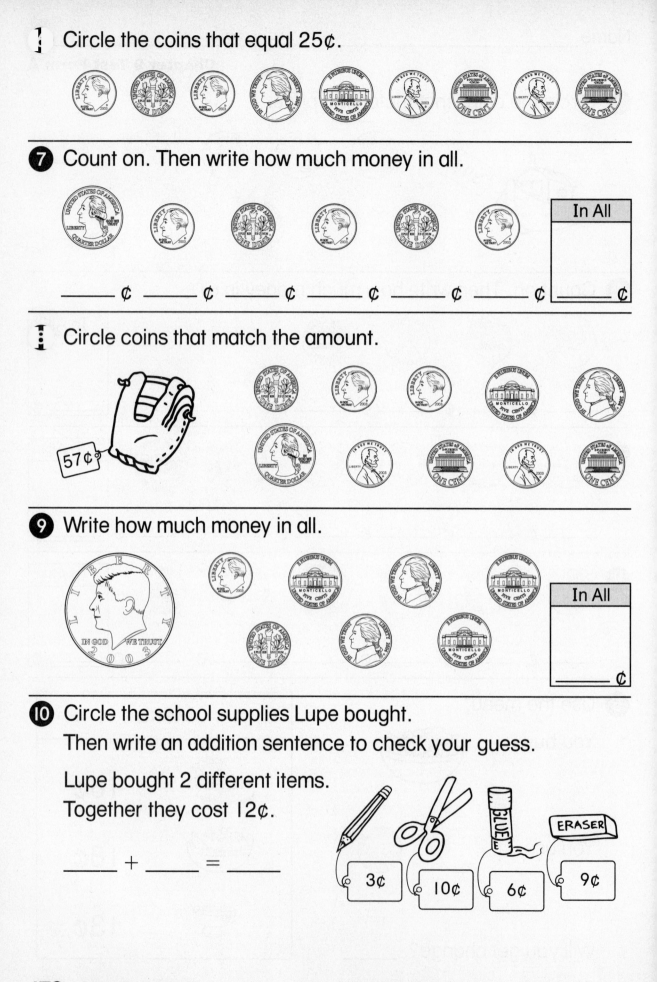

6 Circle the coins that equal 25¢.

7 Count on. Then write how much money in all.

In All

_____ ¢ _____ ¢ _____ ¢ _____ ¢ _____ ¢ _____ ¢ | _____ ¢

8 Circle coins that match the amount.

57¢

9 Write how much money in all.

In All

_____ ¢

10 Circle the school supplies Lupe bought.
Then write an addition sentence to check your guess.

Lupe bought 2 different items.
Together they cost 12¢.

_____ + _____ = _____

3¢   10¢   6¢   9¢

Name _____

1 Circle the coins that match the price.

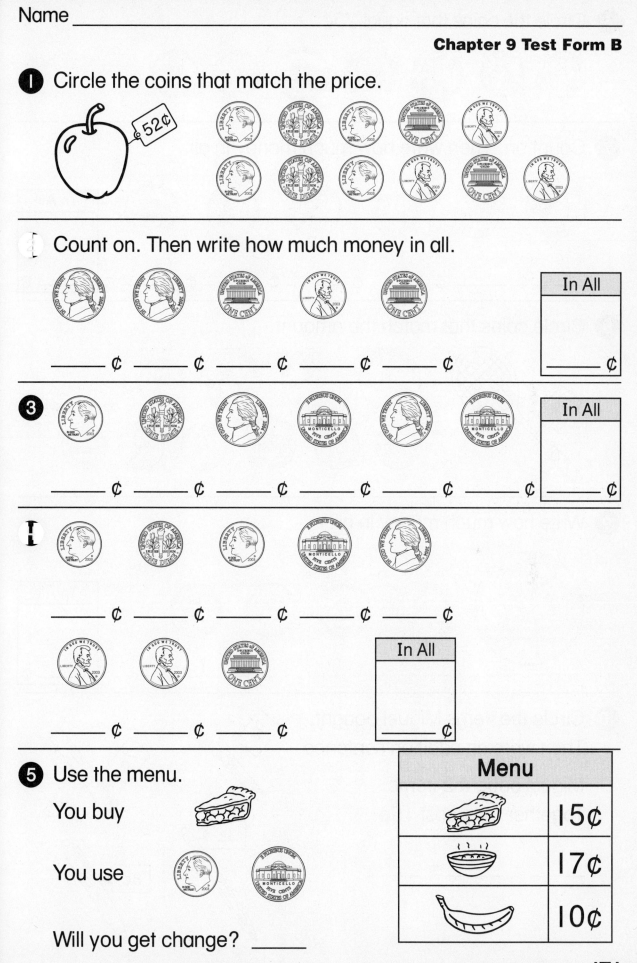

2 Count on. Then write how much money in all.

_____ ¢ _____ ¢ _____ ¢ _____ ¢ _____ ¢

In All
_____ ¢

3

_____ ¢ _____ ¢ _____ ¢ _____ ¢ _____ ¢ _____ ¢

In All
_____ ¢

4

_____ ¢ _____ ¢ _____ ¢ _____ ¢ _____ ¢

_____ ¢ _____ ¢ _____ ¢

In All
_____ ¢

5 Use the menu.

You buy

You use

Will you get change? _____

Menu	
	15¢
	17¢
	10¢

6 Circle the coins that equal 25¢.

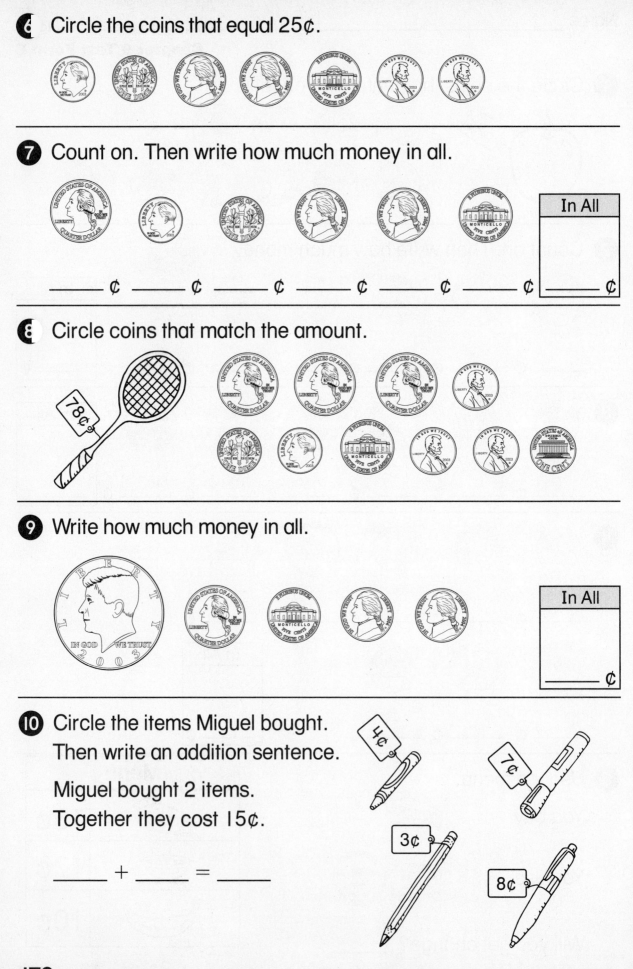

7 Count on. Then write how much money in all.

In All

_____ ¢ _____ ¢ _____ ¢ _____ ¢ _____ ¢ _____ ¢   _____ ¢

8 Circle coins that match the amount.

78¢

9 Write how much money in all.

In All

_____ ¢

10 Circle the items Miguel bought.
Then write an addition sentence.

Miguel bought 2 items.
Together they cost 15¢.

4¢
7¢
3¢
8¢

_____ + _____ = _____

Name _____

Mark the best answer.

1 Which coins match the price?

Ⓐ

Ⓑ

Ⓒ

Ⓓ

2 Which coins match the price?

Ⓐ

Ⓑ

Ⓒ

Ⓓ

Count on. How much money in all?

3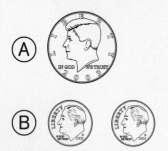

22¢	17¢	12¢	4¢
Ⓐ	Ⓑ	Ⓒ	Ⓓ

4

7¢	34¢	39¢	49¢
Ⓐ	Ⓑ	Ⓒ	Ⓓ

Use the menu.

5 Which coins are needed to buy the sandwich?

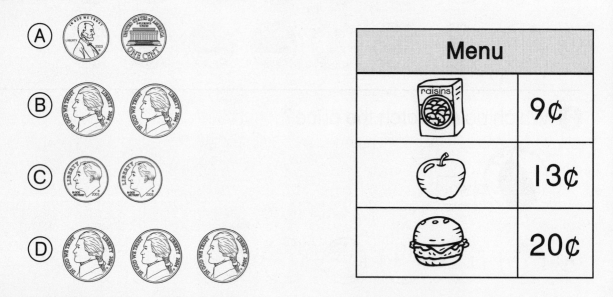

Ⓐ

Ⓑ

Ⓒ

Ⓓ

Menu	
raisins	9¢
🍎	13¢
🍔	20¢

---

6 Which coins equal 25¢?

Ⓐ

Ⓑ

Ⓒ

Ⓓ

7 Which coins match the amount?

23¢

Ⓐ

Ⓑ

Ⓒ

Ⓓ

---

8 Which coins match the amount?

96¢

Ⓐ

Ⓑ

Ⓒ

Ⓓ

9 Which amount equals $1.00?

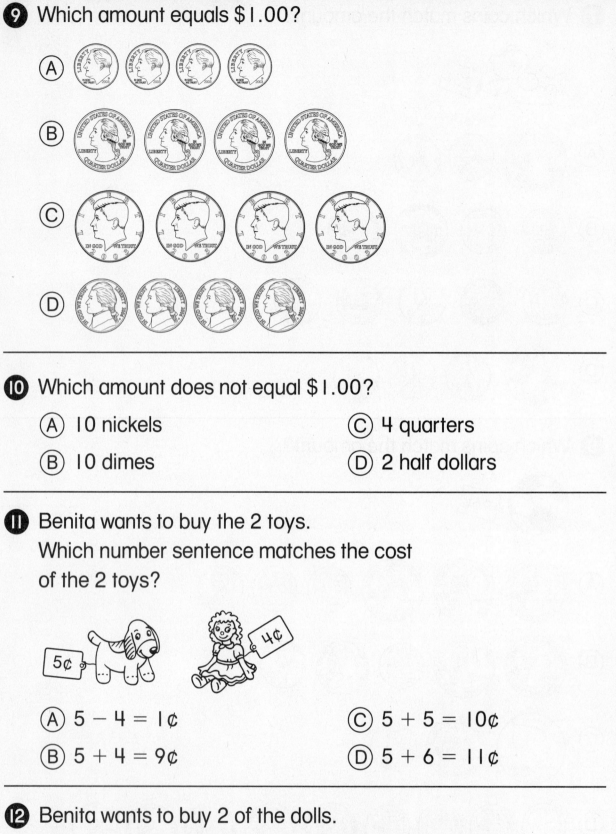

Ⓐ

Ⓑ

Ⓒ

Ⓓ

10 Which amount does not equal $1.00?

Ⓐ 10 nickels   Ⓒ 4 quarters

Ⓑ 10 dimes   Ⓓ 2 half dollars

11 Benita wants to buy the 2 toys.
Which number sentence matches the cost
of the 2 toys?

5¢   4¢

Ⓐ 5 − 4 = 1¢   Ⓒ 5 + 5 = 10¢

Ⓑ 5 + 4 = 9¢   Ⓓ 5 + 6 = 11¢

12 Benita wants to buy 2 of the dolls.
Which number sentence shows the cost of the 2 dolls?

Ⓐ 5 + 5 = 10¢   Ⓒ 10 − 5 = 5¢

Ⓑ 4 + 4 = 8¢   Ⓓ 9 − 5 = 4¢

Name _____

Mark the best answer.

1 Which coins match the price?

Ⓐ

Ⓑ

Ⓒ

Ⓓ

---

2 Which coins match the price?

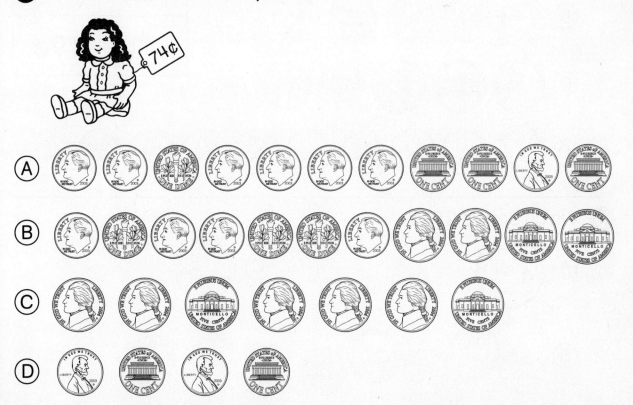

Ⓐ

Ⓑ

Ⓒ

Ⓓ

Count on. How much money in all?

3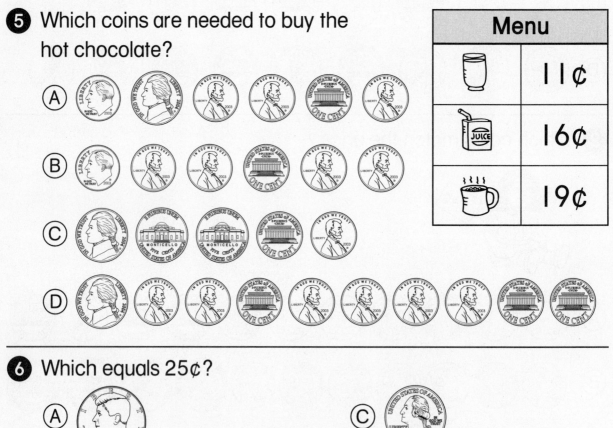

   10¢   37¢   70¢   73¢

   Ⓐ   Ⓑ   Ⓒ   Ⓓ

4

   76¢   61¢   56¢   52¢

   Ⓐ   Ⓑ   Ⓒ   Ⓓ

Use the menu.

5 Which coins are needed to buy the hot chocolate?

Menu	
🥛	11¢
🧃	16¢
☕	19¢

---

6 Which equals 25¢?

7 Which coins match the amount?

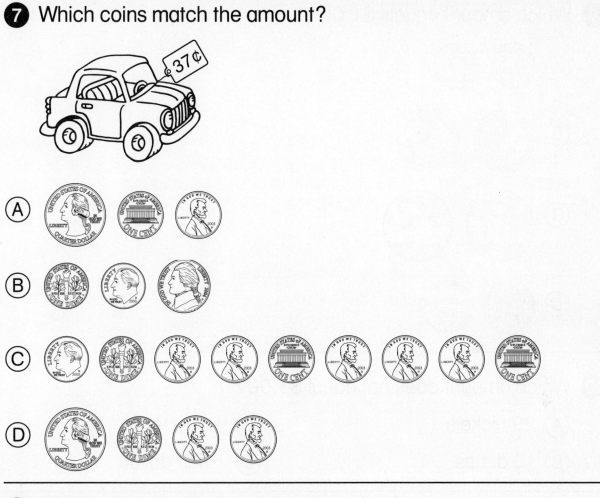

Ⓐ

Ⓑ

Ⓒ

Ⓓ

---

8 Which coins match the amount?

Ⓐ

Ⓑ

Ⓒ

Ⓓ

9 Which amount equals $1.00?

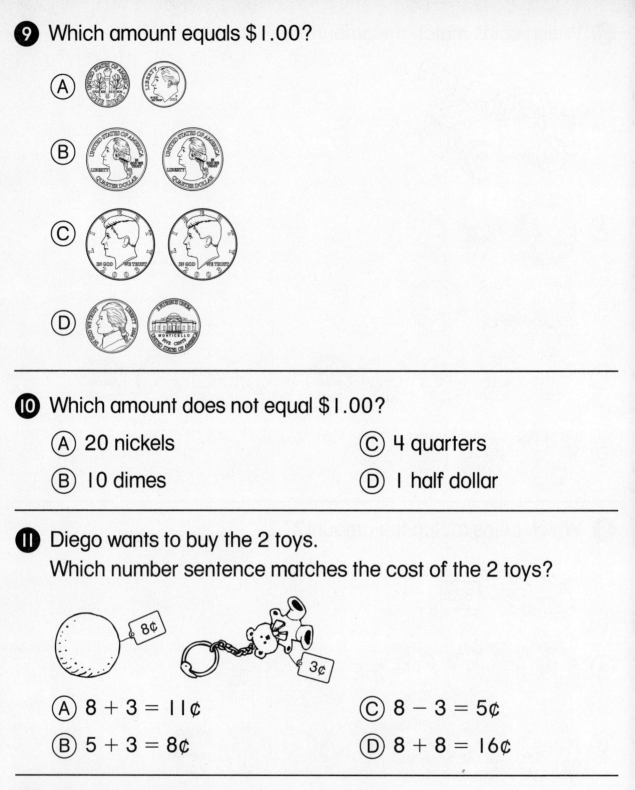

(A)

(B)

(C)

(D)

---

10 Which amount does not equal $1.00?

(A) 20 nickels

(C) 4 quarters

(B) 10 dimes

(D) 1 half dollar

---

11 Diego wants to buy the 2 toys.
Which number sentence matches the cost of the 2 toys?

8¢

3¢

(A) $8 + 3 = 11¢$

(C) $8 - 3 = 5¢$

(B) $5 + 3 = 8¢$

(D) $8 + 8 = 16¢$

---

12 Diego wants to buy 2 of the key chains.
Which number sentence shows the cost of the 2 key chains?

(A) $3 + 8 = 11¢$

(C) $8 - 5 = 3¢$

(B) $3 + 3 = 6¢$

(D) $8 + 8 = 16¢$

Name _____

Mark the best answer.

1 What is the missing number?

9 and 2 more is _____.

10	11	12	13
Ⓐ	Ⓑ	Ⓒ	Ⓓ

---

2 How many fewer dark cubes?

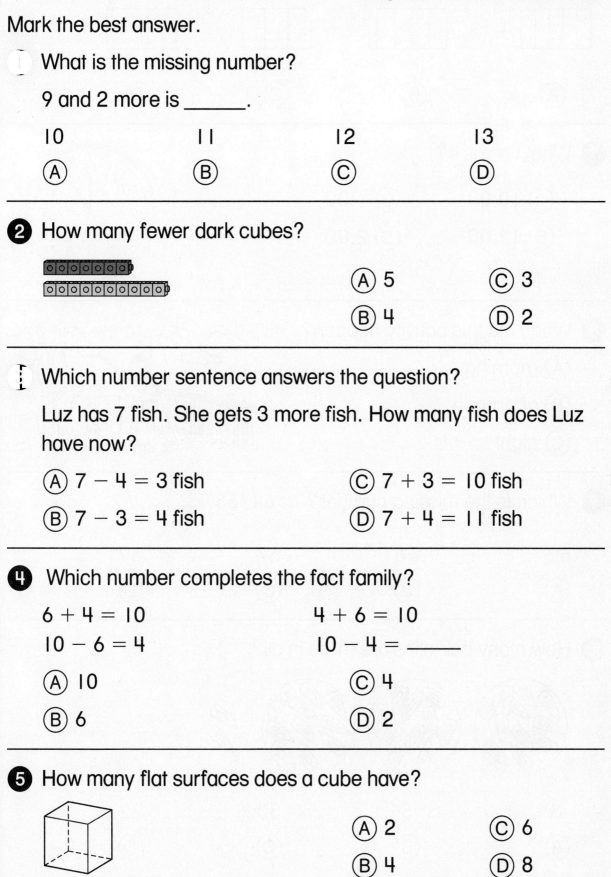

Ⓐ 5   Ⓒ 3

Ⓑ 4   Ⓓ 2

---

3 Which number sentence answers the question?

Luz has 7 fish. She gets 3 more fish. How many fish does Luz have now?

Ⓐ 7 − 4 = 3 fish   Ⓒ 7 + 3 = 10 fish

Ⓑ 7 − 3 = 4 fish   Ⓓ 7 + 4 = 11 fish

---

4 Which number completes the fact family?

6 + 4 = 10   4 + 6 = 10

10 − 6 = 4   10 − 4 = _____

Ⓐ 10   Ⓒ 4

Ⓑ 6   Ⓓ 2

---

5 How many flat surfaces does a cube have?

Ⓐ 2   Ⓒ 6

Ⓑ 4   Ⓓ 8

6 Which shows fourths?

|A| |B| |C| |D|

7 What time is it?

(A) 10:00 (C) 1:00

(B) 12:00 (D) 2:00

8 When did this activity happen?

(A) morning

(B) afternoon

(C) night

9 Which is the missing number?   64, 65, _____, 67

62   66   67   69
(A)   (B)   (C)   (D)

10 How many hair clips are there in all?

3   5   30   32
(A)   (B)   (C)   (D)

11 Which numbers do you say when you count by 5s?

| 41 | 42 | 43 | 44 | 45 | 46 | 47 | 48 | 49 | 50 |

(A) 41, 45, 50

(C) 45

(B) 42, 44, 46, 48, 50

(D) 45, 50

12 There are 3 plates with 2 muffins on each plate.
How many muffins in all?

(A) 2   (C) 5

(B) 3   (D) 6

13 4 tens is ——.

20   30   40   50

(A)   (B)   (C)   (D)

14 Which numbers are in order from least to greatest?

(A) 21, 47, 65

(C) 98, 72, 63

(B) 10, 82, 53

(D) 34, 81, 17

15 Count the tens and ones. What is the number?

Tens	Ones

(A) 84

(B) 58

(C) 49

(D) 48

16 Which number shows how many hundreds, tens, and ones?

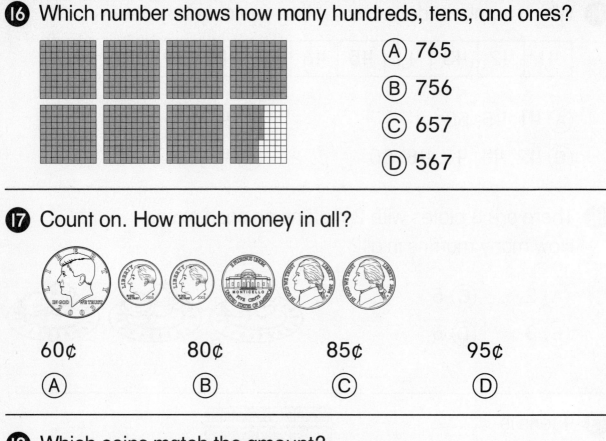

Ⓐ 765

Ⓑ 756

Ⓒ 657

Ⓓ 567

17 Count on. How much money in all?

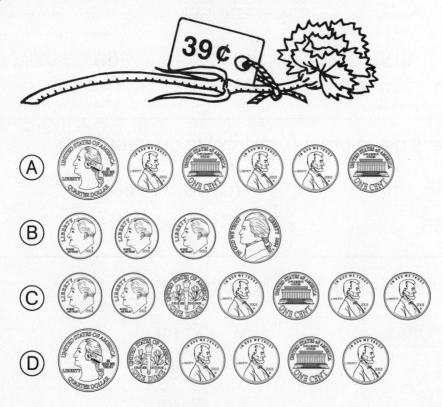

60¢	80¢	85¢	95¢
Ⓐ	Ⓑ	Ⓒ	Ⓓ

18 Which coins match the amount?

39¢

Ⓐ

Ⓑ

Ⓒ

Ⓓ

Name _____

1 Find the object in the classroom and estimate the length. Then measure using cubes.

Estimate		Measure
___ 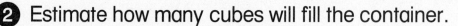		___

2 Estimate how many cubes will fill the container. Then measure using cubes.

Estimate		Measure
___		___

3 Estimate the weight of the object in cubes. Then use a balance to weigh the object.

Estimate		Measure
___		___

4 Circle the thermometer that shows the temperature that might go with the picture.

1 Run around the track
Keep your head down low.
If you run around twice,
How far will you go?

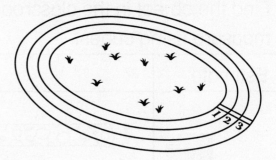

Tell how to find how far you will run.

_____

_____

_____

2 Louisa has a jar of marbles.
5 marbles are green.
20 marbles are red.
Which color is Louisa
less likely to get? Tell why.

_____

_____

_____

Name _____

1 Estimate the length. Then measure using an inch ruler.

Estimate.	Measure.
about ____ inches	____ inches

2 Estimate the length. Then measure using a centimeter ruler.

Estimate.	Measure.
about ____ centimeters	____ centimeters

3 Circle the best estimate for the height of the snail.

I foot

I inch

4 Count how many inches around this shape.

____ inches

5 Write how many cubes will cover this shape.

____ cubes

Circle the best estimate.

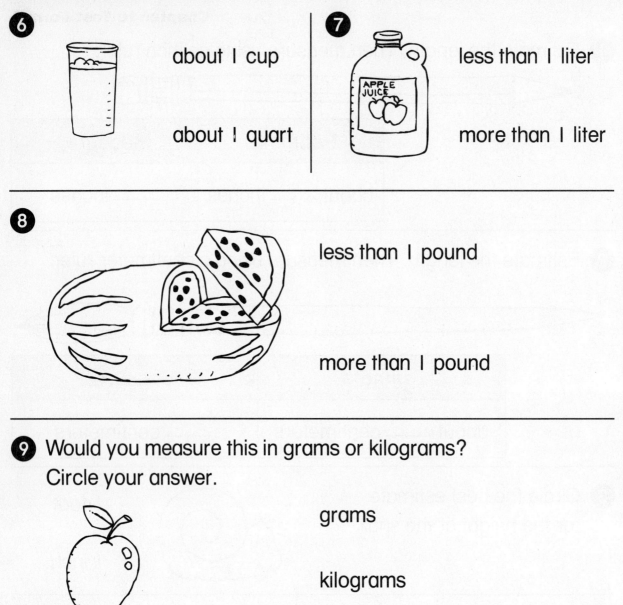

6   about I cup

    about I quart

7   less than I liter

    more than I liter

8   less than I pound

    more than I pound

9 Would you measure this in grams or kilograms?
Circle your answer.

    grams

    kilograms

10 Circle the thermometer that shows the temperature.

°F   30

°F   90

Name _____

1 Estimate the length. Then measure using an inch ruler.

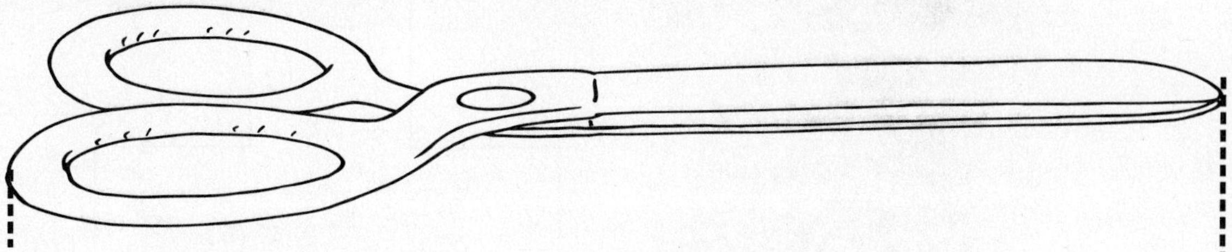

Estimate.	Measure.
about _____ inches	_____ inches

2 Estimate the length. Then measure using a centimeter ruler.

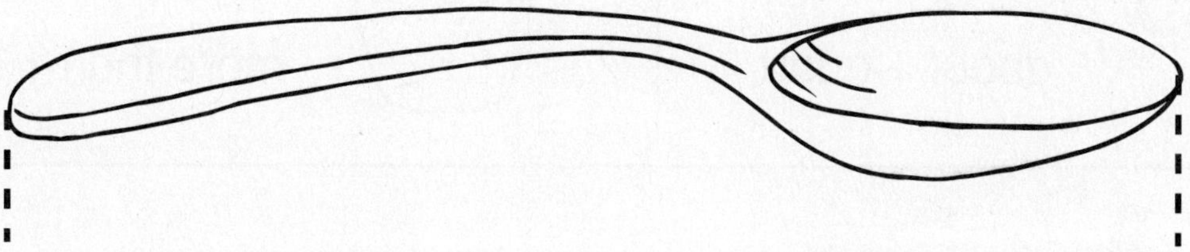

Estimate.	Measure.
about _____ centimeters	_____ centimeters

3 Circle the best estimate for the height of the snap cube.

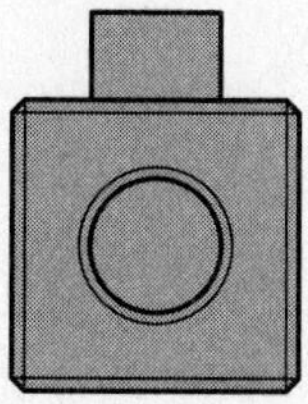

1 inch

1 foot

4 Count the number of inches around this shape.

_____ inches

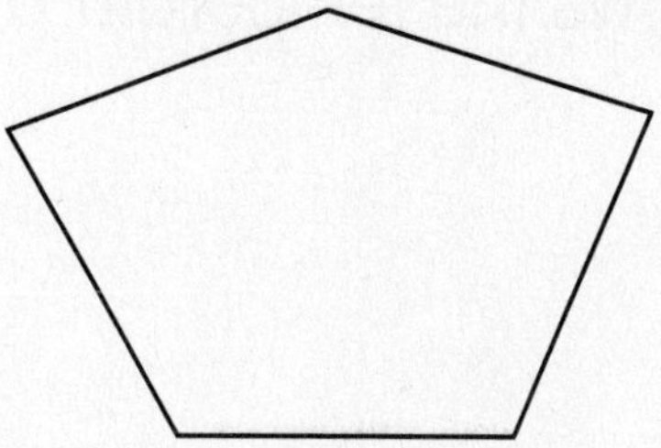

5 Write how many cubes
will cover this shape.

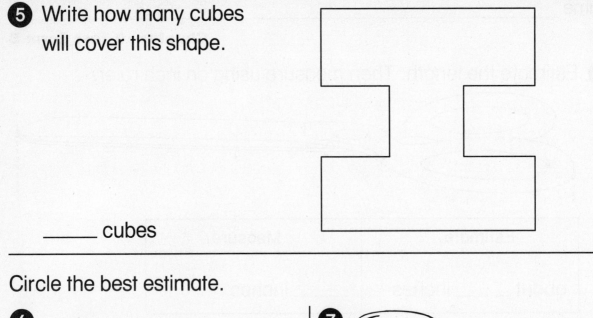

_____ cubes

Circle the best estimate.

6

about I cup

about I quart

7

less than I liter

more than I liter

8

less than I pound

more than I pound

9 Would you measure
this in grams or kilograms?

Circle your answer.

grams

kilograms

10 Circle the thermometer
that shows the temperature.

Name _____

Mark the best answer.

1 How many inches long is the comb?

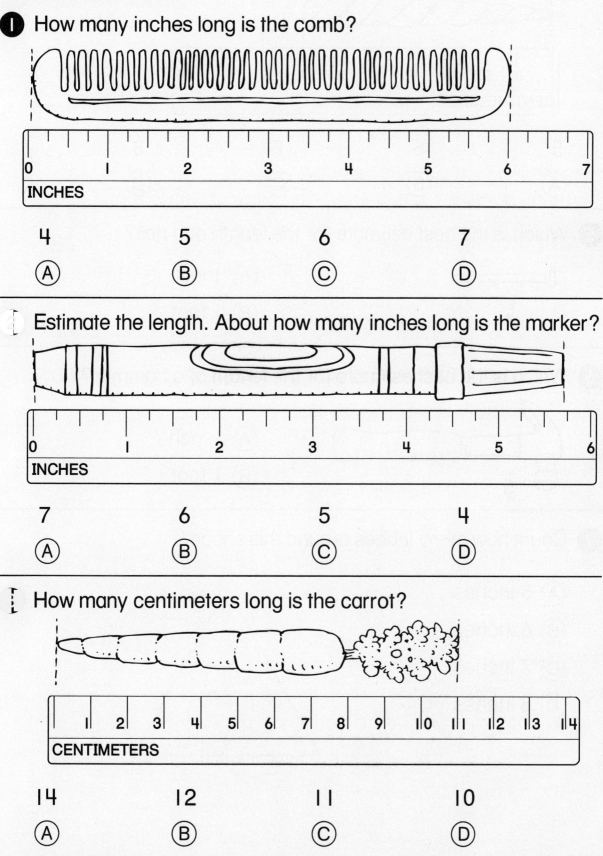

4	5	6	7
Ⓐ	Ⓑ	Ⓒ	Ⓓ

2 Estimate the length. About how many inches long is the marker?

7	6	5	4
Ⓐ	Ⓑ	Ⓒ	Ⓓ

3 How many centimeters long is the carrot?

14	12	11	10
Ⓐ	Ⓑ	Ⓒ	Ⓓ

I Estimate the length. About how many centimeters long is the candle?

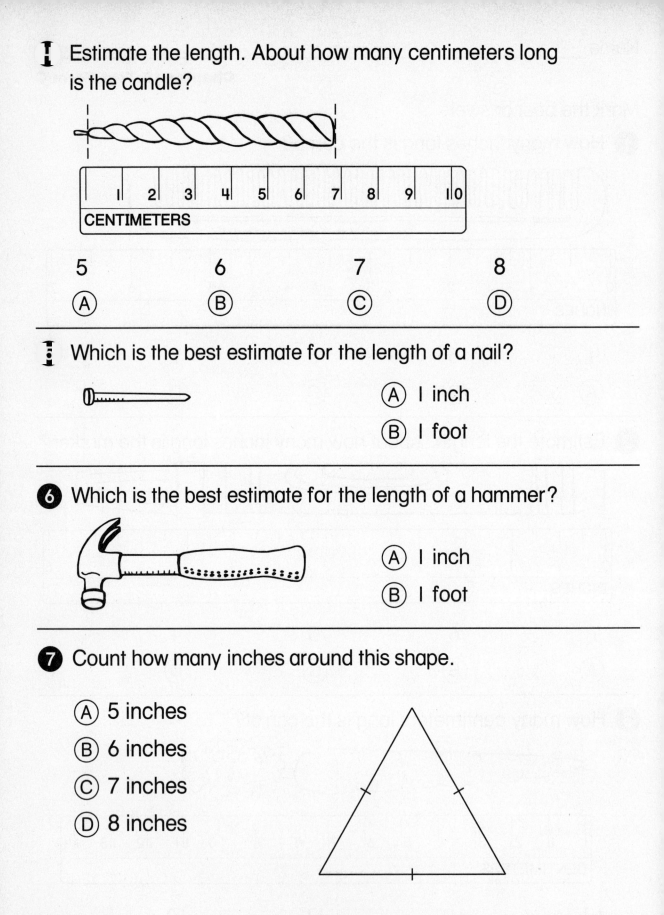

5   6   7   8

Ⓐ   Ⓑ   Ⓒ   Ⓓ

I Which is the best estimate for the length of a nail?

Ⓐ I inch

Ⓑ I foot

---

6 Which is the best estimate for the length of a hammer?

Ⓐ I inch

Ⓑ I foot

---

7 Count how many inches around this shape.

Ⓐ 5 inches

Ⓑ 6 inches

Ⓒ 7 inches

Ⓓ 8 inches

8 How many cubes will cover this shape?

Ⓐ 8 cubes

Ⓑ 7 cubes

Ⓒ 6 cubes

Ⓓ 5 cubes

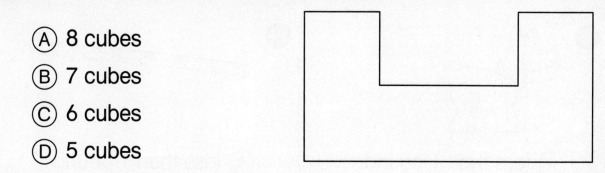

9 Which holds about 1 cup?

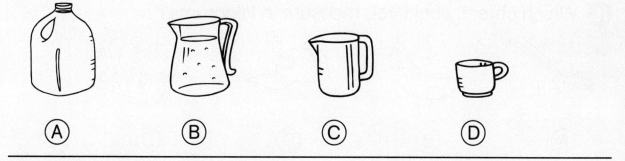

Ⓐ   Ⓑ   Ⓒ   Ⓓ

10 Which holds about 1 quart?

Ⓐ   Ⓑ   Ⓒ   Ⓓ

Estimate. About how much does each container hold?

11

Ⓐ less than 1 liter

Ⓑ more than 1 liter

12

Ⓐ less than 1 liter

Ⓑ more than 1 liter

Estimate. About how much does each object weigh?

13
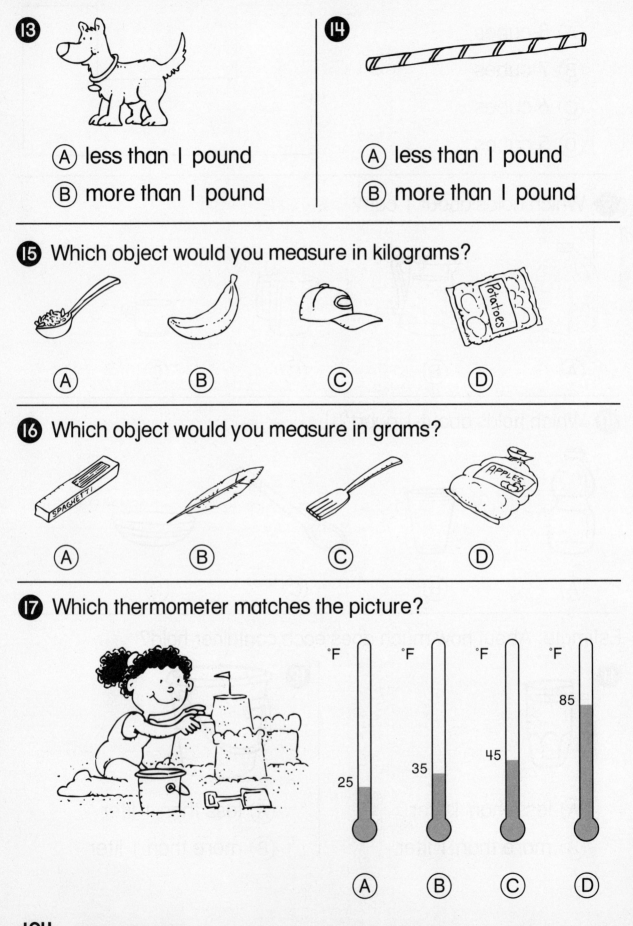
A) less than 1 pound
B) more than 1 pound

14
A) less than 1 pound
B) more than 1 pound

15 Which object would you measure in kilograms?

A) B) C) D) Potatoes

16 Which object would you measure in grams?

A) SPAGHETTI B) C) D) APPLES

17 Which thermometer matches the picture?

°F 25 °F 35 °F 45 °F 85

A) B) C) D)

Name _____

Mark the best answer.

1 How many inches long is the celery stalk?

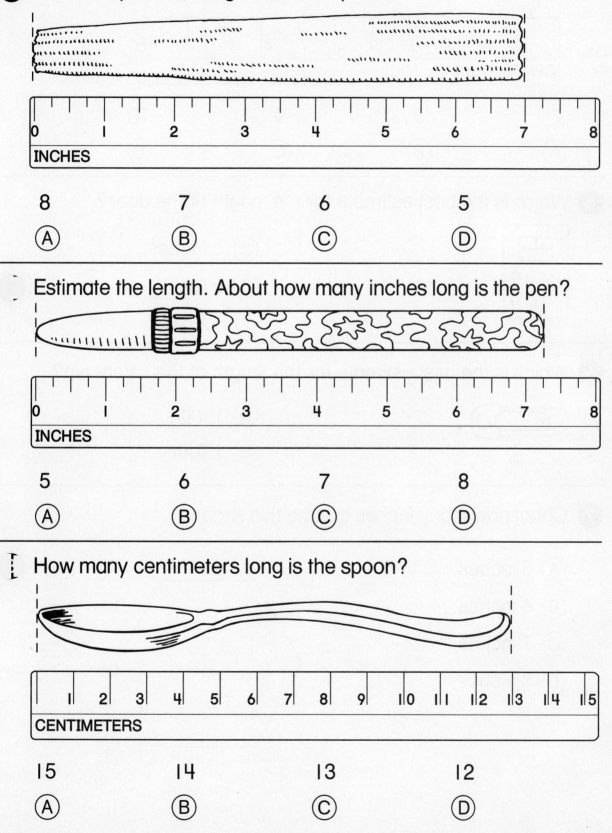

8	7	6	5
Ⓐ	Ⓑ	Ⓒ	Ⓓ

2 Estimate the length. About how many inches long is the pen?

5	6	7	8
Ⓐ	Ⓑ	Ⓒ	Ⓓ

3 How many centimeters long is the spoon?

15	14	13	12
Ⓐ	Ⓑ	Ⓒ	Ⓓ

] Estimate the length. About how many centimeters long is the ribbon?

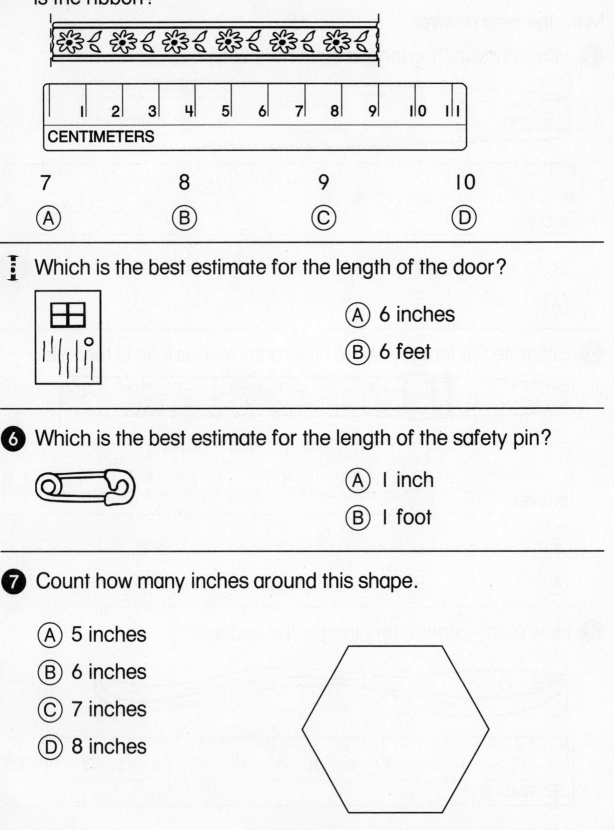

7	8	9	10
Ⓐ	Ⓑ	Ⓒ	Ⓓ

Ξ Which is the best estimate for the length of the door?

Ⓐ 6 inches

Ⓑ 6 feet

---

6 Which is the best estimate for the length of the safety pin?

Ⓐ I inch

Ⓑ I foot

---

7 Count how many inches around this shape.

Ⓐ 5 inches

Ⓑ 6 inches

Ⓒ 7 inches

Ⓓ 8 inches

8 How many cubes will cover this shape?

　(A) 2 cubes

　(B) 3 cubes

　(C) 4 cubes

　(D) 5 cubes

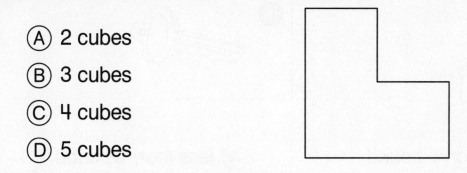

---

9 Which holds about 1 cup?

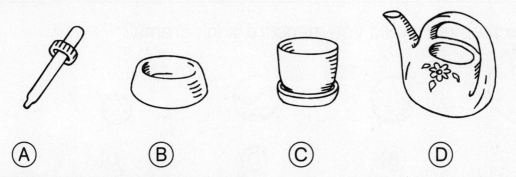

(A)　　　　(B)　　　　(C)　　　　(D)

---

10 Which holds about 1 quart?

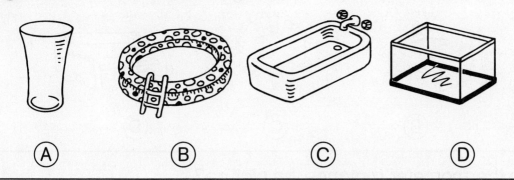

(A)　　　　(B)　　　　(C)　　　　(D)

Estimate. About how much does each container hold?

11
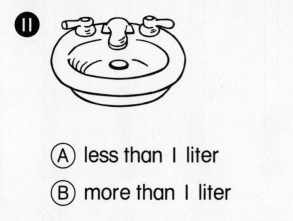

　(A) less than 1 liter

　(B) more than 1 liter

12

　(A) less than 1 liter

　(B) more than 1 liter

Estimate. About how much does each object weigh?

13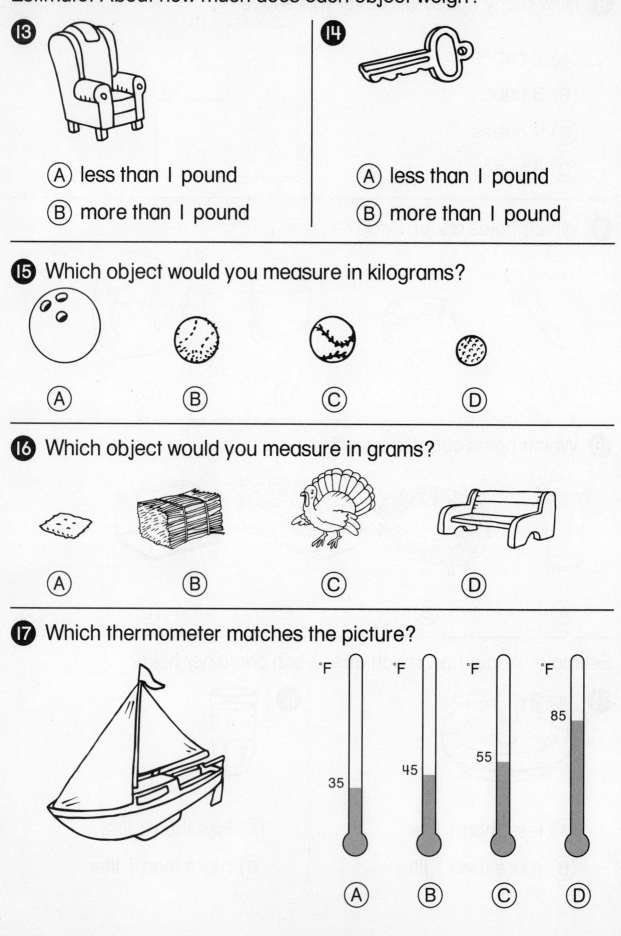

    Ⓐ less than 1 pound

    Ⓑ more than 1 pound

14

    Ⓐ less than 1 pound

    Ⓑ more than 1 pound

15 Which object would you measure in kilograms?

    Ⓐ   Ⓑ   Ⓒ   Ⓓ

16 Which object would you measure in grams?

    Ⓐ   Ⓑ   Ⓒ   Ⓓ

17 Which thermometer matches the picture?

    °F 35   °F 45   °F 55   °F 85

    Ⓐ   Ⓑ   Ⓒ   Ⓓ

Name _____

1 Find each sum. Use cubes if you like.

3	3	6	5	2	5
+ 3	+ 4	+ 7	+ 6	+ 3	+ 4

2 Fill in the missing number to find the sum of 10.

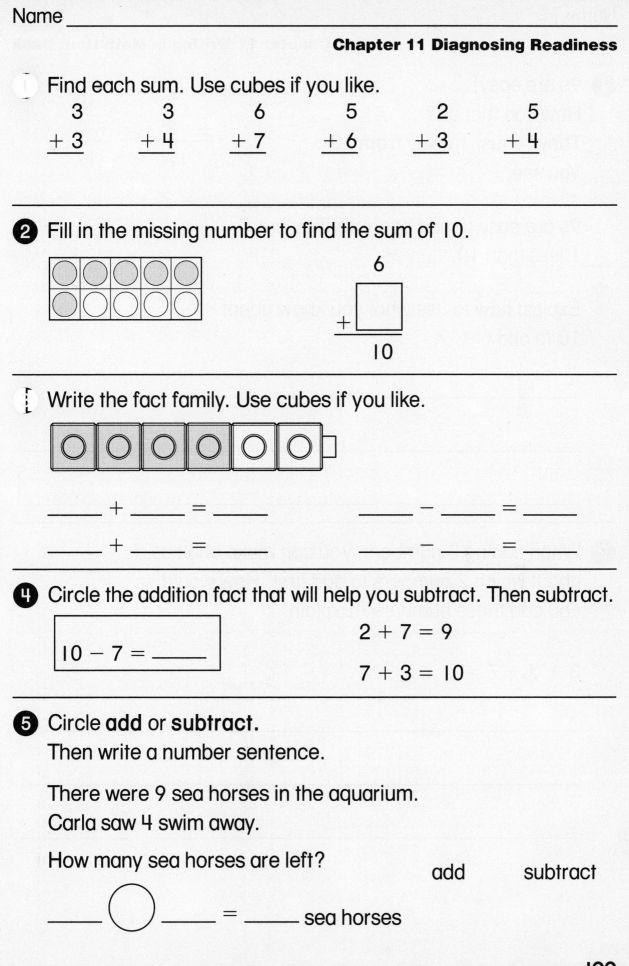

```
      6
   ┌─────┐
   │     │
 + └─────┘
  ─────────
     10
```

3 Write the fact family. Use cubes if you like.

_____ + _____ = _____   _____ − _____ = _____

_____ + _____ = _____   _____ − _____ = _____

4 Circle the addition fact that will help you subtract. Then subtract.

| 10 − 7 = _____ |

2 + 7 = 9

7 + 3 = 10

5 Circle **add** or **subtract**.
Then write a number sentence.

There were 9 sea horses in the aquarium.
Carla saw 4 swim away.

How many sea horses are left?

add   subtract

_____ ◯ _____ = _____ sea horses

Name _____

1 9s are easy!
How can that be?
They're just 1 away from 10
You see.

$$\begin{array}{r} 9 \\ +\ 8 \\ \hline 17 \end{array} \qquad \begin{array}{r} 10 \\ +\ 7 \\ \hline 17 \end{array}$$

9s are easy to add because they are
1 less than 10.

Explain how to use what you know about
10 to add 6 + 9.

_____

_____

_____

2 When adding 3 numbers, you can make choices
about which 2 numbers to add first. How would
you add these numbers? Explain.

3 + 3 + 7 = _____

_____

_____

_____

Name _____

1 Add.

```
   7        9        8        6        6        3
 + 5      + 8      + 8      + 7        4        7
                                     + 3      + 7
```

2 Subtract.

```
  14       15       11       13       14       16
 - 8      - 9      - 7      - 5      - 7      - 9
```

3 Add the doubles. Then use the doubles to help you add.

(Think)   6 + 6 = _____   so 6 + 7 = _____

and 6 + 5 = _____

4 Draw the counters. Then write the sums.

```
┌──┬──┬──┬──┬──┐
│  │  │  │  │  │          9       10
├──┼──┼──┼──┼──┤        + 5      + 4
│  │  │  │  │  │
└──┴──┴──┴──┴──┘
```

5 Write related addition and subtraction facts
to go with the picture.

___ + ___ = _____   ___ − ___ = _____

6 Add. Then use the addition fact to help you subtract.

$7 + 9 =$ _____

so $16 - 9 =$ _____

Use the numbers to write a fact family.

_____ $+$ _____ $=$ _____

_____ $+$ _____ $=$ _____

_____ $-$ _____ $=$ _____

_____ $-$ _____ $=$ _____

8 Make a table to answer the question.

Sara has pencils and pens.
The box holds 3 items.
How many different ways can
Sara fill the box?

Pencil 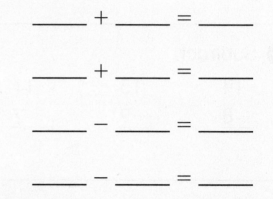	Pen

There are _____ different ways.

9 Solve each problem.

John has 7 baseball cards and 8 football cards.
How many cards does he have in all?

_____ ◯ _____ $=$ _____ cards

John gives 6 cards to his friend.
How many cards does he have left?

_____ ◯ _____ $=$ _____ cards

Name _____

1 Add.

```
   7        9        8        6        9        7
 + 6      + 9      + 4      + 8        2        5
                                     + 5      + 5
```

2 Subtract.

```
  14       13       11       15       12       14
 − 7      − 9      − 6      − 6      − 7      − 5
```

3 Add the doubles. Then use the doubles to help you add.

(Think) $8 + 8 =$ _____   so $8 + 9 =$ _____

and $8 + 7 =$ _____

4 Draw the counters. Then write the sums.

```
┌───┬───┬───┬───┬───┐
│   │   │   │   │   │
├───┼───┼───┼───┼───┤
│   │   │   │   │   │
└───┴───┴───┴───┴───┘
```

```
    9       10
  + 4      + 3
```

5 Write related addition and subtraction facts
to go with the picture.

△ △ △ △ △

▢ ▢ ▢ ▢ ▢ ▢

_____ + _____ = _____   _____ − _____ = _____

6 Add. Then use the addition fact to help you subtract.

$7 + 8 =$ ____

so $15 - 8 =$ ____

Use the numbers to write a fact family.

____ $+$ ____ $=$ ____

____ $+$ ____ $=$ ____

____ $-$ ____ $=$ ____

____ $-$ ____ $=$ ____

Make a table to answer the question.

Jamie has apples and bananas.
His basket holds 4 pieces of fruit.
How many different ways can
Jamie fill the basket?

There are ____ different ways.

Apples 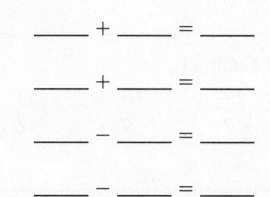	Bananas

---

9 Solve each problem.

Jen has 6 crayons and 8 pencils.
How many objects does she have in all?

____ ◯ ____ $=$ ____ objects

Jen gives 5 pencils to her friend.
How many objects does she have left?

____ ◯ ____ $=$ ____ objects

Mark the best answer.
Add.

1   6
  $+ 6$
   (A) 6
   (B) 10
   (C) 12
   (D) 16

2   7
  $+ 8$
   (A) 12
   (B) 13
   (C) 14
   (D) 15

Subtract.

3   16
  $- 7$
   (A) 9
   (B) 10
   (C) 11
   (D) 23

4   7
     3
  $+ 2$
   (A) 10
   (B) 12
   (C) 15
   (D) 17

5 Which doubles fact helps you add 6 + 7?

3 + 3   4 + 4   6 + 6   8 + 8

(A)   (B)   (C)   (D)

6 Add.

6 + 7 =

11   12   13   14

(A)   (B)   (C)   (D)

7 Which doubles fact helps you add 8 + 9?

4 + 4   8 + 8   7 + 7   5 + 5

(A)   (B)   (C)   (D)

8 Add.

$8 + 9 =$

14	15	16	17
Ⓐ	Ⓑ	Ⓒ	Ⓓ

Use the picture for Exercises 9 and 10.

$$\begin{array}{r} 9 \\ + 4 \\ \hline \end{array}$$

9 Which addition fact could you use to solve the problem?

$5 + 3$	$10 + 0$	$10 + 3$	$9 + 5$
Ⓐ	Ⓑ	Ⓒ	Ⓓ

---

10 Find the sum.

8	10	13	14
Ⓐ	Ⓑ	Ⓒ	Ⓓ

Use the picture for Exercises 11 and 12.

$$\begin{array}{r} 9 \\ + 8 \\ \hline \end{array}$$

11 Which addition fact could you use to solve the problem?

Ⓐ $7 + 7$

Ⓑ $10 + 7$

Ⓒ $10 + 10$

Ⓓ $9 + 7$

12 Find the sum.

Ⓐ 14

Ⓑ 16

Ⓒ 17

Ⓓ 20

Use the picture for Exercises 13 and 14.

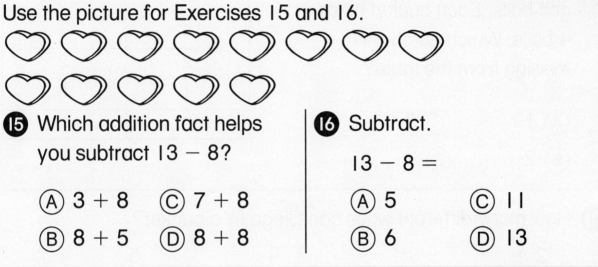

13 Which related addition fact goes with the picture?

(A) $6 + 6 = 12$

(B) $6 + 8 = 14$

(C) $14 + 0 = 14$

(D) $8 + 8 = 16$

14 Which related subtraction fact goes with the picture?

(A) $8 - 8 = 0$

(B) $8 - 6 = 2$

(C) $14 - 6 = 8$

(D) $14 - 0 = 14$

Use the picture for Exercises 15 and 16.

♡ ♡ ♡ ♡ ♡ ♡ ♡ ♡
♡ ♡ ♡ ♡ ♡

15 Which addition fact helps you subtract $13 - 8$?

(A) $3 + 8$ (C) $7 + 8$

(B) $8 + 5$ (D) $8 + 8$

16 Subtract.

$13 - 8 =$

(A) 5   (C) 11

(B) 6   (D) 13

Use the picture for Exercises 17 and 18.

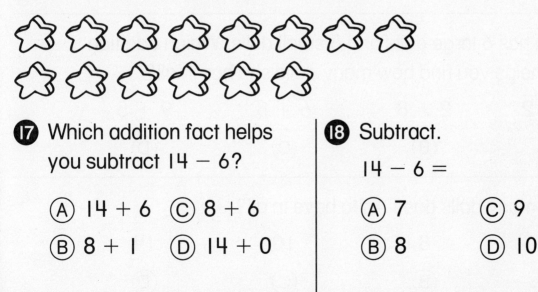

17 Which addition fact helps you subtract $14 - 6$?

(A) $14 + 6$ (C) $8 + 6$

(B) $8 + 1$ (D) $14 + 0$

18 Subtract.

$14 - 6 =$

(A) 7   (C) 9

(B) 8   (D) 10

Which addition fact belongs to this fact family?

Ⓐ 8 + 7 = 15

Ⓑ 9 + 6 = 15

Ⓒ 7 + 7 = 14

Ⓓ 8 + 8 = 16

Use the table to answer Exercises 20 and 21.

20 Diego has tennis balls and golf balls. Each bucket holds 4 balls. Which number is missing from the table?

Ⓐ 1   Ⓒ 3

Ⓑ 2   Ⓓ 4

Tennis Balls	Golf Balls
4	0
3	1
2	2
1	3
0	

---

21 How many different ways can Diego fill a bucket?

2   3   4   5

Ⓐ   Ⓑ   Ⓒ   Ⓓ

---

22 Anita has 6 large dolls and 8 small dolls. Which addition fact helps you find how many dolls she has in all?

6 + 2   2 + 8   6 + 8   9 + 5

Ⓐ   Ⓑ   Ⓒ   Ⓓ

---

23 How many dolls does Anita have in all?

2   8   10   14

Ⓐ   Ⓑ   Ⓒ   Ⓓ

Name _____

Mark the best answer.

Add.

1 8
   + 6

(A) 2
(B) 12
(C) 14
(D) 16

2 7
   + 4

(A) 11
(B) 10
(C) 4
(D) 3

3 Subtract.

   14
   − 9

(A) 4
(B) 5
(C) 15
(D) 23

4 Add.

   8
   4
   + 3

(A) 7
(B) 12
(C) 15
(D) 17

5 Which doubles fact helps you add 5 + 6?

3 + 3   5 + 5   8 + 8   10 + 10

(A)   (B)   (C)   (D)

6 Add.

5 + 6 =

10   11   12   13

(A)   (B)   (C)   (D)

7 Which doubles fact helps you add 7 + 6?

4 + 4   5 + 5   6 + 6   8 + 8

(A)   (B)   (C)   (D)

8 Add.

$7 + 6 =$

12	13	14	15
Ⓐ	Ⓑ	Ⓒ	Ⓓ

Use the picture for Exercises 9 and 10.

$$\begin{array}{r} 9 \\ + 5 \\ \hline \end{array}$$

9 Which addition fact could you use to solve the problem?

$1 + 4$	$10 + 4$	$11 + 3$	$14 + 0$
Ⓐ	Ⓑ	Ⓒ	Ⓓ

---

10 Find the sum.

4	5	10	14
Ⓐ	Ⓑ	Ⓒ	Ⓓ

Use the picture for Exercises 11 and 12.

$$\begin{array}{r} 9 \\ + 6 \\ \hline \end{array}$$

11 Which addition fact could you use to solve the problem?

Ⓐ $5 + 5$

Ⓑ $10 + 5$

Ⓒ $12 + 3$

Ⓓ $15 + 0$

12 Find the sum.

Ⓐ 5

Ⓑ 10

Ⓒ 15

Ⓓ 20

Use the picture for Exercises 13 and 14.

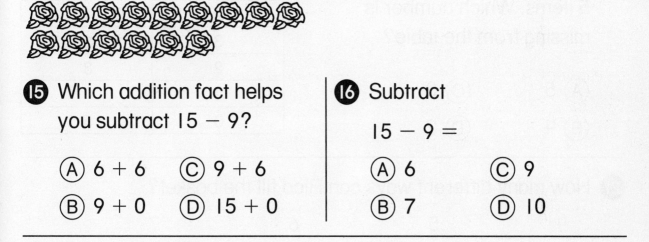

13 Which related addition fact goes with the picture?

- (A) 4 + 9 = 13
- (B) 9 + 9 = 18
- (C) 10 + 3 = 13
- (D) 13 + 0 = 13

14 Which related subtraction fact goes with the picture?

- (A) 9 − 4 = 5
- (B) 9 − 9 = 0
- (C) 9 − 5 = 4
- (D) 13 − 4 = 9

Use the picture for Exercises 15 and 16.

15 Which addition fact helps you subtract 15 − 9?

- (A) 6 + 6
- (C) 9 + 6
- (B) 9 + 0
- (D) 15 + 0

16 Subtract

15 − 9 =

- (A) 6
- (C) 9
- (B) 7
- (D) 10

Use the picture for Exercises 17 and 18.

17 Which addition fact helps you subtract 11 − 4?

- (A) 7 + 7
- (B) 4 + 7
- (C) 10 + 1
- (D) 11 + 4

18 Subtract.

11 − 4 =

- (A) 11
- (B) 8
- (C) 7
- (D) 4

19 Which addition fact belongs to this fact family?

- Ⓐ 6 + 7 = 13
- Ⓑ 6 + 6 = 12
- Ⓒ 7 + 7 = 14
- Ⓓ 13 + 6 = 19

Use the table to answer Exercises 20 and 21.

20 Rico has hockey pucks and sticks. Each basket holds 5 items. Which number is missing from the table?

Hockey Pucks	Hockey Sticks
5	0
4	1
3	2
2	3
1	
0	5

- Ⓐ 5
- Ⓒ 3
- Ⓑ 4
- Ⓓ 2

21 How many different ways can Rico fill the basket?

4   5   6   7

Ⓐ   Ⓑ   Ⓒ   Ⓓ

22 Carmen has 7 large bows and 9 small bows. Which addition fact helps you find how many bows she has in all?

7 + 7   7 + 9   9 + 9   10 + 6

Ⓐ   Ⓑ   Ⓒ   Ⓓ

23 How many bows does Carmen have in all?

7   9   10   16

Ⓐ   Ⓑ   Ⓒ   Ⓓ

Name _____

Add to find the sum. Use cubes if you like.

1

_____ and _____ is _____.

2

_____ and _____ is _____.

Use cubes. Write the numbers.

3 | 52 |

10 less than 52 is _____.

1 more than 52 is _____.

4 | 75 |

10 more than 75 is _____.

1 less than 75 is _____.

Use cubes. Circle **less** or **greater**.

5 7 is _____ than 10.   less   greater

6 11 is _____ than 5.   less   greater

Subtract to find the difference.
Use counters if you like.

7

_____ take away _____ is _____.

8

_____ take away _____ is _____.

Name _____

1 All of the grade 1 classes wanted to sell the most popcorn.
Which class sold the most? Which class sold the least?
How much popcorn did the first graders sell?

Popcorn Sales

Grade 1 Class	Week 1	Week 2	Week 3	Total
Miss Riley	$11.00	$22.00	$30.00	$63.00
Mrs. Scott	$12.00	$31.00	$42.00	$85.00
Mr. Bell	$12.00	$24.00	$35.00	$71.00
Total				

_____

_____

_____

2 **Popcorn Sale Totals**

Grade 1	$289.00
Grade 2	$168.00
Difference	

Tell how to find the difference. Write a number sentence
that shows the difference between the total sales.

_____

_____

Name _____

Write each number sentence.

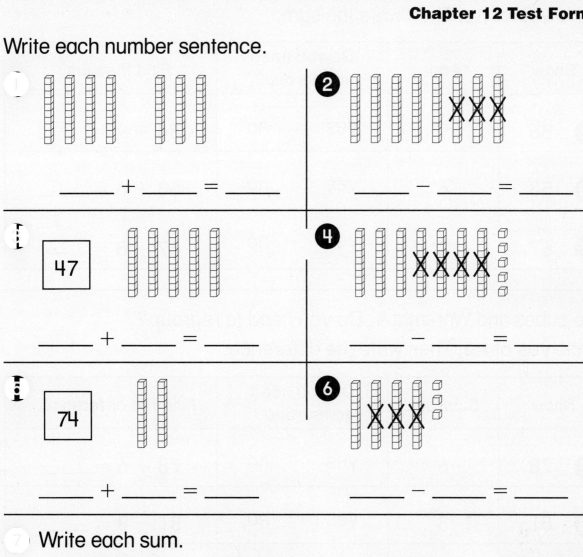

1. _____ + _____ = _____

2. _____ − _____ = _____

3. 47 _____ + _____ = _____

4. _____ − _____ = _____

5. 74 _____ + _____ = _____

6. _____ − _____ = _____

7. Write each sum.

Tens	Ones
3	7
+ 4	2

Tens	Ones
5	4
+ 3	1

Tens	Ones
6	2
+ 1	6

Tens	Ones
1	7
+ 8	2

8. Write each difference.

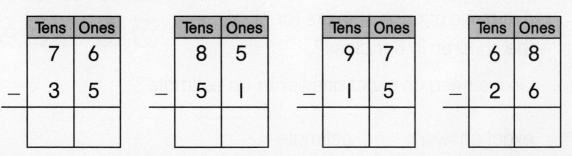

Tens	Ones
7	6
− 3	5

Tens	Ones
8	5
− 5	1

Tens	Ones
9	7
− 1	5

Tens	Ones
6	8
− 2	6

Use cubes and Workmat 4. Do you need to regroup?
Circle **yes** or **no**. Then write the sum.

Show.	Add.	Do you need to regroup?		Find the sum.
9 86	9	yes	no	86 + 9 = _____
10 53	6	yes	no	53 + 6 = _____
11 67	8	yes	no	67 + 8 = _____

Use cubes and Workmat 4. Do you need to regroup?
Circle **yes** or **no**. Then write the difference.

Show.	Subtract.	Do you need to regroup?		Find the difference.
12 78	6	yes	no	78 − 6 = _____
13 81	8	yes	no	81 − 8 = _____
14 94	5	yes	no	94 − 5 = _____

15 Circle **exact answer** or **estimate**.

Juanita has 2 sheets of stickers.
Each sheet has 15 stickers.
There are 27 children in her class.
Are there enough stickers for all of
the children in her class?

Do we need an exact answer or an estimate?

exact answer   estimate

Name _____

Write each number sentence.

1

___ + ___ = ___

2

___ − ___ = ___

3

| 35 |

___ + ___ = ___

4

___ − ___ = ___

5

| 54 |

___ + ___ = ___

6

___ − ___ = ___

7 Write each sum.

Tens	Ones
2	3
+ 3	4

Tens	Ones
6	2
+ 2	1

Tens	Ones
5	1
+ 2	8

Tens	Ones
3	3
+ 3	5

8 Write each difference.

Tens	Ones
8	4
− 2	3

Tens	Ones
7	9
− 3	6

Tens	Ones
6	7
− 4	3

Tens	Ones
9	3
− 6	1

Use cubes and Workmat 4. Do you need to regroup?
Circle **yes** or **no**. Then write the sum.

Show.	Add.	Do you need to regroup?		Find the sum.
9 58	7	yes	no	$58 + 7 =$ _____
10 24	9	yes	no	$24 + 9 =$ _____
11 72	6	yes	no	$72 + 6 =$ _____

Use cubes and Workmat 4. Do you need to regroup?
Circle **yes** or **no**. Then write the difference.

Show.	Subtract.	Do you need to regroup?		Find the difference.
12 63	5	yes	no	$63 - 5 =$ _____
13 78	8	yes	no	$78 - 8 =$ _____
14 34	7	yes	no	$34 - 7 =$ _____

Circle **exact answer** or **estimate**.

15 Marla has 2 sheets of stamps.
Each sheet has 18 stamps.
There are 32 letters to be mailed.
Are there enough stamps for
all of the letters?

Do we need an exact answer or an estimate?

exact answer   estimate

Name _____

Mark the best answer.
Use this picture for problems 1 and 2.

1 Which number sentence matches the picture?

Ⓐ 30 + 30

Ⓑ 30 + 40

Ⓒ 30 + 50

Ⓓ 30 + 60

2 What is the sum?

Ⓐ 90

Ⓑ 80

Ⓒ 70

Ⓓ 60

Use this picture for problems 3 and 4.

3 Which number sentence matches the picture?

Ⓐ 20 + 40

Ⓑ 20 + 50

Ⓒ 20 + 60

Ⓓ 20 + 70

4 What is the sum?

Ⓐ 90

Ⓑ 80

Ⓒ 40

Ⓓ 8

Use this picture for problems 5 and 6.

5 Which number sentence matches the picture?

Ⓐ 70 − 30

Ⓑ 40 − 10

Ⓒ 40 − 20

Ⓓ 40 − 30

6 What is the difference?

Ⓐ 10

Ⓑ 20

Ⓒ 30

Ⓓ 40

Use this picture for problems 7 and 8.

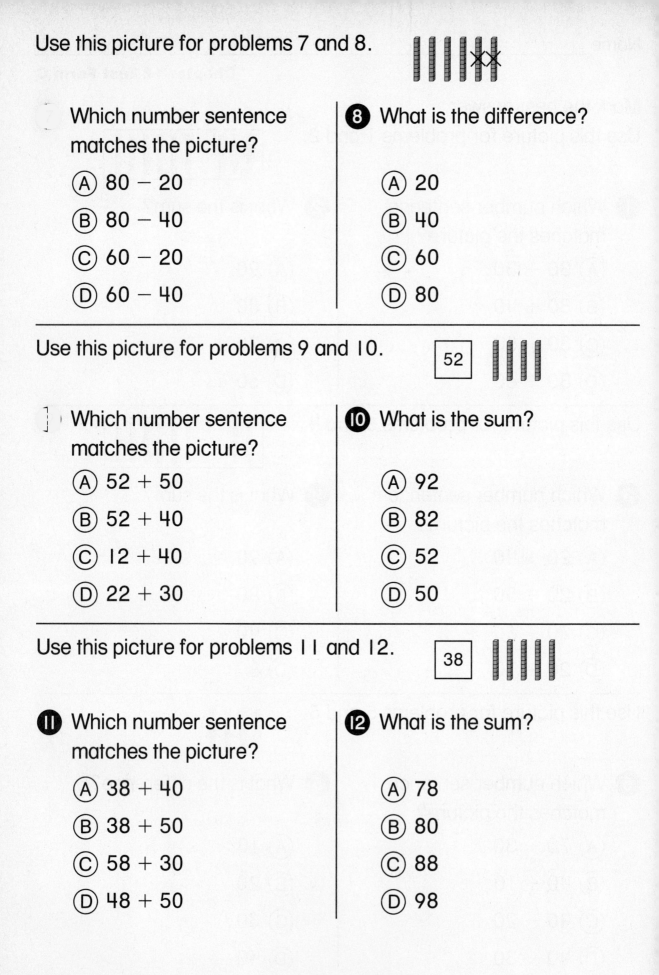

Which number sentence matches the picture?

(A) 80 − 20

(B) 80 − 40

(C) 60 − 20

(D) 60 − 40

8 What is the difference?

(A) 20

(B) 40

(C) 60

(D) 80

Use this picture for problems 9 and 10.

52

Which number sentence matches the picture?

(A) 52 + 50

(B) 52 + 40

(C) 12 + 40

(D) 22 + 30

10 What is the sum?

(A) 92

(B) 82

(C) 52

(D) 50

Use this picture for problems 11 and 12.

38

11 Which number sentence matches the picture?

(A) 38 + 40

(B) 38 + 50

(C) 58 + 30

(D) 48 + 50

12 What is the sum?

(A) 78

(B) 80

(C) 88

(D) 98

Use this picture for problems 13 and 14.

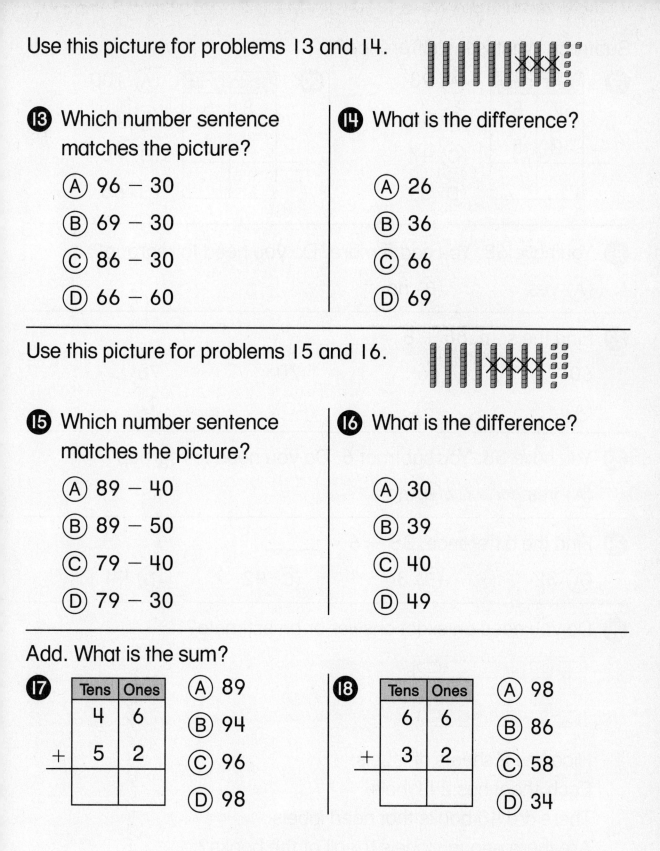

13 Which number sentence matches the picture?

Ⓐ 96 − 30

Ⓑ 69 − 30

Ⓒ 86 − 30

Ⓓ 66 − 60

14 What is the difference?

Ⓐ 26

Ⓑ 36

Ⓒ 66

Ⓓ 69

Use this picture for problems 15 and 16.

15 Which number sentence matches the picture?

Ⓐ 89 − 40

Ⓑ 89 − 50

Ⓒ 79 − 40

Ⓓ 79 − 30

16 What is the difference?

Ⓐ 30

Ⓑ 39

Ⓒ 40

Ⓓ 49

Add. What is the sum?

17

Tens	Ones
4	6
+ 5	2

Ⓐ 89

Ⓑ 94

Ⓒ 96

Ⓓ 98

18

Tens	Ones
6	6
+ 3	2

Ⓐ 98

Ⓑ 86

Ⓒ 58

Ⓓ 34

Subtract. What is the difference?

19

Tens	Ones
7	8
− 2	5

Ⓐ 93

Ⓑ 53

Ⓒ 47

Ⓓ 35

20

Tens	Ones
8	5
− 1	5

Ⓐ 100

Ⓑ 75

Ⓒ 70

Ⓓ 65

---

21 You have 68. You add 8 more. Do you need to regroup?

Ⓐ yes   Ⓑ no

---

22 Find the sum. 68 + 8 = _____

60   66   70   76

Ⓐ   Ⓑ   Ⓒ   Ⓓ

---

23 You have 38. You subtract 6. Do you need to regroup?

Ⓐ yes   Ⓑ no

---

24 Find the difference. 38 − 6 = _____

Ⓐ 32   Ⓑ 36   Ⓒ 42   Ⓓ 44

---

25 Do you need an exact answer or an estimate?

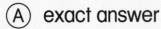
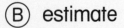

Rico has 2 sheets of labels.

Each sheet has 24 labels.

There are 40 books that need labels.

Are there enough labels for all of the books?

Ⓐ exact answer

Ⓑ estimate

Name _____

Mark the best answer.

Use this picture for problems 1 and 2.

1 Which number sentence matches the picture?

Ⓐ 30 + 10

Ⓑ 30 + 20

Ⓒ 30 + 30

Ⓓ 30 + 40

2 What is the sum?

Ⓐ 30

Ⓑ 40

Ⓒ 50

Ⓓ 60

Use this picture for problems 3 and 4.

3 Which number sentence matches the picture?

Ⓐ 20 + 40

Ⓑ 20 + 50

Ⓒ 20 + 60

Ⓓ 20 + 70

4 What is the sum?

Ⓐ 50

Ⓑ 60

Ⓒ 70

Ⓓ 80

Use this picture for problems 5 and 6.

5 Which number sentence matches the picture?

Ⓐ 70 − 30

Ⓑ 70 − 10

Ⓒ 70 − 20

Ⓓ 60 − 30

6 What is the difference?

Ⓐ 10

Ⓑ 20

Ⓒ 30

Ⓓ 40

Use this picture for problems 7 and 8.

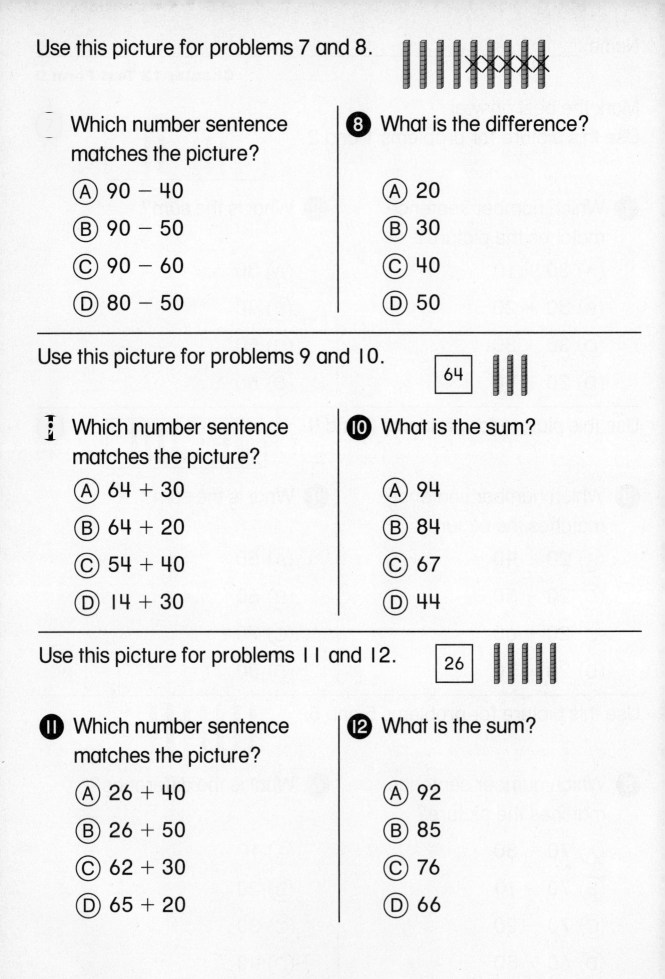

Which number sentence matches the picture?

A) 90 − 40

B) 90 − 50

C) 90 − 60

D) 80 − 50

8 What is the difference?

A) 20

B) 30

C) 40

D) 50

Use this picture for problems 9 and 10.

Which number sentence matches the picture?

A) 64 + 30

B) 64 + 20

C) 54 + 40

D) 14 + 30

10 What is the sum?

A) 94

B) 84

C) 67

D) 44

Use this picture for problems 11 and 12.

11 Which number sentence matches the picture?

A) 26 + 40

B) 26 + 50

C) 62 + 30

D) 65 + 20

12 What is the sum?

A) 92

B) 85

C) 76

D) 66

Use this picture for problems 13 and 14.

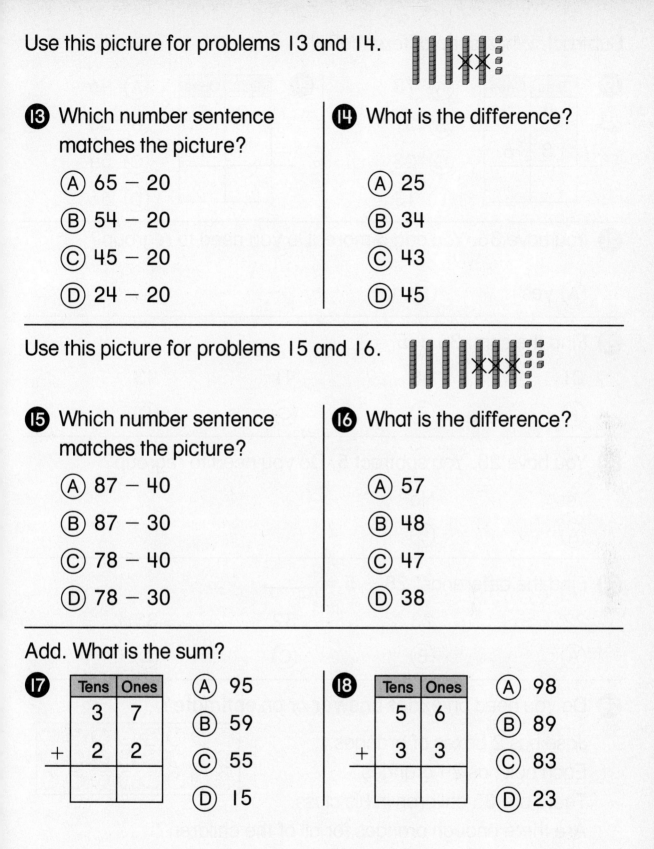

13 Which number sentence matches the picture?

- (A) 65 − 20
- (B) 54 − 20
- (C) 45 − 20
- (D) 24 − 20

14 What is the difference?

- (A) 25
- (B) 34
- (C) 43
- (D) 45

Use this picture for problems 15 and 16.

15 Which number sentence matches the picture?

- (A) 87 − 40
- (B) 87 − 30
- (C) 78 − 40
- (D) 78 − 30

16 What is the difference?

- (A) 57
- (B) 48
- (C) 47
- (D) 38

Add. What is the sum?

17

Tens	Ones
3	7
+ 2	2

- (A) 95
- (B) 59
- (C) 55
- (D) 15

18

Tens	Ones
5	6
+ 3	3

- (A) 98
- (B) 89
- (C) 83
- (D) 23

Subtract. What is the difference?

19

Tens	Ones
4	9
− 3	6

Ⓐ 73

Ⓑ 31

Ⓒ 23

Ⓓ 13

20

Tens	Ones
9	5
− 4	1

Ⓐ 46

Ⓑ 53

Ⓒ 54

Ⓓ 66

21 You have 36. You add 5 more. Do you need to regroup?

Ⓐ yes   Ⓑ no

22 Find the sum. 36 + 5 = _____

31   38   41   43

Ⓐ   Ⓑ   Ⓒ   Ⓓ

23 You have 28. You subtract 5. Do you need to regroup?

Yes   No

Ⓐ   Ⓑ

24 Find the difference. 28 − 5 = _____

22   23   32   33

Ⓐ   Ⓑ   Ⓒ   Ⓓ

25 Do you need an **exact answer** or an **estimate?**

Jose has 2 boxes of oranges.
Each box has 24 oranges.
There are 35 children in his class.
Are there enough oranges for all of the children?

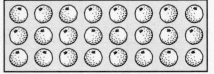

Ⓐ   exact answer

Ⓑ   estimate

Name _____

Mark the best answer.

1 Which number shows one way to make 7?

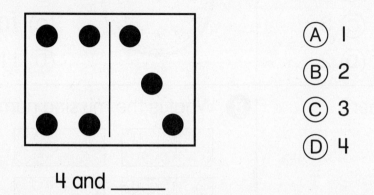

4 and _____

Ⓐ 1

Ⓑ 2

Ⓒ 3

Ⓓ 4

---

2 Which number sentence answers the question?

Rico has 5 baseball cards. Tomás gives him 3 more baseball cards. How many baseball cards does Rico have now?

Ⓐ 5 + 3 = 8

Ⓑ 4 + 2 = 6

Ⓒ 5 − 3 = 2

Ⓓ 4 − 2 = 2

---

3 Which two addition sentences tell about the picture?

📷 📷 📷
📷 📷 📷
📷 📷 📷
📷 📷 📷

Ⓐ 4 + 6 = 10; 6 + 4 = 10

Ⓑ 4 + 7 = 11; 7 + 4 = 11

Ⓒ 4 + 8 = 12; 8 + 4 = 12

Ⓓ 4 + 9 = 13; 9 + 4 = 13

4 What are the related addition and subtraction facts for the picture?

⚾⚾⚾   ⚾⚾⚾
⚾⚾   ⚾⚾⚾

Ⓐ 5 + 6 = 11; 11 − 6 = 5

Ⓑ 5 + 5 = 10; 10 − 5 = 5

Ⓒ 4 + 6 = 10; 10 − 4 = 6

Ⓓ 5 + 4 = 9; 9 − 4 = 5

5 How many flat surfaces does this solid figure have?

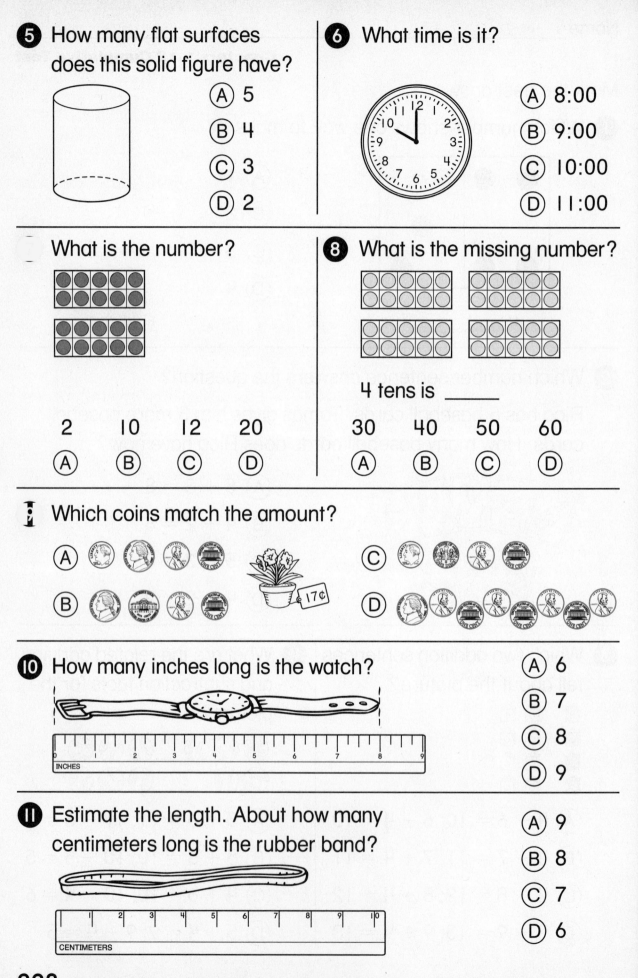

Ⓐ 5
Ⓑ 4
Ⓒ 3
Ⓓ 2

6 What time is it?

Ⓐ 8:00
Ⓑ 9:00
Ⓒ 10:00
Ⓓ 11:00

What is the number?

2	10	12	20
Ⓐ	Ⓑ	Ⓒ	Ⓓ

8 What is the missing number?

4 tens is _____

30	40	50	60
Ⓐ	Ⓑ	Ⓒ	Ⓓ

Which coins match the amount?

Ⓐ

Ⓑ

17¢

Ⓒ

Ⓓ

10 How many inches long is the watch?

Ⓐ 6
Ⓑ 7
Ⓒ 8
Ⓓ 9

INCHES

11 Estimate the length. About how many centimeters long is the rubber band?

Ⓐ 9
Ⓑ 8
Ⓒ 7
Ⓓ 6

CENTIMETERS

12 Which is the best estimate for the length of a doll?

Ⓐ 1 inch

Ⓑ 1 foot

---

13 Which holds about 1 cup?

Ⓐ

Ⓒ

Ⓑ

Ⓓ

14 Which object would you measure in kilograms?

Ⓐ

Ⓒ

Ⓑ

Ⓓ

---

15 Add.

8
5
+ 2

Ⓐ 10

Ⓑ 13

Ⓒ 15

Ⓓ 17

16 Which doubles fact helps you add 6 + 7

Ⓐ 5 + 5   Ⓒ 9 + 9

Ⓑ 6 + 6   Ⓓ 8 + 8

Use the picture for Exercises 17 and 18.

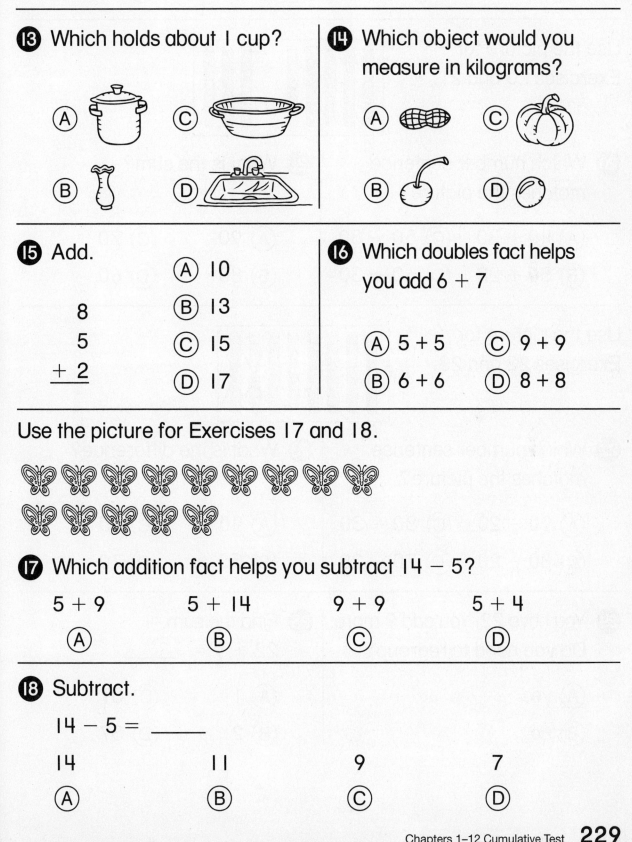

17 Which addition fact helps you subtract 14 − 5?

5 + 9   5 + 14   9 + 9   5 + 4

Ⓐ   Ⓑ   Ⓒ   Ⓓ

---

18 Subtract.

14 − 5 = _____

14   11   9   7

Ⓐ   Ⓑ   Ⓒ   Ⓓ

19 Miguel has 5 apples and 7 bananas. Which addition fact helps you find how many pieces of fruit he has in all?

5 + 7   5 + 5   7 + 7   10 + 2

(A)   (B)   (C)   (D)

Use the picture for Exercises 20 and 21.

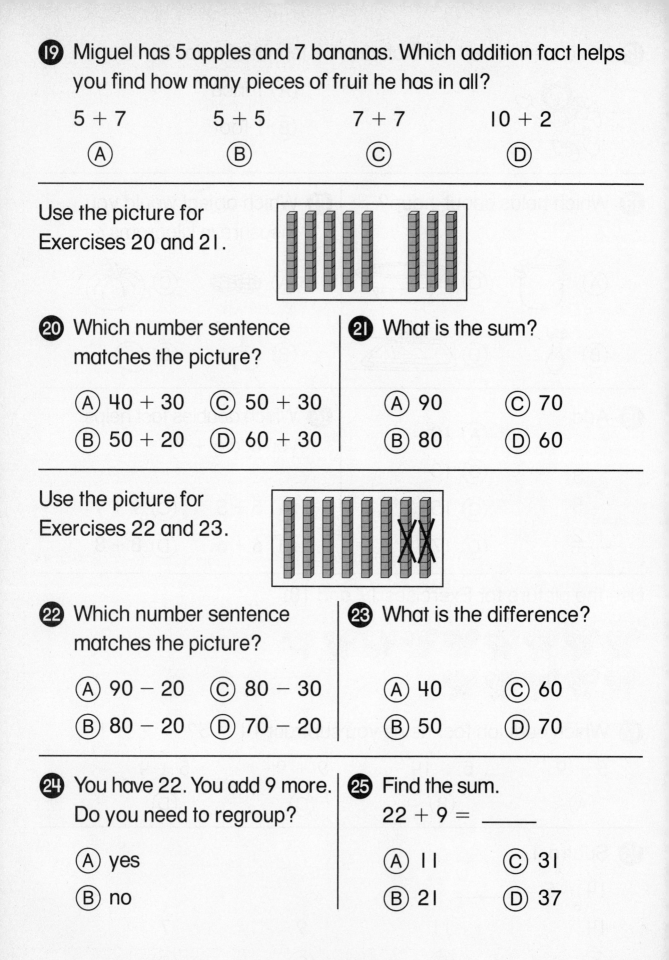

20 Which number sentence matches the picture?

(A) 40 + 30   (C) 50 + 30

(B) 50 + 20   (D) 60 + 30

21 What is the sum?

(A) 90   (C) 70

(B) 80   (D) 60

Use the picture for Exercises 22 and 23.

22 Which number sentence matches the picture?

(A) 90 − 20   (C) 80 − 30

(B) 80 − 20   (D) 70 − 20

23 What is the difference?

(A) 40   (C) 60

(B) 50   (D) 70

24 You have 22. You add 9 more. Do you need to regroup?

(A) yes

(B) no

25 Find the sum.

22 + 9 = _____

(A) 11   (C) 31

(B) 21   (D) 37

Basic-Facts Timed Test 1–4

Name _____

Give each answer.

1. 7 + 2 = __9__
2. 3 + 1 = __4__
3. 2 + 2 = __4__
4. 4 + 1 = __5__
5. 8 + 2 = __10__
6. 5 + 3 = __8__
7. 6 + 1 = __7__
8. 3 + 2 = __5__
9. 4 + 2 = __6__
10. 8 + 1 = __9__
11. 6 + 3 = __9__
12. 5 + 1 = __6__
13. 7 − 3 = __4__

14. 6 − 1 = __5__
15. 9 − 2 = __7__
16. 8 − 3 = __5__
17. 6 − 2 = __4__
18. 10 − 1 = __9__
19. 7 − 2 = __5__
20. 9 − 3 = __6__
21. 4 − 2 = __2__
22. 11 − 3 = __8__
23. 10 − 1 = __9__
24. 11 − 2 = __9__
25. 8 − 2 = __6__

page 27

Name _____

Give each answer.

1. 2 + 7 = __9__
2. 6 + 1 = __7__
3. 2 + 4 = __6__
4. 4 + 0 = __4__
5. 8 + 1 = __9__
6. 7 + 3 = __10__
7. 6 + 1 = __7__
8. 3 + 8 = __11__
9. 10 + 2 = __12__
10. 6 + 4 = __10__
11. 9 + 3 = __12__
12. 0 + 9 = __9__
13. 7 − 3 = __4__

14. 9 − 7 = __2__
15. 12 − 5 = __7__
16. 8 − 3 = __5__
17. 7 − 2 = __5__
18. 11 − 4 = __7__
19. 7 − 4 = __3__
20. 9 − 6 = __3__
21. 10 − 2 = __8__
22. 11 − 8 = __3__
23. 10 − 1 = __9__
24. 5 − 4 = __1__
25. 10 − 6 = __4__

page 28

Name _____

Give each answer.

1. 12 − 7 = __5__
2. 10 − 9 = __1__
3. 5 − 2 = __3__
4. 7 − 2 = __5__
5. 11 − 6 = __5__
6. 8 − 4 = __4__
7. 12 − 5 = __7__
8. 7 − 3 = __4__
9. 11 − 5 = __6__
10. 10 − 7 = __3__
11. 9 − 0 = __9__
12. 7 − 1 = __6__
13. 10 − 6 = __4__

14. 6 + 5 = __11__
15. 5 − 5 = __0__
16. 8 − 3 = __5__
17. 8 + 2 = __10__
18. 11 − 7 = __4__
19. 6 + 4 = __10__
20. 9 − 2 = __7__
21. 8 + 4 = __12__
22. 11 − 10 = __1__
23. 7 − 7 = __0__
24. 6 + 1 = __7__
25. 9 − 4 = __5__

page 29

Name _____

Give each answer.

1. 7 + 8 = __15__
2. 3 + 9 = __12__
3. 8 + 3 = __11__
4. 9 + 0 = __9__
5. 8 + 5 = __13__
6. 11 + 3 = __14__
7. 6 + 9 = __15__
8. 7 + 5 = __12__
9. 11 + 2 = __13__
10. 12 + 4 = __16__
11. 6 + 6 = __12__
12. 15 + 0 = __15__
13. 12 − 9 = __3__

14. 6 + 6 = __12__
15. 14 − 9 = __5__
16. 13 − 12 = __1__
17. 16 − 10 = __6__
18. 10 + 2 = __12__
19. 13 − 7 = __6__
20. 8 + 8 = __16__
21. 14 − 3 = __11__
22. 15 − 5 = __10__
23. 8 + 4 = __12__
24. 14 + 2 = __16__
25. 13 − 1 = __12__

page 30

231

Basic-Facts Timed Test 5–8

Name _____

Basic-Facts Timed Test 5

Give each answer.

1. 12 − 9 = **3**
2. 10 − 3 = **7**
3. 15 − 2 = **13**
4. 7 − 1 = **6**
5. 13 − 6 = **7**
6. 16 − 4 = **12**
7. 15 − 11 = **4**
8. 9 − 8 = **1**
9. 13 − 3 = **10**
10. 8 − 6 = **2**
11. 11 − 0 = **11**
12. 14 − 6 = **8**
13. 10 − 6 = **4**

14. 7 + 8 = **15**
15. 15 − 13 = **2**
16. 12 − 3 = **9**
17. 8 + 5 = **13**
18. 11 − 7 = **4**
19. 3 + 12 = **15**
20. 16 − 11 = **5**
21. 8 + 4 = **12**
22. 11 − 5 = **6**
23. 16 − 7 = **9**
24. 10 + 4 = **14**
25. 15 − 7 = **8**

page 31

Name _____

Basic-Facts Timed Test 6

Give each answer.

1. 8 + 7 = **15**
2. 6 + 5 = **11**
3. 9 + 4 = **13**
4. 16 + 0 = **16**
5. 8 + 3 = **11**
6. 9 + 9 = **18**
7. 6 + 7 = **13**
8. 4 + 8 = **12**
9. 11 + 2 = **13**
10. 6 + 4 = **10**
11. 3 + 11 = **14**
12. 17 + 1 = **18**
13. 16 − 6 = **10**

14. 15 + 2 = **17**
15. 18 − 5 = **13**
16. 16 − 14 = **2**
17. 6 + 12 = **18**
18. 11 − 4 = **7**
19. 5 + 10 = **15**
20. 15 − 6 = **9**
21. 17 − 14 = **3**
22. 15 − 8 = **7**
23. 18 − 12 = **6**
24. 10 + 7 = **17**
25. 11 − 6 = **5**

page 32

Name _____

Basic-Facts Timed Test 7

Give each answer.

1. 12 − 10 = **2**
2. 18 − 3 = **15**
3. 15 − 8 = **7**
4. 17 − 14 = **3**
5. 13 − 5 = **8**
6. 16 − 2 = **14**
7. 17 − 5 = **12**
8. 18 − 9 = **9**
9. 14 − 0 = **14**
10. 16 − 9 = **7**
11. 17 − 11 = **6**
12. 18 − 8 = **10**
13. 15 + 3 = **18**

14. 11 + 4 = **15**
15. 17 − 5 = **12**
16. 12 − 8 = **4**
17. 7 + 9 = **16**
18. 11 − 7 = **4**
19. 5 + 12 = **17**
20. 16 − 11 = **5**
21. 11 + 3 = **14**
22. 11 − 10 = **1**
23. 17 − 4 = **13**
24. 12 + 4 = **16**
25. 18 − 5 = **13**

page 33

Name _____

Basic-Facts Timed Test 8

Give each answer.

1. 10 + 8 = **18**
2. 15 + 2 = **17**
3. 4 + 14 = **18**
4. 10 + 1 = **11**
5. 8 + 4 = **12**
6. 9 + 9 = **18**
7. 5 + 12 = **17**
8. 11 + 5 = **16**
9. 3 + 14 = **17**
10. 17 + 1 = **18**
11. 3 + 13 = **16**
12. 14 + 1 = **15**
13. 16 − 6 = **10**

14. 11 + 7 = **18**
15. 18 − 5 = **13**
16. 17 − 6 = **11**
17. 9 + 8 = **17**
18. 12 − 4 = **8**
19. 15 − 10 = **5**
20. 4 + 12 = **16**
21. 18 − 9 = **9**
22. 15 − 8 = **7**
23. 18 − 7 = **11**
24. 11 + 6 = **17**
25. 13 + 3 = **16**

page 34

Basic-Facts Timed Test 9–12

Basic-Facts Timed Test 9

Name _____

Give each answer.

1. $17 - 10 = 7$
2. $10 - 10 = 0$
3. $18 - 12 = 6$
4. $16 - 14 = 2$
5. $8 - 5 = 3$
6. $16 - 5 = 11$
7. $18 - 13 = 5$
8. $17 - 9 = 8$
9. $14 - 10 = 4$
10. $16 - 4 = 12$
11. $17 - 12 = 5$
12. $18 - 11 = 7$
13. $12 + 6 = 18$
14. $11 + 4 = 15$
15. $17 - 6 = 11$
16. $18 - 13 = 5$
17. $14 + 4 = 18$
18. $16 - 4 = 12$
19. $4 + 10 = 14$
20. $16 - 11 = 5$
21. $2 + 16 = 18$
22. $16 - 10 = 6$
23. $15 - 13 = 2$
24. $12 + 4 = 16$
25. $18 - 6 = 12$

page 35

Basic-Facts Timed Test 10

Name _____

Give each answer.

1. $9 + 8 = 17$
2. $11 + 2 = 13$
3. $4 + 10 = 14$
4. $10 + 6 = 16$
5. $8 + 5 = 13$
6. $6 + 6 = 12$
7. $5 + 11 = 16$
8. $9 + 5 = 14$
9. $3 + 12 = 15$
10. $16 + 1 = 17$
11. $4 + 9 = 13$
12. $14 + 2 = 16$
13. $15 - 5 = 10$
14. $11 + 4 = 15$
15. $16 - 5 = 11$
16. $15 - 6 = 9$
17. $9 + 7 = 16$
18. $12 - 8 = 4$
19. $14 - 10 = 4$
20. $5 + 12 = 17$
21. $16 - 8 = 8$
22. $15 - 7 = 8$
23. $13 - 7 = 6$
24. $8 + 6 = 14$
25. $12 + 4 = 16$

page 36

Basic-Facts Timed Test 11

Name _____

Give each answer.

1. $16 - 10 = 6$
2. $8 - 8 = 0$
3. $16 - 8 = 8$
4. $17 - 14 = 3$
5. $14 - 6 = 8$
6. $13 - 8 = 5$
7. $12 - 5 = 7$
8. $17 - 8 = 9$
9. $14 - 11 = 3$
10. $16 - 7 = 9$
11. $17 - 12 = 5$
12. $13 - 6 = 7$
13. $9 + 9 = 18$
14. $8 + 9 = 17$
15. $16 - 6 = 10$
16. $18 - 9 = 9$
17. $5 + 6 = 11$
18. $16 - 4 = 12$
19. $7 + 6 = 13$
20. $15 - 7 = 8$
21. $4 + 8 = 12$
22. $16 - 7 = 9$
23. $15 - 9 = 6$
24. $7 + 7 = 14$
25. $12 - 6 = 6$

page 37

Basic-Facts Timed Test 12

Name _____

Give each answer.

1. $8 + 8 = 16$
2. $11 + 7 = 18$
3. $4 + 11 = 15$
4. $10 + 4 = 14$
5. $8 + 9 = 17$
6. $6 + 6 = 12$
7. $5 + 8 = 13$
8. $9 + 6 = 15$
9. $2 + 12 = 14$
10. $7 + 8 = 15$
11. $4 + 9 = 13$
12. $11 + 2 = 13$
13. $14 - 4 = 10$
14. $8 + 9 = 17$
15. $11 - 5 = 6$
16. $14 - 6 = 8$
17. $9 + 7 = 16$
18. $13 - 8 = 5$
19. $15 - 10 = 5$
20. $4 + 12 = 16$
21. $16 - 8 = 8$
22. $15 - 9 = 6$
23. $16 - 7 = 9$
24. $8 + 10 = 18$
25. $7 + 8 = 15$

page 38

Diagnosing Readiness for Grade 1

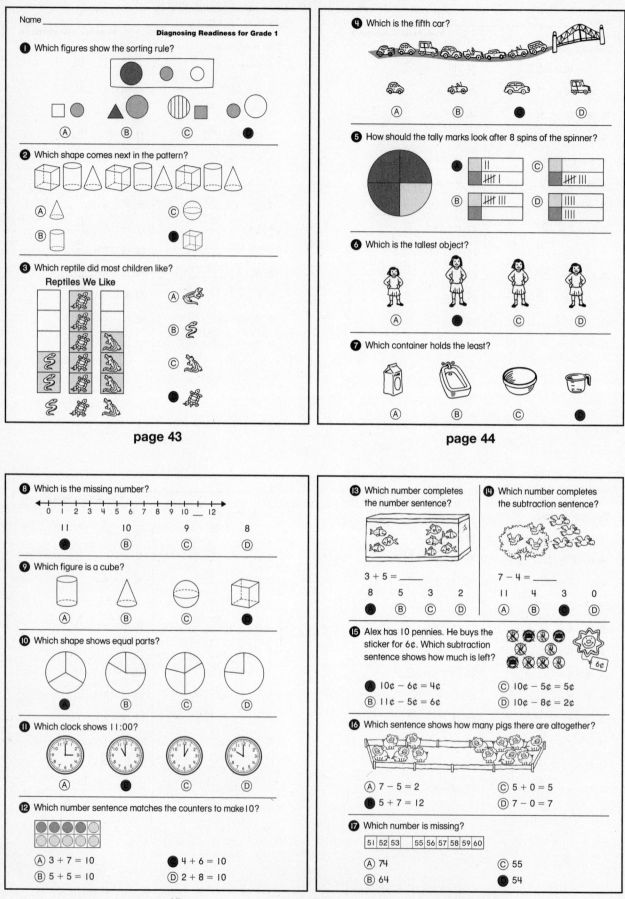

Name _____

Diagnosing Readiness for Grade 1

1 Which figures show the sorting rule?

Ⓐ   Ⓑ   Ⓒ   Ⓓ

2 Which shape comes next in the pattern?

Ⓐ

Ⓑ

Ⓒ

Ⓓ

3 Which reptile did most children like?

Reptiles We Like

Ⓐ
Ⓑ
Ⓒ
Ⓓ

page 43

4 Which is the fifth car?

Ⓐ   Ⓑ   Ⓒ   Ⓓ

5 How should the tally marks look after 8 spins of the spinner?

Ⓐ   Ⓒ

Ⓑ   Ⓓ

6 Which is the tallest object?

Ⓐ   Ⓑ   Ⓒ   Ⓓ

7 Which container holds the least?

Ⓐ   Ⓑ   Ⓒ   Ⓓ

page 44

8 Which is the missing number?

0 1 2 3 4 5 6 7 8 9 10 __ 12

11	10	9	8
Ⓐ	Ⓑ	Ⓒ	Ⓓ

9 Which figure is a cube?

Ⓐ   Ⓑ   Ⓒ   Ⓓ

10 Which shape shows equal parts?

Ⓐ   Ⓑ   Ⓒ   Ⓓ

11 Which clock shows 11:00?

Ⓐ   Ⓑ   Ⓒ   Ⓓ

12 Which number sentence matches the counters to make 10?

Ⓐ 3 + 7 = 10   Ⓒ 4 + 6 = 10
Ⓑ 5 + 5 = 10   Ⓓ 2 + 8 = 10

page 45

13 Which number completes the number sentence?

3 + 5 = _____

8	5	3	2
Ⓐ	Ⓑ	Ⓒ	Ⓓ

14 Which number completes the subtraction sentence?

7 − 4 = _____

11	4	3	0
Ⓐ	Ⓑ	Ⓒ	Ⓓ

15 Alex has 10 pennies. He buys the sticker for 6¢. Which subtraction sentence shows how much is left?

6¢

Ⓐ 10¢ − 6¢ = 4¢   Ⓒ 10¢ − 5¢ = 5¢
Ⓑ 11¢ − 5¢ = 6¢   Ⓓ 10¢ − 8¢ = 2¢

16 Which sentence shows how many pigs there are altogether?

Ⓐ 7 − 5 = 2   Ⓒ 5 + 0 = 5
Ⓑ 5 + 7 = 12   Ⓓ 7 − 0 = 7

17 Which number is missing?

| 51 | 52 | 53 | | 55 | 56 | 57 | 58 | 59 | 60 |

Ⓐ 74   Ⓒ 55
Ⓑ 64   Ⓓ 54

page 46

Diagnosing Readiness for Chapter 1, Forms A and B

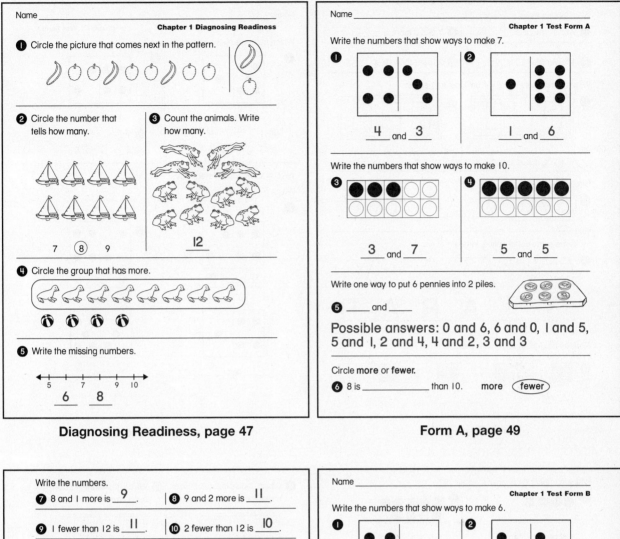

Diagnosing Readiness, page 47

Form A, page 49

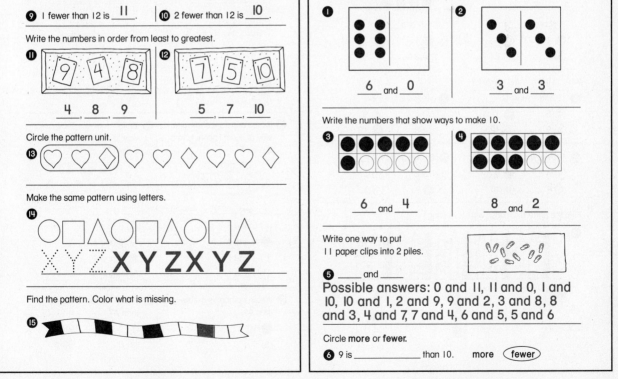

page 50

Form B, page 51

Chapter Tests Forms A and B in the Assessment Sourcebook parallel Chapter Tests in the Student Edition item for item. See the Teacher's Edition for item analysis of these tests.

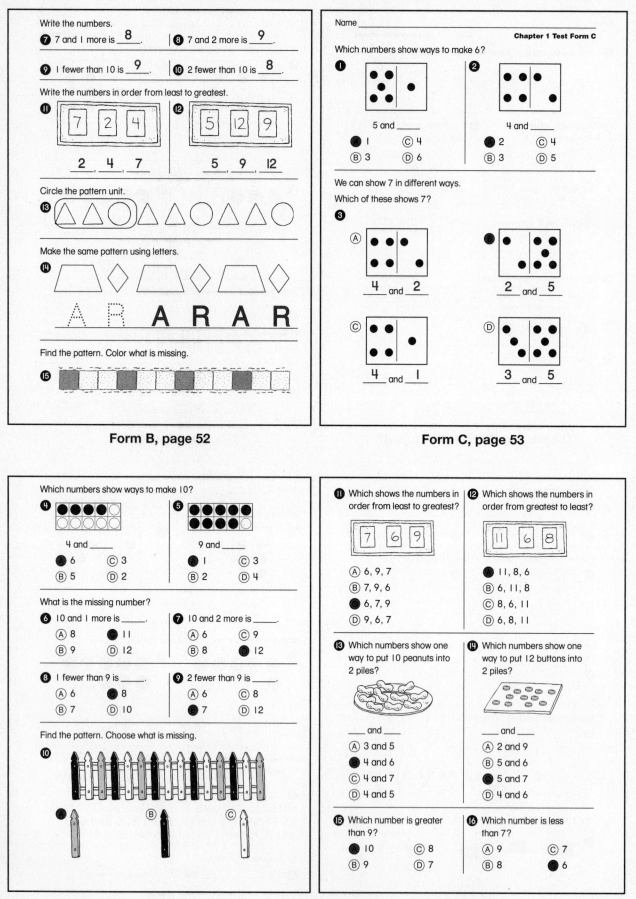

Form B, page 52

Write the numbers.

7 7 and 1 more is __8__. | **8** 7 and 2 more is __9__.

9 1 fewer than 10 is __9__. | **10** 2 fewer than 10 is __8__.

Write the numbers in order from least to greatest.

11 [7] [2] [4] → __2__, __4__, __7__

12 [5] [12] [9] → __5__, __9__, __12__

Circle the pattern unit.

13

Make the same pattern using letters.

14

A R A R A R

Find the pattern. Color what is missing.

15

Form C, page 53

Name _____

Chapter 1 Test Form C

Which numbers show ways to make 6?

1 5 and ____
(A) 1 (C) 4
(B) 3 (D) 6

2 4 and ____
(A) 2 (C) 4
(B) 3 (D) 5

We can show 7 in different ways.
Which of these shows 7?

3
(A) __4__ and __2__
(B) __2__ and __5__
(C) __4__ and __1__
(D) __3__ and __5__

---

page 54

Which numbers show ways to make 10?

4 4 and ____
(A) 6 (C) 3
(B) 5 (D) 2

5 9 and ____
(A) 1 (C) 3
(B) 2 (D) 4

What is the missing number?

6 10 and 1 more is ____.
(A) 8 (C) 9
(B) 9 (D) 11

7 10 and 2 more is ____.
(A) 6 (C) 9
(B) 8 (D) 12

8 1 fewer than 9 is ____.
(A) 6 (C) 8
(B) 7 (D) 10

9 2 fewer than 9 is ____.
(A) 6 (C) 8
(B) 7 (D) 12

Find the pattern. Choose what is missing.

10
(A) (B) (C)

---

page 55

11 Which shows the numbers in order from least to greatest?
[7] [6] [9]
(A) 6, 9, 7
(B) 7, 9, 6
(C) 6, 7, 9
(D) 9, 6, 7

12 Which shows the numbers in order from greatest to least?
[11] [6] [8]
(A) 11, 8, 6
(B) 6, 11, 8
(C) 8, 6, 11
(D) 6, 8, 11

13 Which numbers show one way to put 10 peanuts into 2 piles?
____ and ____
(A) 3 and 5
(B) 4 and 6
(C) 4 and 7
(D) 4 and 5

14 Which numbers show one way to put 12 buttons into 2 piles?
____ and ____
(A) 2 and 9
(B) 5 and 6
(C) 5 and 7
(D) 4 and 6

15 Which number is greater than 9?
(A) 10 (C) 8
(B) 9 (D) 7

16 Which number is less than 7?
(A) 9 (C) 7
(B) 8 (D) 6

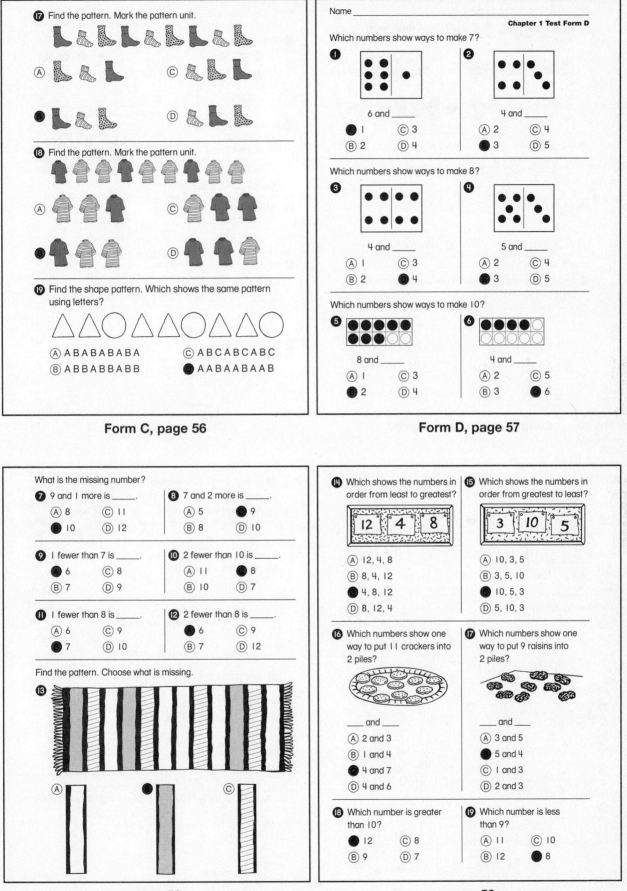

17 Find the pattern. Mark the pattern unit.

Ⓐ
Ⓒ
Ⓑ
Ⓓ

18 Find the pattern. Mark the pattern unit.

Ⓐ
Ⓒ
Ⓑ
Ⓓ

19 Find the shape pattern. Which shows the same pattern using letters?

Ⓐ A B A B A B A B A
Ⓒ A B C A B C A B C
Ⓑ A B B A B B A B B
Ⓓ A A B A A B A A B

Form C, page 56

Name _____

Chapter 1 Test Form D

Which numbers show ways to make 7?

1
6 and _____
Ⓐ I   Ⓒ 3
Ⓑ 2   Ⓓ 4

2
4 and _____
Ⓐ 2   Ⓒ 4
Ⓑ 3   Ⓓ 5

Which numbers show ways to make 8?

3
4 and _____
Ⓐ I   Ⓒ 3
Ⓑ 2   Ⓓ 4

4
5 and _____
Ⓐ 2   Ⓒ 4
Ⓑ 3   Ⓓ 5

Which numbers show ways to make 10?

5
8 and _____
Ⓐ I   Ⓒ 3
Ⓑ 2   Ⓓ 4

6
4 and _____
Ⓐ 2   Ⓒ 5
Ⓑ 3   Ⓓ 6

Form D, page 57

What is the missing number?

7 9 and I more is _____.
Ⓐ 8   Ⓒ II
Ⓑ 10   Ⓓ 12

8 7 and 2 more is _____.
Ⓐ 5   Ⓒ 9
Ⓑ 8   Ⓓ 10

9 I fewer than 7 is _____.
Ⓐ 6   Ⓒ 8
Ⓑ 7   Ⓓ 9

10 2 fewer than 10 is _____.
Ⓐ II   Ⓒ 8
Ⓑ 10   Ⓓ 7

11 I fewer than 8 is _____.
Ⓐ 6   Ⓒ 9
Ⓑ 7   Ⓓ 10

12 2 fewer than 8 is _____.
Ⓐ 6   Ⓒ 9
Ⓑ 7   Ⓓ 12

Find the pattern. Choose what is missing.

13

Ⓐ
Ⓑ
Ⓒ

page 58

14 Which shows the numbers in order from least to greatest?

12   4   8

Ⓐ 12, 4, 8
Ⓑ 8, 4, 12
Ⓒ 4, 8, 12
Ⓓ 8, 12, 4

15 Which shows the numbers in order from greatest to least?

3   10   5

Ⓐ 10, 3, 5
Ⓑ 3, 5, 10
Ⓒ 10, 5, 3
Ⓓ 5, 10, 3

16 Which numbers show one way to put II crackers into 2 piles?

_____ and _____
Ⓐ 2 and 3
Ⓑ I and 4
Ⓒ 4 and 7
Ⓓ 4 and 6

17 Which numbers show one way to put 9 raisins into 2 piles?

_____ and _____
Ⓐ 3 and 5
Ⓑ 5 and 4
Ⓒ I and 3
Ⓓ 2 and 3

18 Which number is greater than 10?
Ⓐ 12   Ⓒ 8
Ⓑ 9   Ⓓ 7

19 Which number is less than 9?
Ⓐ II   Ⓒ 10
Ⓑ 12   Ⓓ 8

page 59

Chapters 1 and 2

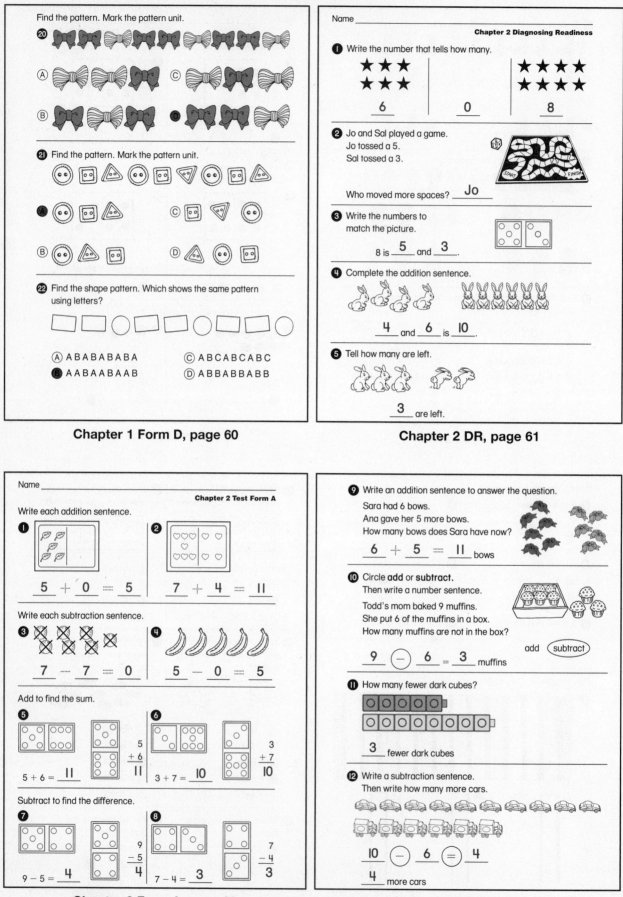

Chapter 1 Form D, page 60

Find the pattern. Mark the pattern unit.

⑳

Ⓐ Ⓒ

Ⓑ Ⓓ

㉑ Find the pattern. Mark the pattern unit.

Ⓐ Ⓒ

Ⓑ Ⓓ

㉒ Find the shape pattern. Which shows the same pattern using letters?

Ⓐ A B A B A B A B A   Ⓒ A B C A B C A B C
Ⓑ A A B A A B A A B   Ⓓ A B B A B B A B B

Chapter 2 DR, page 61

Name _____

Chapter 2 Diagnosing Readiness

❶ Write the number that tells how many.

★ ★ ★
★ ★ ★ | ★ ★ ★ ★
          | ★ ★ ★ ★

_6_ _0_ _8_

❷ Jo and Sal played a game.
Jo tossed a 5.
Sal tossed a 3.

Who moved more spaces? _Jo_

❸ Write the numbers to match the picture.

8 is _5_ and _3_.

❹ Complete the addition sentence.

_4_ and _6_ is _10_.

❺ Tell how many are left.

_3_ are left.

Chapter 2 Form A, page 63

Name _____

Chapter 2 Test Form A

Write each addition sentence.

❶ _5_ ＋ _0_ ＝ _5_

❷ _7_ ＋ _4_ ＝ _11_

Write each subtraction sentence.

❸ _7_ − _7_ ＝ _0_

❹ _5_ − _0_ ＝ _5_

Add to find the sum.

❺ 5 + 6 = _11_

  5
+ 6
_11_

❻ 3 + 7 = _10_

  3
+ 7
_10_

Subtract to find the difference.

❼ 9 − 5 = _4_

  9
− 5
_4_

❽ 7 − 4 = _3_

  7
− 4
_3_

page 64

❾ Write an addition sentence to answer the question.

Sara had 6 bows.
Ana gave her 5 more bows.
How many bows does Sara have now?

_6_ ＋ _5_ ＝ _11_ bows

❿ Circle add or subtract.
Then write a number sentence.

Todd's mom baked 9 muffins.
She put 6 of the muffins in a box.
How many muffins are not in the box?

_9_ ⊖ _6_ = _3_ muffins

add (subtract)

⓫ How many fewer dark cubes?

_3_ fewer dark cubes

⓬ Write a subtraction sentence.
Then write how many more cars.

_10_ ⊖ _6_ ⊜ _4_

_4_ more cars

Chapter Tests Forms A and B in the Assessment Sourcebook parallel Chapter Tests in the Student Edition item for item. See the Teacher's Edition for item analysis of these tests.

Chapter 2 Form B and Form C

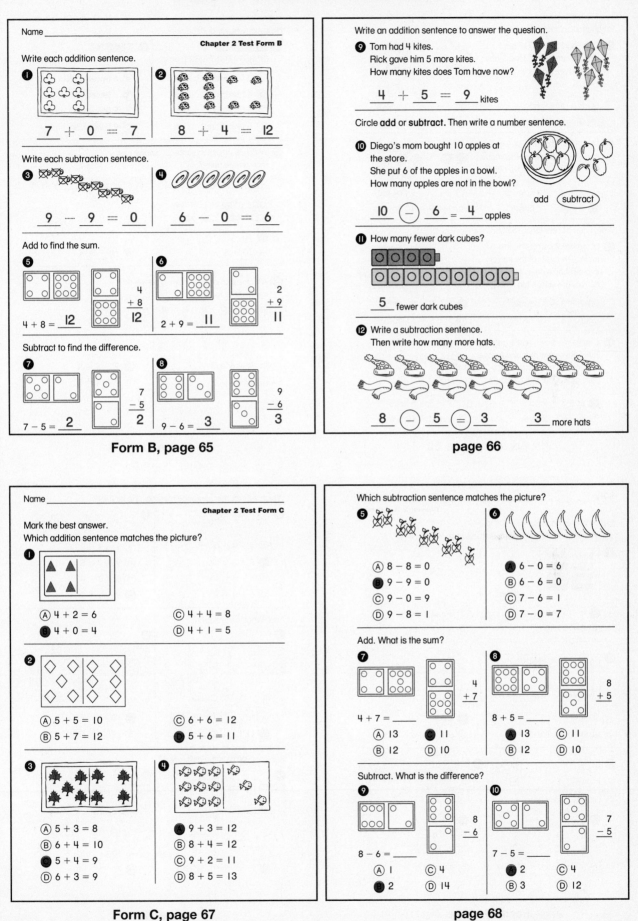

Name _____

Write each addition sentence.

❶ 7 + 0 = 7

❷ 8 + 4 = 12

Write each subtraction sentence.

❸ 9 - 9 = 0

❹ 6 - 0 = 6

Add to find the sum.

❺ 4 + 8 = 12

❻ 2 + 9 = 11

Subtract to find the difference.

❼ 7 - 5 = 2

❽ 9 - 6 = 3

Form B, page 65

Write an addition sentence to answer the question.

❾ Tom had 4 kites.
Rick gave him 5 more kites.
How many kites does Tom have now?

4 + 5 = 9 kites

Circle **add** or **subtract**. Then write a number sentence.

❿ Diego's mom bought 10 apples at the store.
She put 6 of the apples in a bowl.
How many apples are not in the bowl?

add   ⟨subtract⟩

10 ⊖ 6 = 4 apples

⓫ How many fewer dark cubes?

5 fewer dark cubes

⓬ Write a subtraction sentence.
Then write how many more hats.

8 ⊖ 5 ⊜ 3   3 more hats

page 66

Name _____

Mark the best answer.
Which addition sentence matches the picture?

❶
- (A) 4 + 2 = 6
- (B) ● 4 + 0 = 4
- (C) 4 + 4 = 8
- (D) 4 + 1 = 5

❷
- (A) 5 + 5 = 10
- (B) 5 + 7 = 12
- (C) 6 + 6 = 12
- (D) ● 5 + 6 = 11

❸
- (A) 5 + 3 = 8
- (B) 6 + 4 = 10
- (C) ● 5 + 4 = 9
- (D) 6 + 3 = 9

❹
- (A) ● 9 + 3 = 12
- (B) 8 + 4 = 12
- (C) 9 + 2 = 11
- (D) 8 + 5 = 13

Form C, page 67

Which subtraction sentence matches the picture?

❺
- (A) 8 - 8 = 0
- (B) ● 9 - 9 = 0
- (C) 9 - 0 = 9
- (D) 9 - 8 = 1

❻
- (A) ● 6 - 0 = 6
- (B) 6 - 6 = 0
- (C) 7 - 6 = 1
- (D) 7 - 0 = 7

Add. What is the sum?

❼ 4 + 7 = ____
- (A) 13
- (B) 12
- (C) ● 11
- (D) 10

❽ 8 + 5 = ____
- (A) 13
- (B) 12
- (C) 11
- (D) 10

Subtract. What is the difference?

❾ 8 - 6 = ____
- (A) 1
- (B) ● 2
- (C) 4
- (D) 14

❿ 7 - 5 = ____
- (A) ● 2
- (B) 3
- (C) 4
- (D) 12

page 68

Chapter Tests Forms A and B in the Assessment Sourcebook parallel Chapter Tests in the Student Edition item for item. See the Teacher's Edition for item analysis of these tests.

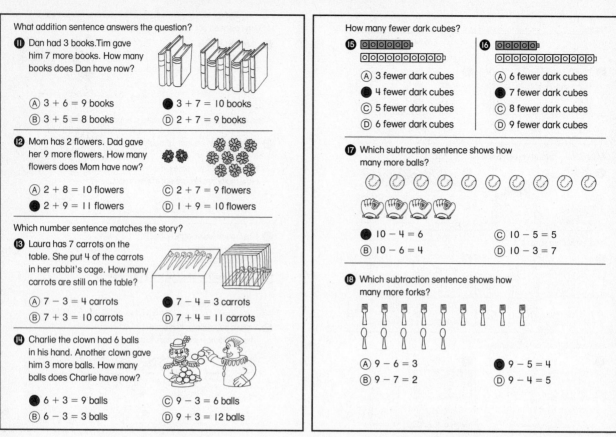

What addition sentence answers the question?

11 Dan had 3 books. Tim gave him 7 more books. How many books does Dan have now?

- Ⓐ 3 + 6 = 9 books
- Ⓑ 3 + 5 = 8 books
- ● 3 + 7 = 10 books
- Ⓓ 2 + 7 = 9 books

12 Mom has 2 flowers. Dad gave her 9 more flowers. How many flowers does Mom have now?

- Ⓐ 2 + 8 = 10 flowers
- ● 2 + 9 = 11 flowers
- Ⓒ 2 + 7 = 9 flowers
- Ⓓ 1 + 9 = 10 flowers

Which number sentence matches the story?

13 Laura has 7 carrots on the table. She put 4 of the carrots in her rabbit's cage. How many carrots are still on the table?

- Ⓐ 7 − 3 = 4 carrots
- Ⓑ 7 + 3 = 10 carrots
- ● 7 − 4 = 3 carrots
- Ⓓ 7 + 4 = 11 carrots

14 Charlie the clown had 6 balls in his hand. Another clown gave him 3 more balls. How many balls does Charlie have now?

- ● 6 + 3 = 9 balls
- Ⓑ 6 − 3 = 3 balls
- Ⓒ 9 − 3 = 6 balls
- Ⓓ 9 + 3 = 12 balls

How many fewer dark cubes?

15
- Ⓐ 3 fewer dark cubes
- ● 4 fewer dark cubes
- Ⓒ 5 fewer dark cubes
- Ⓓ 6 fewer dark cubes

16
- Ⓐ 6 fewer dark cubes
- ● 7 fewer dark cubes
- Ⓒ 8 fewer dark cubes
- Ⓓ 9 fewer dark cubes

17 Which subtraction sentence shows how many more balls?

- ● 10 − 4 = 6
- Ⓑ 10 − 6 = 4
- Ⓒ 10 − 5 = 5
- Ⓓ 10 − 3 = 7

18 Which subtraction sentence shows how many more forks?

- Ⓐ 9 − 6 = 3
- Ⓑ 9 − 7 = 2
- ● 9 − 5 = 4
- Ⓓ 9 − 4 = 5

Form C, page 69

page 70

Name _____

Chapter 2 Test Form D

Mark the best answer.

Which addition sentence matches the picture?

1
- ● 8 + 0 = 8
- Ⓑ 8 + 1 = 9
- Ⓒ 8 + 2 = 10
- Ⓓ 8 + 3 = 11

2
- Ⓐ 4 + 6 = 10
- Ⓑ 3 + 7 = 10
- ● 4 + 7 = 11
- Ⓓ 6 + 6 = 12

3
- ● 5 + 3 = 8
- Ⓑ 6 + 3 = 9
- Ⓒ 5 + 4 = 9
- Ⓓ 6 + 4 = 10

4
- ● 4 + 3 = 7
- Ⓑ 4 + 4 = 8
- Ⓒ 5 + 3 = 8
- Ⓓ 5 + 4 = 9

Which subtraction sentence matches the picture?

5
- Ⓐ 4 − 4 = 0
- ● 5 − 5 = 0
- Ⓒ 5 − 4 = 1
- Ⓓ 6 − 4 = 2

6
- Ⓐ 9 − 9 = 0
- Ⓑ 9 − 1 = 8
- Ⓒ 8 − 0 = 8
- ● 9 − 0 = 9

Add. What is the sum?

7
8
+ 3

8 + 3 = ____
- Ⓐ 10
- ● 11
- Ⓒ 12
- Ⓓ 13

8
9
+ 4

9 + 4 = ____
- ● 13
- Ⓑ 12
- Ⓒ 11
- Ⓓ 10

Subtract. What is the difference?

9
7
− 5

7 − 5 = ____
- Ⓐ 1
- ● 2
- Ⓒ 3
- Ⓓ 12

10
10
− 3

10 − 3 = ____
- Ⓐ 10
- ● 7
- Ⓒ 3
- Ⓓ 1

Form D, page 71

page 72

Chapters 2 and 3

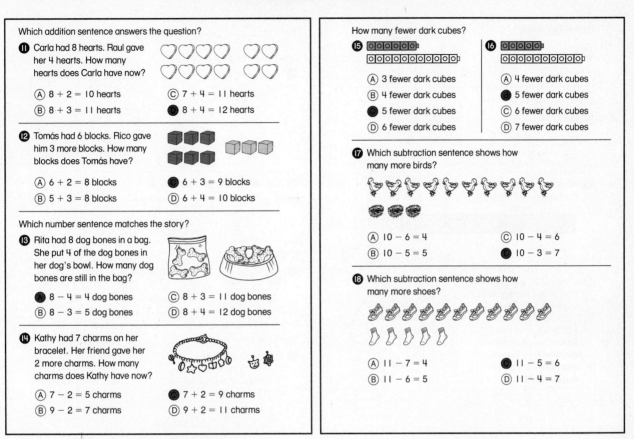

Which addition sentence answers the question?

⑪ Carla had 8 hearts. Raul gave her 4 hearts. How many hearts does Carla have now?

Ⓐ 8 + 2 = 10 hearts   Ⓒ 7 + 4 = 11 hearts
Ⓑ 8 + 3 = 11 hearts   ● 8 + 4 = 12 hearts

⑫ Tomás had 6 blocks. Rico gave him 3 more blocks. How many blocks does Tomás have?

Ⓐ 6 + 2 = 8 blocks   ● 6 + 3 = 9 blocks
Ⓑ 5 + 3 = 8 blocks   Ⓓ 6 + 4 = 10 blocks

Which number sentence matches the story?

⑬ Rita had 8 dog bones in a bag. She put 4 of the dog bones in her dog's bowl. How many dog bones are still in the bag?

● 8 − 4 = 4 dog bones   Ⓒ 8 + 3 = 11 dog bones
Ⓑ 8 − 3 = 5 dog bones   Ⓓ 8 + 4 = 12 dog bones

⑭ Kathy had 7 charms on her bracelet. Her friend gave her 2 more charms. How many charms does Kathy have now?

Ⓐ 7 − 2 = 5 charms   ● 7 + 2 = 9 charms
Ⓑ 9 − 2 = 7 charms   Ⓓ 9 + 2 = 11 charms

Chapter 2 Form D, page 73

How many fewer dark cubes?

⑮   ⑯

Ⓐ 3 fewer dark cubes   Ⓐ 4 fewer dark cubes
Ⓑ 4 fewer dark cubes   ● 5 fewer dark cubes
● 5 fewer dark cubes   Ⓒ 6 fewer dark cubes
Ⓓ 6 fewer dark cubes   Ⓓ 7 fewer dark cubes

⑰ Which subtraction sentence shows how many more birds?

Ⓐ 10 − 6 = 4   Ⓒ 10 − 4 = 6
Ⓑ 10 − 5 = 5   ● 10 − 3 = 7

⑱ Which subtraction sentence shows how many more shoes?

Ⓐ 11 − 7 = 4   ● 11 − 5 = 6
Ⓑ 11 − 6 = 5   Ⓓ 11 − 4 = 7

page 74

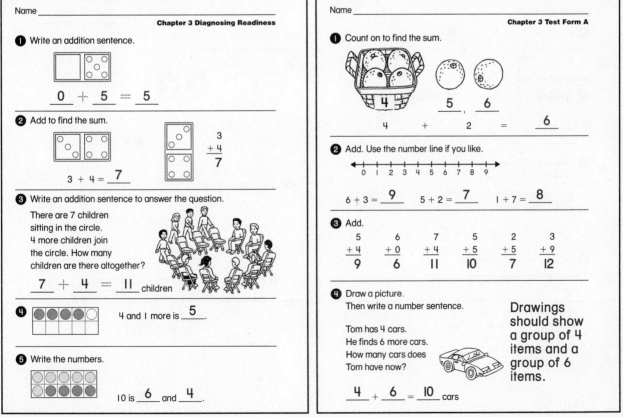

Name _____

Chapter 3 Diagnosing Readiness

❶ Write an addition sentence.

0 + 5 = 5

❷ Add to find the sum.

3 + 4 = 7

$\begin{array}{r} 3 \\ +\ 4 \\ \hline 7 \end{array}$

❸ Write an addition sentence to answer the question.

There are 7 children sitting in the circle. 4 more children join the circle. How many children are there altogether?

7 + 4 = 11 children

❹ 4 and 1 more is 5.

❺ Write the numbers.

10 is 6 and 4.

Chapter 3 DR, page 75

Name _____

Chapter 3 Test Form A

❶ Count on to find the sum.

4 , 5 , 6

4 + 2 = 6

❷ Add. Use the number line if you like.

6 + 3 = 9   5 + 2 = 7   1 + 7 = 8

❸ Add.

$\begin{array}{r} 5 \\ +\ 4 \\ \hline 9 \end{array}$ $\begin{array}{r} 6 \\ +\ 0 \\ \hline 6 \end{array}$ $\begin{array}{r} 7 \\ +\ 4 \\ \hline 11 \end{array}$ $\begin{array}{r} 5 \\ +\ 5 \\ \hline 10 \end{array}$ $\begin{array}{r} 2 \\ +\ 5 \\ \hline 7 \end{array}$ $\begin{array}{r} 3 \\ +\ 9 \\ \hline 12 \end{array}$

❹ Draw a picture. Then write a number sentence.

Tom has 4 cars. He finds 6 more cars. How many cars does Tom have now?

Drawings should show a group of 4 items and a group of 6 items.

4 + 6 = 10 cars

Chapter 3 Form A, page 77

Chapter Tests Forms A and B in the Assessment Sourcebook parallel Chapter Tests in the Student Edition item for item. See the Teacher's Edition for item analysis of these tests.

241

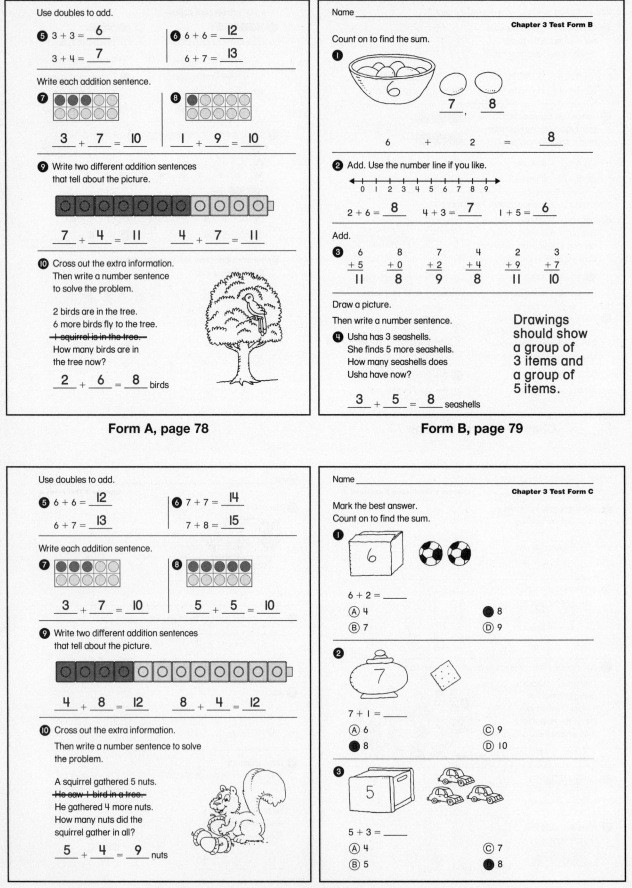

Form A, page 78

Use doubles to add.

5 3 + 3 = __6__   **6** 6 + 6 = __12__

   3 + 4 = __7__   6 + 7 = __13__

Write each addition sentence.

7 __3__ + __7__ = __10__   **8** __1__ + __9__ = __10__

9 Write two different addition sentences that tell about the picture.

__7__ + __4__ = __11__   __4__ + __7__ = __11__

10 Cross out the extra information. Then write a number sentence to solve the problem.

2 birds are in the tree.
6 more birds fly to the tree.
~~1 squirrel is in the tree.~~
How many birds are in the tree now?

__2__ + __6__ = __8__ birds

Form B, page 79

Name _____

Chapter 3 Test Form B

Count on to find the sum.

1 __7__ , __8__

6 + 2 = __8__

2 Add. Use the number line if you like.

0 1 2 3 4 5 6 7 8 9

2 + 6 = __8__   4 + 3 = __7__   1 + 5 = __6__

Add.

3
6 + 5 = __11__   8 + 0 = __8__   7 + 2 = __9__   4 + 4 = __8__   2 + 9 = __11__   3 + 7 = __10__

Draw a picture.
Then write a number sentence.

4 Usha has 3 seashells.
She finds 5 more seashells.
How many seashells does Usha have now?

Drawings should show a group of 3 items and a group of 5 items.

__3__ + __5__ = __8__ seashells

page 80

Use doubles to add.

5 6 + 6 = __12__   **6** 7 + 7 = __14__

   6 + 7 = __13__   7 + 8 = __15__

Write each addition sentence.

7 __3__ + __7__ = __10__   **8** __5__ + __5__ = __10__

9 Write two different addition sentences that tell about the picture.

__4__ + __8__ = __12__   __8__ + __4__ = __12__

10 Cross out the extra information. Then write a number sentence to solve the problem.

A squirrel gathered 5 nuts.
~~He saw 1 bird in a tree.~~
He gathered 4 more nuts.
How many nuts did the squirrel gather in all?

__5__ + __4__ = __9__ nuts

Form C, page 81

Name _____

Chapter 3 Test Form C

Mark the best answer.
Count on to find the sum.

1

6 + 2 = ____
Ⓐ 4   ● 8
Ⓑ 7   Ⓓ 9

2

7 + 1 = ____
Ⓐ 6   Ⓒ 9
● 8   Ⓓ 10

3

5 + 3 = ____
Ⓐ 4   Ⓒ 7
Ⓑ 5   ● 8

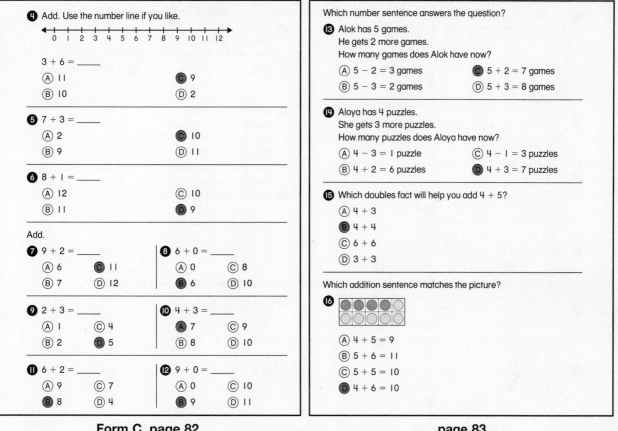

4 Add. Use the number line if you like.

0 1 2 3 4 5 6 7 8 9 10 11 12

$3 + 6 =$ _____

Ⓐ 11   Ⓒ 9
Ⓑ 10   Ⓓ 2

5 $7 + 3 =$ _____

Ⓐ 2   Ⓒ 10
Ⓑ 9   Ⓓ 11

6 $8 + 1 =$ _____

Ⓐ 12   Ⓒ 10
Ⓑ 11   Ⓓ 9

Add.

7 $9 + 2 =$ _____   **8** $6 + 0 =$ _____

Ⓐ 6   Ⓒ 11   Ⓐ 0   Ⓒ 8
Ⓑ 7   Ⓓ 12   Ⓑ 6   Ⓓ 10

9 $2 + 3 =$ _____   **10** $4 + 3 =$ _____

Ⓐ 1   Ⓒ 4   Ⓐ 7   Ⓒ 9
Ⓑ 2   Ⓓ 5   Ⓑ 8   Ⓓ 10

11 $6 + 2 =$ _____   **12** $9 + 0 =$ _____

Ⓐ 9   Ⓒ 7   Ⓐ 0   Ⓒ 10
Ⓑ 8   Ⓓ 4   Ⓑ 9   Ⓓ 11

Form C, page 82

Which number sentence answers the question?

13 Alok has 5 games.
He gets 2 more games.
How many games does Alok have now?

Ⓐ $5 - 2 = 3$ games   Ⓒ $5 + 2 = 7$ games
Ⓑ $5 - 3 = 2$ games   Ⓓ $5 + 3 = 8$ games

14 Aloya has 4 puzzles.
She gets 3 more puzzles.
How many puzzles does Aloya have now?

Ⓐ $4 - 3 = 1$ puzzle   Ⓒ $4 - 1 = 3$ puzzles
Ⓑ $4 + 2 = 6$ puzzles   Ⓓ $4 + 3 = 7$ puzzles

15 Which doubles fact will help you add $4 + 5$?

Ⓐ $4 + 3$
Ⓑ $4 + 4$
Ⓒ $6 + 6$
Ⓓ $3 + 3$

Which addition sentence matches the picture?

16

Ⓐ $4 + 5 = 9$
Ⓑ $5 + 6 = 11$
Ⓒ $5 + 5 = 10$
Ⓓ $4 + 6 = 10$

page 83

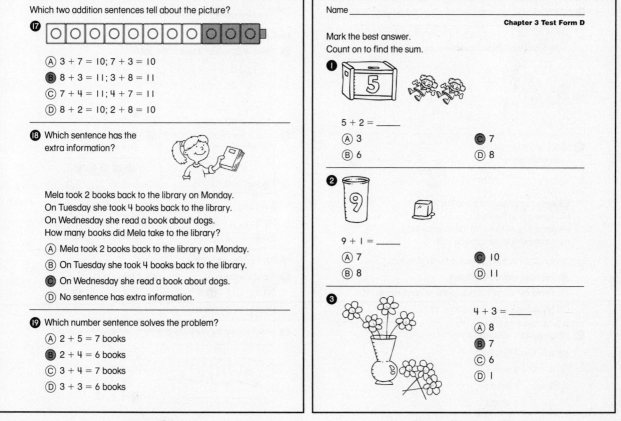

Which two addition sentences tell about the picture?

17

Ⓐ $3 + 7 = 10; 7 + 3 = 10$
Ⓑ $8 + 3 = 11; 3 + 8 = 11$
Ⓒ $7 + 4 = 11; 4 + 7 = 11$
Ⓓ $8 + 2 = 10; 2 + 8 = 10$

18 Which sentence has the extra information?

Mela took 2 books back to the library on Monday.
On Tuesday she took 4 books back to the library.
On Wednesday she read a book about dogs.
How many books did Mela take to the library?

Ⓐ Mela took 2 books back to the library on Monday.
Ⓑ On Tuesday she took 4 books back to the library.
Ⓒ On Wednesday she read a book about dogs.
Ⓓ No sentence has extra information.

19 Which number sentence solves the problem?

Ⓐ $2 + 5 = 7$ books
Ⓑ $2 + 4 = 6$ books
Ⓒ $3 + 4 = 7$ books
Ⓓ $3 + 3 = 6$ books

page 84

Name _____

Chapter 3 Test Form D

Mark the best answer.
Count on to find the sum.

1

$5 + 2 =$ _____

Ⓐ 3   Ⓒ 7
Ⓑ 6   Ⓓ 8

2

$9 + 1 =$ _____

Ⓐ 7   Ⓒ 10
Ⓑ 8   Ⓓ 11

3

$4 + 3 =$ _____

Ⓐ 8
Ⓑ 7
Ⓒ 6
Ⓓ 1

Form D, page 85

Chapter 3 Form D and Cumulative Test

4 Add. Use the number line if you like.

0 1 2 3 4 5 6 7 8 9 10 11 12

5 + 1 = ____

Ⓐ 8   ● 6
Ⓑ 7   Ⓓ 4

5 9 + 3 = ____

● 12   Ⓒ 8
Ⓑ 11   Ⓓ 6

6 6 + 2 = ____

Ⓐ 4   Ⓒ 7
Ⓑ 5   ● 8

Add.

7 8 + 3 = ____

Ⓐ 5   ● 11
Ⓑ 6   Ⓓ 12

8 9 + 0 = ____

Ⓐ 0   ● 9
Ⓑ 6   Ⓓ 10

9 1 + 3 = ____

Ⓐ 1   ● 4
Ⓑ 2   Ⓓ 5

10 7 + 3 = ____

Ⓐ 6   Ⓒ 9
Ⓑ 7   ● 10

11 4 + 2 = ____

Ⓐ 8   ● 6
Ⓑ 7   Ⓓ 2

12 7 + 0 = ____

Ⓐ 0   Ⓒ 8
● 7   Ⓓ 10

Form D, page 86

Which number sentence answers the question?

13 Rita has 8 crayons.
She gets 2 more crayons.
How many crayons does Rita have now?

Ⓐ 8 − 2 = 6 crayons   ● 8 + 2 = 10 crayons
Ⓑ 8 − 6 = 2 crayons   Ⓓ 8 + 3 = 11 crayons

14 Benito has 3 postcards.
He gets 3 more postcards.
How many postcards does Benito have now?

● 3 + 3 = 6 postcards   Ⓒ 6 − 3 = 3 postcards
Ⓑ 3 + 2 = 5 postcards   Ⓓ 3 − 3 = 0 postcards

15 Which doubles fact will help you add 3 + 4?

Ⓐ 2 + 3
● 3 + 3
Ⓒ 6 + 6
Ⓓ 5 + 5

Which addition sentence matches the picture?

16

Ⓐ 6 + 3 = 9
Ⓑ 7 + 2 = 9
● 7 + 3 = 10
Ⓓ 6 + 4 = 10

page 87

---

17 Which two addition sentences tell about the picture?

Ⓐ 2 + 5 = 7; 5 + 2 = 7
● 2 + 6 = 8; 6 + 2 = 8
Ⓒ 3 + 5 = 8; 5 + 3 = 8
Ⓓ 3 + 6 = 9; 6 + 3 = 9

18 Which sentence has the extra information?

Eduardo threw 5 strikes in the first inning.
His team played the Tigers.
He threw 4 more strikes in the second inning.
How many strikes did Eduardo throw?

Ⓐ Eduardo threw 5 strikes in the first inning.
● His team played the Tigers.
Ⓒ He threw 4 more strikes in the second inning.
Ⓓ No sentence has extra information.

19 Which number sentence solves the problem?

● 5 + 4 = 9 strikes
Ⓑ 4 + 4 = 8 strikes
Ⓒ 4 + 3 = 7 strikes
Ⓓ 3 + 3 = 6 strikes

page 88

Name ____

Chapters 1–3 Cumulative Test

Mark the best answer.

1 Which shapes come next in the pattern?

Ⓐ ○ ○
Ⓑ ○ □
Ⓒ □ ○
● □ □

2 What is the missing number?

8 is 2 and ____.

Ⓐ 4   ● 6
Ⓑ 5   Ⓓ 7

3 What are the missing numbers?

7 is ____ and ____.

Ⓐ 4 and 4   Ⓒ 5 and 1
Ⓑ 4 and 5   ● 5 and 2

What is the missing number?

4 7 and 2 more is ____.

Ⓐ 7   ● 9
Ⓑ 8   Ⓓ 10

5 2 fewer than 6 is ____.

Ⓐ 2   ● 4
Ⓑ 3   Ⓓ 5

6 Which shows the numbers in order from least to greatest?

6   12   9

Ⓐ 12, 9, 6
Ⓑ 9, 6, 12
Ⓒ 6, 12, 9
● 6, 9, 12

Cumulative Test 1–3, page 89

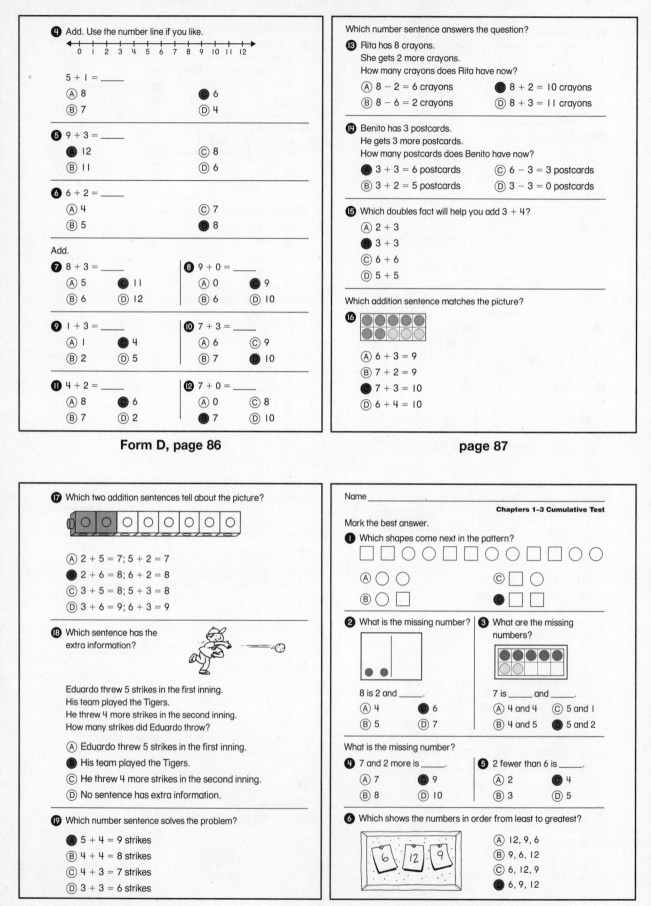

7 What is one way to put 12 pencils into 3 piles?

12 is _____ and _____ and _____.

(A) 1 and 2 and 6   (C) 2 and 4 and 6
(B) 1 and 3 and 7   (D) 2 and 4 and 5

8 Which number is less than 8?

7   8   9   10
(A)   (B)   (C)   (D)

9 Which addition sentence matches the picture?

(A) $4 + 5 = 9$
(B) $4 + 6 = 10$
(C) $5 + 5 = 10$
(D) $5 + 6 = 11$

10 Subtract. What is the difference?

$7 - 3 =$ _____

$7 - 3$

(A) 1
(B) 2
(C) 3
(D) 4

11 Which addition sentence answers the question?

Will had 5 baseball cards. Marta gave him 7 more baseball cards. How many baseball cards does Will have now?

(A) $5 + 6 = 11$ (C) $6 + 7 = 13$
(B) $5 + 7 = 12$ (D) $5 + 8 = 13$

Cumulative Test 1–3, page 90

12 Which number sentence matches the story? Mica had 10 pennies on the table. She put 5 pennies in the jar. How many pennies are still on the table?

(A) $10 + 6 = 16$ (C) $10 - 4 = 6$
(B) $10 + 5 = 15$ (D) $10 - 5 = 5$

13 How many fewer dark cubes are there than white cubes?

(A) 2 fewer   (C) 4 fewer
(B) 3 fewer   (D) 5 fewer

14 Which subtraction sentence shows how many more whistles?

(A) $9 - 3 = 6$
(B) $9 - 5 = 4$
(C) $9 - 6 = 3$
(D) $9 - 7 = 2$

15 Add. What is the sum?

$4 + 6 =$ _____

(A) 8   (B) 9   (C) 10   (D) 11

16 Add. Use the number line if you like.

0 1 2 3 4 5 6 7 8 9 10 11 12

$8 + 2 =$ _____

(A) 6   (C) 10
(B) 8   (D) 11

page 91

17 Which number sentence matches the story?
Carmen has 4 rings.
She gets 5 more rings.
How many rings does Carmen have now?

(A) $4 + 5 = 9$ rings   (C) $5 - 4 = 1$ ring
(B) $4 + 4 = 8$ rings   (D) $5 - 1 = 4$ rings

18 Use doubles to add. What is the sum?

$7 + 7 = 14$ $7 + 8 =$ _____

(A) 13   (C) 15
(B) 14   (D) 16

19 Which sentence has the extra information?

3 girls are playing basketball.
2 more girls come and play basketball.
1 girl has blue basketball shoes.
How many girls are playing basketball now?

(A) 3 girls are playing basketball.
(B) 2 more girls come to play basketball.
(C) 1 girl has blue basketball shoes.
(D) All information is needed.

20 Which number sentence solves the problem in Question 19?

(A) $5 + 1 = 6$ girls
(B) $3 + 3 = 6$ girls
(C) $4 + 2 = 6$ girls
(D) $3 + 2 = 5$ girls

page 92

Name _____

Chapter 4 Diagnosing Readiness

1 Tell how many are left. Then write a subtraction sentence. How many birds are left?

8 minus 1 equals _7_ .   8 _ 1 _ 7

2 Cross out the dots to show subtraction. Subtract to find the difference.

$9 - 3 = $ _6_

$9 - 3 = 6$

3 Write the subtraction sentence. Then write how many more or how many fewer.

How many fewer bones than dogs?

7 (−) 3 (=) 4   _4_ fewer bones

4 Use the picture. Circle **add** or **subtract**. Then write a number sentence.
There are 5 teddy bears and 2 lambs. How many animals are on both shelves?

add   subtract

5 (+) 2 = 7

Chapter 4 DR, page 93

Item Analysis for Diagnosis and Intervention: Chapters 1–3 Cumulative Test is on page 281 in the Assessment Sourcebook.

245

Chapter 4 Form A and Form B

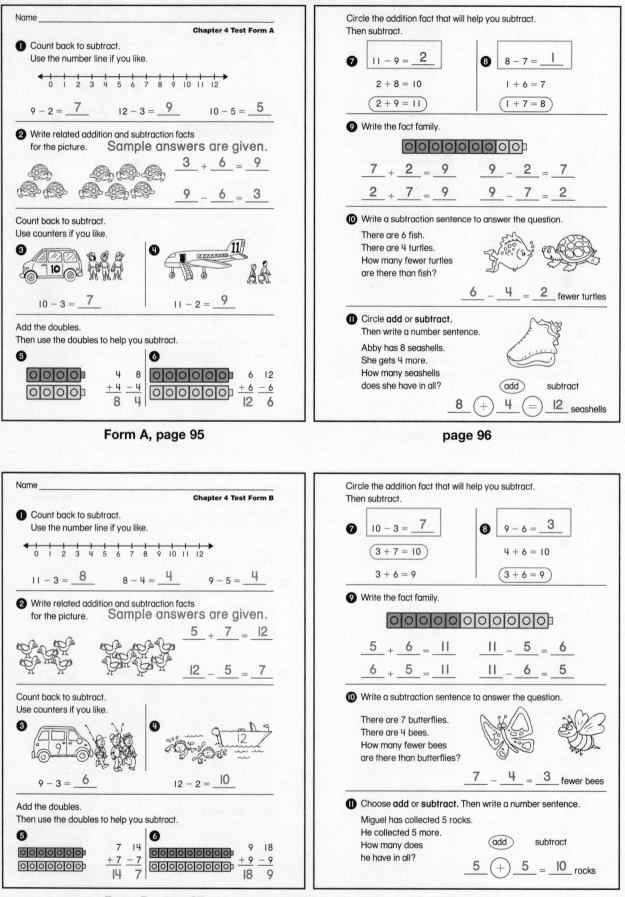

Name _____

Chapter 4 Test Form A

❶ Count back to subtract.
Use the number line if you like.

0 1 2 3 4 5 6 7 8 9 10 11 12

$9 - 2 = \underline{7}$ $12 - 3 = \underline{9}$ $10 - 5 = \underline{5}$

❷ Write related addition and subtraction facts
for the picture. **Sample answers are given.**

$\underline{3} + \underline{6} = \underline{9}$

$\underline{9} - \underline{6} = \underline{3}$

Count back to subtract.
Use counters if you like.

❸ $10 - 3 = \underline{7}$

❹ $11 - 2 = \underline{9}$

Add the doubles.
Then use the doubles to help you subtract.

❺
$\begin{array}{c} 4 \\ +4 \\ \hline 8 \end{array}$ $\begin{array}{c} 8 \\ -4 \\ \hline 4 \end{array}$

❻
$\begin{array}{c} 6 \\ +6 \\ \hline 12 \end{array}$ $\begin{array}{c} 12 \\ -6 \\ \hline 6 \end{array}$

Form A, page 95

Circle the addition fact that will help you subtract.
Then subtract.

❼ $11 - 9 = \underline{2}$

$2 + 8 = 10$

$(2 + 9 = 11)$

❽ $8 - 7 = \underline{1}$

$1 + 6 = 7$

$(1 + 7 = 8)$

❾ Write the fact family.

$\underline{7} + \underline{2} = \underline{9}$ $\underline{9} - \underline{2} = \underline{7}$

$\underline{2} + \underline{7} = \underline{9}$ $\underline{9} - \underline{7} = \underline{2}$

❿ Write a subtraction sentence to answer the question.

There are 6 fish.
There are 4 turtles.
How many fewer turtles
are there than fish?

$\underline{6} - \underline{4} = \underline{2}$ fewer turtles

⓫ Circle **add** or **subtract**.
Then write a number sentence.

Abby has 8 seashells.
She gets 4 more.
How many seashells
does she have in all?

(add) subtract

$8 \oplus 4 \ominus \underline{12}$ seashells

page 96

Name _____

Chapter 4 Test Form B

❶ Count back to subtract.
Use the number line if you like.

0 1 2 3 4 5 6 7 8 9 10 11 12

$11 - 3 = \underline{8}$ $8 - 4 = \underline{4}$ $9 - 5 = \underline{4}$

❷ Write related addition and subtraction facts
for the picture. **Sample answers are given.**

$\underline{5} + \underline{7} = \underline{12}$

$\underline{12} - \underline{5} = \underline{7}$

Count back to subtract.
Use counters if you like.

❸ $9 - 3 = \underline{6}$

❹ $12 - 2 = \underline{10}$

Add the doubles.
Then use the doubles to help you subtract.

❺
$\begin{array}{c} 7 \\ +7 \\ \hline 14 \end{array}$ $\begin{array}{c} 14 \\ -7 \\ \hline 7 \end{array}$

❻
$\begin{array}{c} 9 \\ +9 \\ \hline 18 \end{array}$ $\begin{array}{c} 18 \\ -9 \\ \hline 9 \end{array}$

Form B, page 97

Circle the addition fact that will help you subtract.
Then subtract.

❼ $10 - 3 = \underline{7}$

$(3 + 7 = 10)$

$3 + 6 = 9$

❽ $9 - 6 = \underline{3}$

$4 + 6 = 10$

$(3 + 6 = 9)$

❾ Write the fact family.

$\underline{5} + \underline{6} = \underline{11}$ $\underline{11} - \underline{5} = \underline{6}$

$\underline{6} + \underline{5} = \underline{11}$ $\underline{11} - \underline{6} = \underline{5}$

❿ Write a subtraction sentence to answer the question.

There are 7 butterflies.
There are 4 bees.
How many fewer bees
are there than butterflies?

$\underline{7} - \underline{4} = \underline{3}$ fewer bees

⓫ Choose **add** or **subtract**. Then write a number sentence.

Miguel has collected 5 rocks.
He collected 5 more.
How many does
he have in all?

(add) subtract

$5 \oplus 5 = \underline{10}$ rocks

page 98

Chapter Tests Forms A and B in the Assessment Sourcebook parallel Chapter Tests in the Student
Edition item for item. See the Teacher's Edition for item analysis of these tests.

Chapter 4 Form C

Name _____

Mark the best answer.

1 Use the number line if you like.
What is the difference?

```
|--|--|--|--|--|--|--|--|--|--|--|--|-->
0  1  2  3  4  5  6  7  8  9  10 11 12
```

7 − 3 = ____

(A) 10

(B) 9

● 4

(D) 3

2 What are the related addition and subtraction facts for the picture?

(A) 6 + 5 = 11; 11 − 5 = 6

● 6 + 4 = 10; 10 − 4 = 6

(C) 5 + 4 = 9; 9 − 5 = 4

(D) 5 + 5 = 10; 10 − 5 = 5

Form C, page 99

Count back to subtract.
Mark the answer.

3 6 − 2 = ____

(A) 4

(B) 3

(C) 2

(D) 1

4 12 − 3 = ____

(A) 8

● 9

(C) 10

(D) 11

Use the picture to answer questions 5 and 6.

5 Add the doubles.
What is the sum?

```
  2
+ 2
```

(A) 0

(B) 2

● 4

(D) 8

6 What is the related subtraction fact?

(A) 4 − 1 = 3

● 4 − 2 = 2

(C) 4 − 3 = 1

(D) 4 − 4 = 0

page 100

Use the picture to answer questions 7 and 8.

7 Add the doubles.
What is the sum?

```
  7
+ 7
```

(A) 0

(B) 7

● 14

(D) 16

8 What is the related subtraction fact?

(A) 14 − 6 = 8

(B) 14 − 14 = 0

(C) 14 − 8 = 6

● 14 − 7 = 7

Which addition fact will help you subtract?

9 8 − 5 = ____

(A) 5 + 4 = 9

(B) 3 + 8 = 11

● 3 + 5 = 8

(D) 5 + 8 = 13

10 10 − 2 = ____

● 2 + 8 = 10

(B) 2 + 7 = 9

(C) 8 + 1 = 9

(D) 10 + 2 = 12

page 101

11 Which number completes the fact family?

8 + 4 = 12   4 + 8 = 12

12 − 8 = 4   12 − 4 = ____

(A) 4

(B) 6

● 8

(D) 12

12 Which number sentence completes the fact family?

7 + 1 = 8   1 + 7 = 8   8 − 1 = 7

(A) 8 − 2 = 6

(B) 8 − 1 = 9

(C) 7 + 2 = 9

● 8 − 7 = 1

13 Which subtraction sentence answers the question?

There are 9 lizards.
There are 8 snakes.
How many fewer snakes are there than lizards?

(A) 8 − 1 = 7

(B) 9 − 1 = 8

● 9 − 8 = 1

(D) 9 − 2 = 7

14 Which number sentence answers the question?

Maria has 11 beads.
She lost 7 beads.
How many beads does Maria have now?

(A) 11 + 7 = 18

(B) 7 + 4 = 11

● 11 − 7 = 4

(D) 11 − 11 = 0

page 102

Chapter 4 Form D

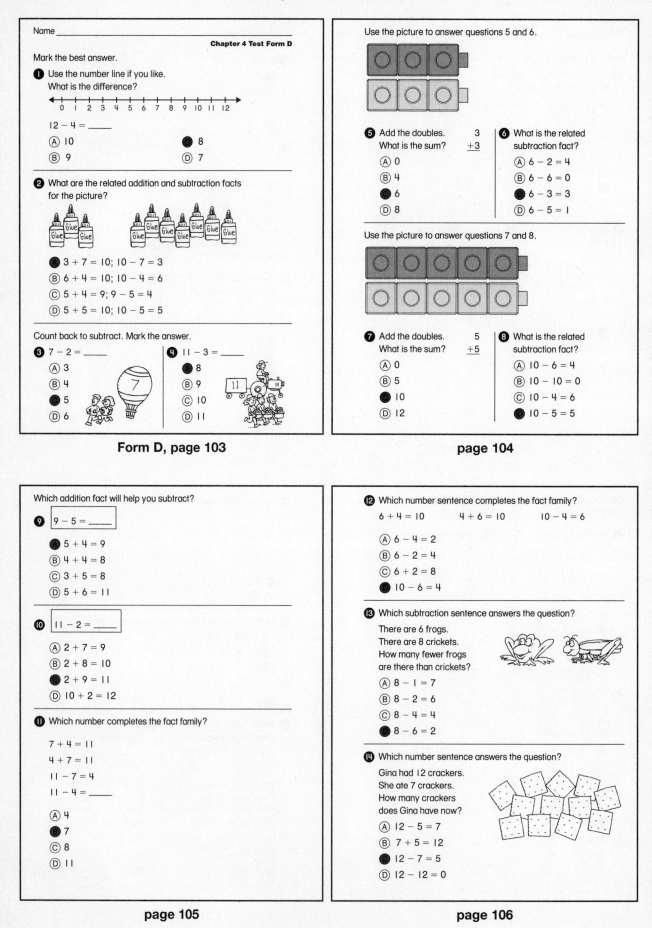

Name _____

Mark the best answer.

1 Use the number line if you like.

What is the difference?

$12 - 4 =$ _____

Ⓐ 10   ● 8

Ⓑ 9   Ⓓ 7

2 What are the related addition and subtraction facts for the picture?

● $3 + 7 = 10; 10 - 7 = 3$

Ⓑ $6 + 4 = 10; 10 - 4 = 6$

Ⓒ $5 + 4 = 9; 9 - 5 = 4$

Ⓓ $5 + 5 = 10; 10 - 5 = 5$

Count back to subtract. Mark the answer.

3 $7 - 2 =$ _____

Ⓐ 3

Ⓑ 4

● 5

Ⓓ 6

4 $11 - 3 =$ _____

● 8

Ⓑ 9

Ⓒ 10

Ⓓ 11

Form D, page 103

Use the picture to answer questions 5 and 6.

5 Add the doubles.
What is the sum?

$\begin{array}{r} 3 \\ +3 \\ \hline \end{array}$

Ⓐ 0

Ⓑ 4

● 6

Ⓓ 8

6 What is the related subtraction fact?

Ⓐ $6 - 2 = 4$

Ⓑ $6 - 6 = 0$

● $6 - 3 = 3$

Ⓓ $6 - 5 = 1$

Use the picture to answer questions 7 and 8.

7 Add the doubles.
What is the sum?

$\begin{array}{r} 5 \\ +5 \\ \hline \end{array}$

Ⓐ 0

Ⓑ 5

● 10

Ⓓ 12

8 What is the related subtraction fact?

Ⓐ $10 - 6 = 4$

Ⓑ $10 - 10 = 0$

Ⓒ $10 - 4 = 6$

● $10 - 5 = 5$

page 104

Which addition fact will help you subtract?

9 $9 - 5 =$ _____

● $5 + 4 = 9$

Ⓑ $4 + 4 = 8$

Ⓒ $3 + 5 = 8$

Ⓓ $5 + 6 = 11$

10 $11 - 2 =$ _____

Ⓐ $2 + 7 = 9$

Ⓑ $2 + 8 = 10$

● $2 + 9 = 11$

Ⓓ $10 + 2 = 12$

11 Which number completes the fact family?

$7 + 4 = 11$

$4 + 7 = 11$

$11 - 7 = 4$

$11 - 4 =$ _____

Ⓐ 4

● 7

Ⓒ 8

Ⓓ 11

page 105

---

12 Which number sentence completes the fact family?

$6 + 4 = 10$ $4 + 6 = 10$ $10 - 4 = 6$

Ⓐ $6 - 4 = 2$

Ⓑ $6 - 2 = 4$

Ⓒ $6 + 2 = 8$

● $10 - 6 = 4$

13 Which subtraction sentence answers the question?

There are 6 frogs.
There are 8 crickets.
How many fewer frogs
are there than crickets?

Ⓐ $8 - 1 = 7$

Ⓑ $8 - 2 = 6$

Ⓒ $8 - 4 = 4$

● $8 - 6 = 2$

14 Which number sentence answers the question?

Gina had 12 crackers.
She ate 7 crackers.
How many crackers
does Gina have now?

Ⓐ $12 - 5 = 7$

Ⓑ $7 + 5 = 12$

● $12 - 7 = 5$

Ⓓ $12 - 12 = 0$

page 106

248

Chapter 5

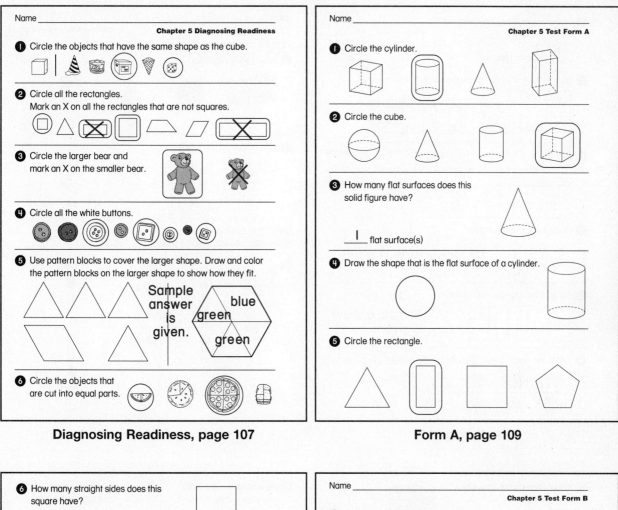

Chapter 5 Diagnosing Readiness

1. Circle the objects that have the same shape as the cube.

2. Circle all the rectangles.
   Mark an X on all the rectangles that are not squares.

3. Circle the larger bear and mark an X on the smaller bear.

4. Circle all the white buttons.

5. Use pattern blocks to cover the larger shape. Draw and color the pattern blocks on the larger shape to show how they fit.

   Sample answer is given.
   blue
   green
   green

6. Circle the objects that are cut into equal parts.

Diagnosing Readiness, page 107

Chapter 5 Test Form A

1. Circle the cylinder.

2. Circle the cube.

3. How many flat surfaces does this solid figure have?

   ___1___ flat surface(s)

4. Draw the shape that is the flat surface of a cylinder.

5. Circle the rectangle.

Form A, page 109

6. How many straight sides does this square have?

   ___4___ straight sides

7. Look at the first shape. Circle the shape that matches it.

8. Draw a line of symmetry on each shape. Sample answers are given.

9. Divide this square into thirds.
   Sample answer is given.

10. Divide this circle into fourths.
    Sample answer is given.

11. Divide this group in half. Sample answer is given.

© Pearson Education, Inc. 1

page 110

Chapter 5 Test Form B

1. Circle the cylinder.

2. Circle the cone.

3. How many flat surfaces does this solid figure have?

   ___6___ flat surfaces

4. Draw the shape that is the flat surface of a cone.

5. Circle the triangle.

Form B, page 111

Chapter Tests Forms A and B in the Assessment Sourcebook parallel Chapter Tests in the Student Edition item for item. See the Teacher's Edition for item analysis of these tests.

249

Chapter 5 Form B and Form C

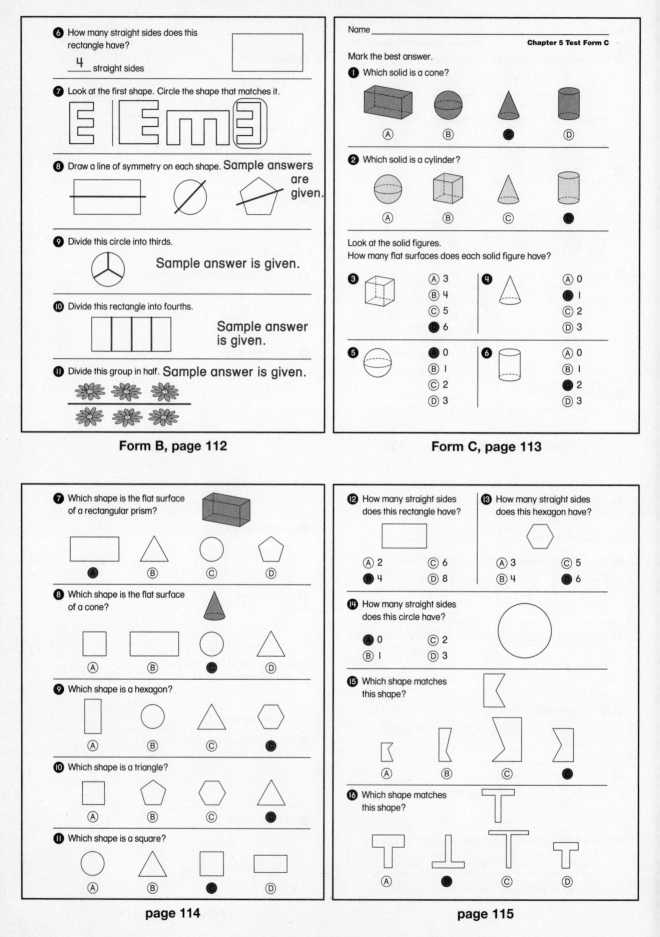

6 How many straight sides does this rectangle have?

___4___ straight sides

7 Look at the first shape. Circle the shape that matches it.

8 Draw a line of symmetry on each shape. **Sample answers are given.**

9 Divide this circle into thirds.

Sample answer is given.

10 Divide this rectangle into fourths.

Sample answer is given.

11 Divide this group in half. **Sample answer is given.**

Form B, page 112

Name _____

Chapter 5 Test Form C

Mark the best answer.

1 Which solid is a cone?
- Ⓐ
- Ⓑ
- ● C
- Ⓓ

2 Which solid is a cylinder?
- Ⓐ
- Ⓑ
- Ⓒ
- ● D

Look at the solid figures.
How many flat surfaces does each solid figure have?

3
- Ⓐ 3
- Ⓑ 4
- Ⓒ 5
- ● 6

4
- Ⓐ 0
- ● 1
- Ⓒ 2
- Ⓓ 3

5
- ● 0
- Ⓑ 1
- Ⓒ 2
- Ⓓ 3

6
- Ⓐ 0
- Ⓑ 1
- ● 2
- Ⓓ 3

Form C, page 113

---

7 Which shape is the flat surface of a rectangular prism?
- ● A
- Ⓑ
- Ⓒ
- Ⓓ

8 Which shape is the flat surface of a cone?
- Ⓐ
- Ⓑ
- ● C
- Ⓓ

9 Which shape is a hexagon?
- Ⓐ
- Ⓑ
- Ⓒ
- ● D

10 Which shape is a triangle?
- Ⓐ
- Ⓑ
- Ⓒ
- ● D

11 Which shape is a square?
- Ⓐ
- Ⓑ
- ● C
- Ⓓ

page 114

---

12 How many straight sides does this rectangle have?
- Ⓐ 2
- ● 4
- Ⓒ 6
- Ⓓ 8

13 How many straight sides does this hexagon have?
- Ⓐ 3
- Ⓑ 4
- Ⓒ 5
- ● 6

14 How many straight sides does this circle have?
- ● 0
- Ⓑ 1
- Ⓒ 2
- Ⓓ 3

15 Which shape matches this shape?
- Ⓐ
- Ⓑ
- Ⓒ
- ● D

16 Which shape matches this shape?
- Ⓐ
- ● B
- Ⓒ
- Ⓓ

page 115

Chapter 5 Form C and Form D

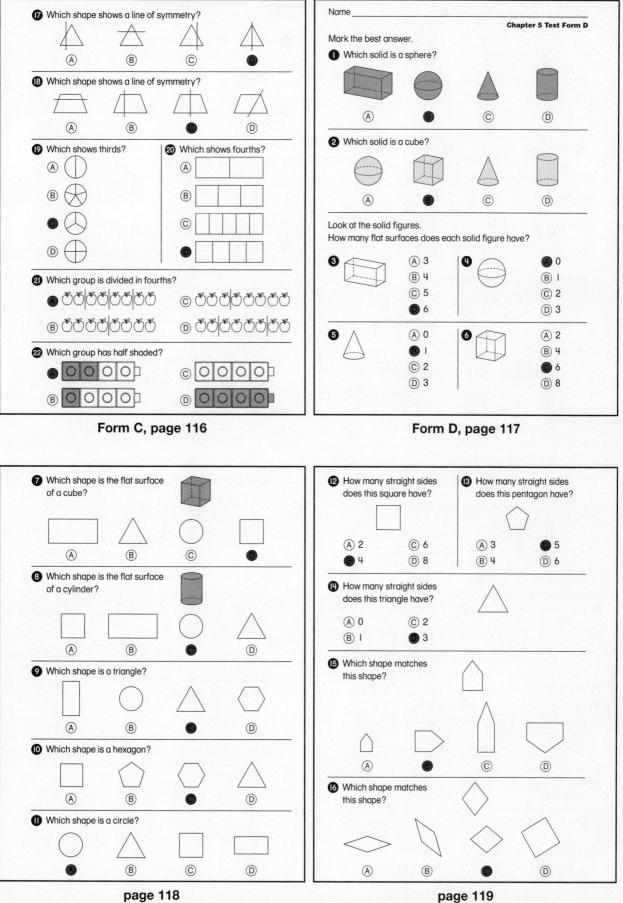

17 Which shape shows a line of symmetry?
Ⓐ Ⓑ Ⓒ Ⓓ

18 Which shape shows a line of symmetry?
Ⓐ Ⓑ Ⓒ Ⓓ

19 Which shows thirds?
Ⓐ
Ⓑ
Ⓒ
Ⓓ

20 Which shows fourths?
Ⓐ
Ⓑ
Ⓒ
Ⓓ

21 Which group is divided in fourths?
Ⓐ Ⓒ
Ⓑ Ⓓ

22 Which group has half shaded?
Ⓐ Ⓒ
Ⓑ Ⓓ

Form C, page 116

Name _____

Mark the best answer.

1 Which solid is a sphere?
Ⓐ Ⓑ Ⓒ Ⓓ

2 Which solid is a cube?
Ⓐ Ⓑ Ⓒ Ⓓ

Look at the solid figures.
How many flat surfaces does each solid figure have?

3
Ⓐ 3
Ⓑ 4
Ⓒ 5
Ⓓ 6

4
Ⓐ 0
Ⓑ 1
Ⓒ 2
Ⓓ 3

5
Ⓐ 0
Ⓑ 1
Ⓒ 2
Ⓓ 3

6
Ⓐ 2
Ⓑ 4
Ⓒ 6
Ⓓ 8

Form D, page 117

---

7 Which shape is the flat surface of a cube?
Ⓐ Ⓑ Ⓒ Ⓓ

8 Which shape is the flat surface of a cylinder?
Ⓐ Ⓑ Ⓒ Ⓓ

9 Which shape is a triangle?
Ⓐ Ⓑ Ⓒ Ⓓ

10 Which shape is a hexagon?
Ⓐ Ⓑ Ⓒ Ⓓ

11 Which shape is a circle?
Ⓐ Ⓑ Ⓒ Ⓓ

page 118

---

12 How many straight sides does this square have?
Ⓐ 2 Ⓒ 6
Ⓑ 4 Ⓓ 8

13 How many straight sides does this pentagon have?
Ⓐ 3 Ⓒ 5
Ⓑ 4 Ⓓ 6

14 How many straight sides does this triangle have?
Ⓐ 0 Ⓒ 2
Ⓑ 1 Ⓓ 3

15 Which shape matches this shape?
Ⓐ Ⓑ Ⓒ Ⓓ

16 Which shape matches this shape?
Ⓐ Ⓑ Ⓒ Ⓓ

page 119

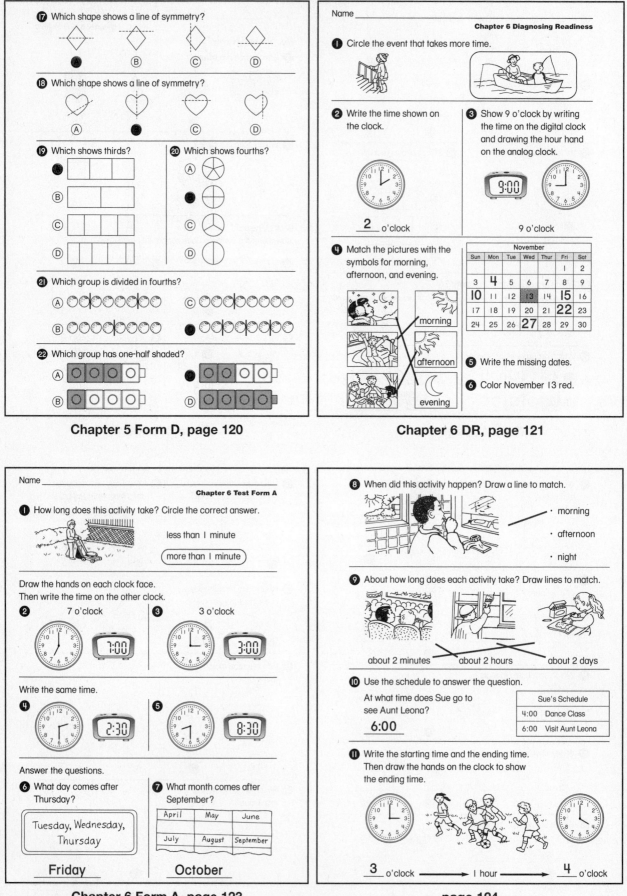

17 Which shape shows a line of symmetry?

Ⓐ Ⓑ Ⓒ Ⓓ

18 Which shape shows a line of symmetry?

Ⓐ Ⓑ Ⓒ Ⓓ

19 Which shows thirds?

Ⓐ
Ⓑ
Ⓒ
Ⓓ

20 Which shows fourths?

Ⓐ
Ⓑ
Ⓒ
Ⓓ

21 Which group is divided in fourths?

Ⓐ   Ⓒ
Ⓑ   Ⓓ

22 Which group has one-half shaded?

Ⓐ   Ⓒ
Ⓑ   Ⓓ

Chapter 5 Form D, page 120

Name _____

Chapter 6 Diagnosing Readiness

1 Circle the event that takes more time.

2 Write the time shown on the clock.

_2_ o'clock

3 Show 9 o'clock by writing the time on the digital clock and drawing the hour hand on the analog clock.

9:00

9 o'clock

4 Match the pictures with the symbols for morning, afternoon, and evening.

morning
afternoon
evening

November

Sun	Mon	Tue	Wed	Thur	Fri	Sat
					1	2
3	4	5	6	7	8	9
10	11	12	13	14	15	16
17	18	19	20	21	22	23
24	25	26	27	28	29	30

5 Write the missing dates.

6 Color November 13 red.

Chapter 6 DR, page 121

Name _____

Chapter 6 Test Form A

1 How long does this activity take? Circle the correct answer.

less than 1 minute

(more than 1 minute)

Draw the hands on each clock face.
Then write the time on the other clock.

2 7 o'clock

7:00

3 3 o'clock

3:00

Write the same time.

4

2:30

5

8:30

Answer the questions.

6 What day comes after Thursday?

Tuesday, Wednesday, Thursday

Friday

7 What month comes after September?

April	May	June
July	August	September

October

Chapter 6 Form A, page 123

---

8 When did this activity happen? Draw a line to match.

· morning
· afternoon
· night

9 About how long does each activity take? Draw lines to match.

about 2 minutes   about 2 hours   about 2 days

10 Use the schedule to answer the question.

At what time does Sue go to see Aunt Leona?

_6:00_

Sue's Schedule	
4:00	Dance Class
6:00	Visit Aunt Leona

11 Write the starting time and the ending time. Then draw the hands on the clock to show the ending time.

_3_ o'clock ——→ 1 hour ——→ _4_ o'clock

page 124

Chapter Tests Forms A and B in the Assessment Sourcebook parallel Chapter Tests in the Student Edition item for item. See the Teacher's Edition for item analysis of these tests.

Chapter 6 Form B and Form C

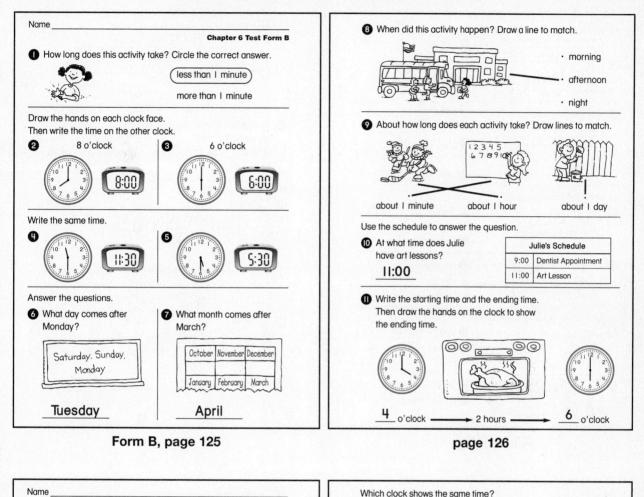

Name _____

1 How long does this activity take? Circle the correct answer.

(less than 1 minute)

more than 1 minute

Draw the hands on each clock face.
Then write the time on the other clock.

2 8 o'clock — `8:00`

3 6 o'clock — `6:00`

Write the same time.

4 `11:30`

5 `5:30`

Answer the questions.

6 What day comes after Monday?

Saturday, Sunday, Monday

Tuesday

7 What month comes after March?

October	November	December
January	February	March

April

8 When did this activity happen? Draw a line to match.

· morning
· afternoon
· night

9 About how long does each activity take? Draw lines to match.

about 1 minute   about 1 hour   about 1 day

Use the schedule to answer the question.

10 At what time does Julie have art lessons?

`11:00`

Julie's Schedule	
9:00	Dentist Appointment
11:00	Art Lesson

11 Write the starting time and the ending time.
Then draw the hands on the clock to show the ending time.

4 o'clock ——→ 2 hours ——→ **6** o'clock

Form B, page 125

page 126

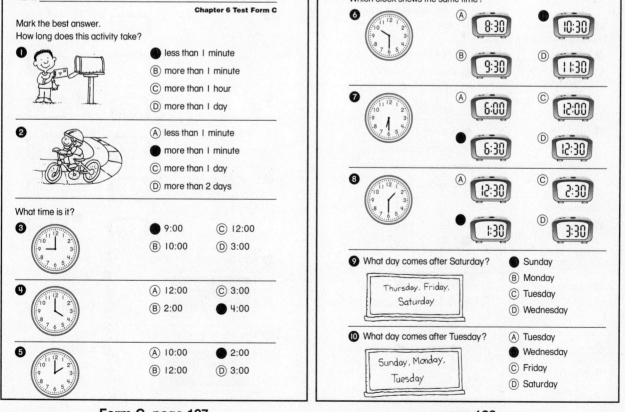

Name _____

Mark the best answer.
How long does this activity take?

1
- Ⓐ less than 1 minute ●
- Ⓑ more than 1 minute
- Ⓒ more than 1 hour
- Ⓓ more than 1 day

2
- Ⓐ less than 1 minute
- Ⓑ more than 1 minute ●
- Ⓒ more than 1 day
- Ⓓ more than 2 days

What time is it?

3
- Ⓐ 9:00 ●   Ⓒ 12:00
- Ⓑ 10:00   Ⓓ 3:00

4
- Ⓐ 12:00   Ⓒ 3:00
- Ⓑ 2:00   Ⓓ 4:00 ●

5
- Ⓐ 10:00   Ⓒ 2:00 ●
- Ⓑ 12:00   Ⓓ 3:00

Which clock shows the same time?

6
- Ⓐ `8:30`   Ⓑ `10:30` ●
- Ⓑ `9:30`   Ⓓ `11:30`

7
- Ⓐ `6:00`   Ⓒ `12:00`
- `6:30` ●   Ⓓ `12:30`

8
- Ⓐ `12:30`   Ⓒ `2:30`
- `1:30` ●   Ⓓ `3:30`

9 What day comes after Saturday?
- Sunday ●
- Ⓑ Monday
- Ⓒ Tuesday
- Ⓓ Wednesday

Thursday, Friday, Saturday

10 What day comes after Tuesday?
- Ⓐ Tuesday
- Wednesday ●
- Ⓒ Friday
- Ⓓ Saturday

Sunday, Monday, Tuesday

Form C, page 127

page 128

Chapter Tests Forms A and B in the Assessment Sourcebook parallel Chapter Tests in the Student
Edition item for item. See the Teacher's Edition for item analysis of these tests.

Chapter 6 Form C and Form D

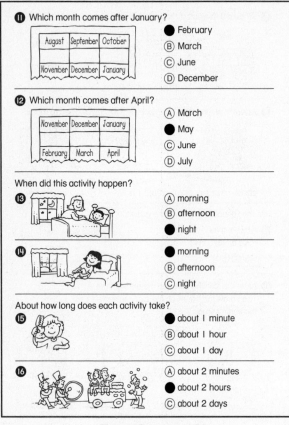

11. Which month comes after January?

| August | September | October |
| November | December | January |

- ● February
- Ⓑ March
- Ⓒ June
- Ⓓ December

12. Which month comes after April?

| November | December | January |
| February | March | April |

- Ⓐ March
- ● May
- Ⓒ June
- Ⓓ July

When did this activity happen?

13.
- Ⓐ morning
- Ⓑ afternoon
- ● night

14.
- ● morning
- Ⓑ afternoon
- Ⓒ night

About how long does each activity take?

15.
- ● about 1 minute
- Ⓑ about 1 hour
- Ⓒ about 1 day

16.
- Ⓐ about 2 minutes
- ● about 2 hours
- Ⓒ about 2 days

Form C, page 129

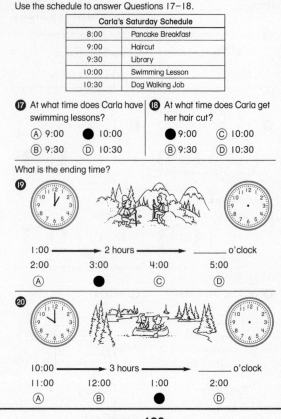

Use the schedule to answer Questions 17–18.

Carla's Saturday Schedule	
8:00	Pancake Breakfast
9:00	Haircut
9:30	Library
10:00	Swimming Lesson
10:30	Dog Walking Job

17. At what time does Carla have swimming lessons?
- Ⓐ 9:00
- Ⓑ 9:30
- ● 10:00
- Ⓓ 10:30

18. At what time does Carla get her hair cut?
- ● 9:00
- Ⓑ 9:30
- Ⓒ 10:00
- Ⓓ 10:30

What is the ending time?

19.
1:00 ➝ 2 hours ➝ _____ o'clock

| 2:00 | 3:00 | 4:00 | 5:00 |
| Ⓐ | ● | Ⓒ | Ⓓ |

20.
10:00 ➝ 3 hours ➝ _____ o'clock

| 11:00 | 12:00 | 1:00 | 2:00 |
| Ⓐ | Ⓑ | ● | Ⓓ |

page 130

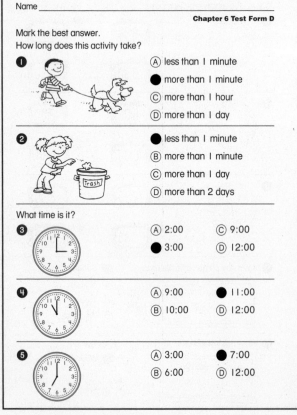

Name _____

Chapter 6 Test Form D

Mark the best answer.
How long does this activity take?

1.
- Ⓐ less than 1 minute
- ● more than 1 minute
- Ⓒ more than 1 hour
- Ⓓ more than 1 day

2.
- ● less than 1 minute
- Ⓑ more than 1 minute
- Ⓒ more than 1 day
- Ⓓ more than 2 days

What time is it?

3.
- Ⓐ 2:00
- ● 3:00
- Ⓒ 9:00
- Ⓓ 12:00

4.
- Ⓐ 9:00
- Ⓑ 10:00
- ● 11:00
- Ⓓ 12:00

5.
- Ⓐ 3:00
- Ⓑ 6:00
- ● 7:00
- Ⓓ 12:00

Form D, page 131

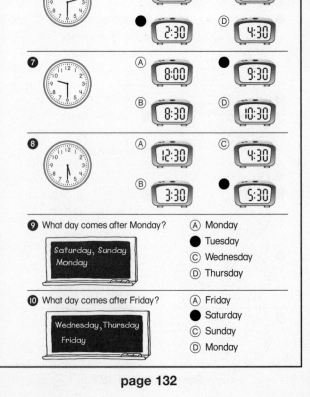

Which clock shows the same time?

6.
- Ⓐ 1:30
- ● 2:30
- Ⓒ 3:30
- Ⓓ 4:30

7.
- Ⓐ 8:00
- Ⓑ 8:30
- ● 9:30
- Ⓓ 10:30

8.
- Ⓐ 12:30
- Ⓑ 3:30
- Ⓒ 4:30
- ● 5:30

9. What day comes after Monday?

Saturday, Sunday Monday

- Ⓐ Monday
- ● Tuesday
- Ⓒ Wednesday
- Ⓓ Thursday

10. What day comes after Friday?

Wednesday, Thursday Friday

- Ⓐ Friday
- ● Saturday
- Ⓒ Sunday
- Ⓓ Monday

page 132

Chapter 6 Form D and Cumulative Test

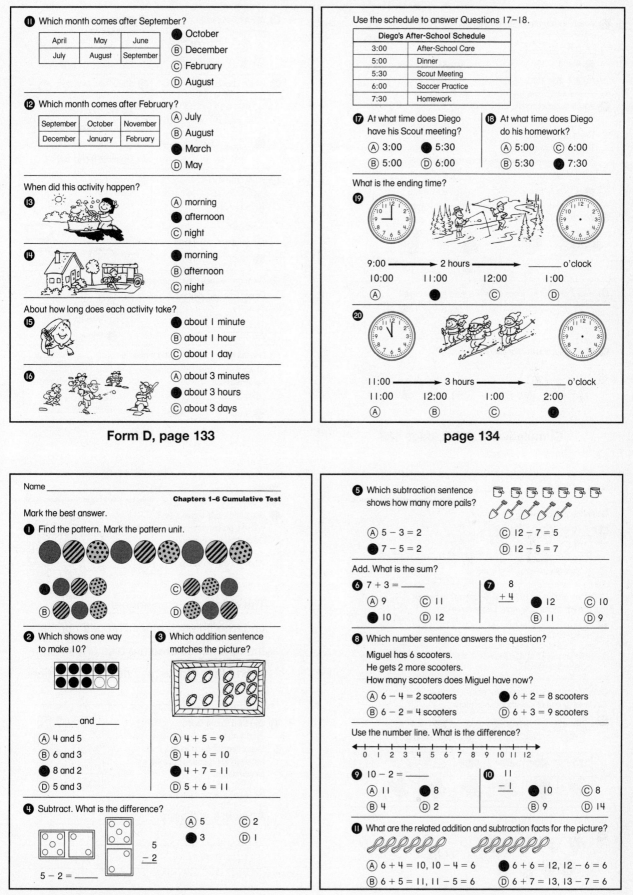

⑪ Which month comes after September?

April	May	June
July	August	September

- ● October
- Ⓑ December
- Ⓒ February
- Ⓓ August

⑫ Which month comes after February?

September	October	November
December	January	February

- Ⓐ July
- Ⓑ August
- ● March
- Ⓓ May

When did this activity happen?

⑬
- Ⓐ morning
- ● afternoon
- Ⓒ night

⑭
- ● morning
- Ⓑ afternoon
- Ⓒ night

About how long does each activity take?

⑮
- ● about 1 minute
- Ⓑ about 1 hour
- Ⓒ about 1 day

⑯
- Ⓐ about 3 minutes
- ● about 3 hours
- Ⓒ about 3 days

Form D, page 133

Use the schedule to answer Questions 17–18.

Diego's After-School Schedule	
3:00	After-School Care
5:00	Dinner
5:30	Scout Meeting
6:00	Soccer Practice
7:30	Homework

⑰ At what time does Diego have his Scout meeting?
- Ⓐ 3:00
- ● 5:30
- Ⓑ 5:00
- Ⓓ 6:00

⑱ At what time does Diego do his homework?
- Ⓐ 5:00
- Ⓒ 6:00
- Ⓑ 5:30
- ● 7:30

What is the ending time?

⑲

9:00 ⟶ 2 hours ⟶ _____ o'clock

10:00	11:00	12:00	1:00
Ⓐ	●	Ⓒ	Ⓓ

⑳

11:00 ⟶ 3 hours ⟶ _____ o'clock

11:00	12:00	1:00	2:00
Ⓐ	Ⓑ	Ⓒ	●

page 134

Name _____

Chapters 1–6 Cumulative Test

Mark the best answer.

❶ Find the pattern. Mark the pattern unit.

- Ⓐ
- Ⓒ
- Ⓑ
- Ⓓ

❷ Which shows one way to make 10?

_____ and _____

- Ⓐ 4 and 5
- Ⓑ 6 and 3
- ● 8 and 2
- Ⓓ 5 and 3

❸ Which addition sentence matches the picture?

- Ⓐ 4 + 5 = 9
- Ⓑ 4 + 6 = 10
- ● 4 + 7 = 11
- Ⓓ 5 + 6 = 11

❹ Subtract. What is the difference?

5
− 2

5 − 2 = _____

- Ⓐ 5
- Ⓒ 2
- ● 3
- Ⓓ 1

❺ Which subtraction sentence shows how many more pails?

- Ⓐ 5 − 3 = 2
- Ⓒ 12 − 7 = 5
- ● 7 − 5 = 2
- Ⓓ 12 − 5 = 7

Add. What is the sum?

❻ 7 + 3 = _____
- Ⓐ 9
- Ⓒ 11
- ● 10
- Ⓓ 12

❼
8
+ 4
- ● 12
- Ⓒ 10
- Ⓑ 11
- Ⓓ 9

❽ Which number sentence answers the question?

Miguel has 6 scooters.
He gets 2 more scooters.
How many scooters does Miguel have now?

- Ⓐ 6 − 4 = 2 scooters
- ● 6 + 2 = 8 scooters
- Ⓑ 6 − 2 = 4 scooters
- Ⓓ 6 + 3 = 9 scooters

Use the number line. What is the difference?

0 1 2 3 4 5 6 7 8 9 10 11 12

❾ 10 − 2 = _____
- Ⓐ 11
- ● 8
- Ⓑ 4
- Ⓓ 2

❿
11
− 1
- ● 10
- Ⓒ 8
- Ⓑ 9
- Ⓓ 14

⓫ What are the related addition and subtraction facts for the picture?

- Ⓐ 6 + 4 = 10, 10 − 4 = 6
- ● 6 + 6 = 12, 12 − 6 = 6
- Ⓑ 6 + 5 = 11, 11 − 5 = 6
- Ⓓ 6 + 7 = 13, 13 − 7 = 6

Cumulative Test 1-6, page 135

page 136

Item Analysis for Diagnosis and Intervention: Chapters 1–6 Cumulative Test is on page 282 in the Assessment Sourcebook.

Chapters 6 and 7

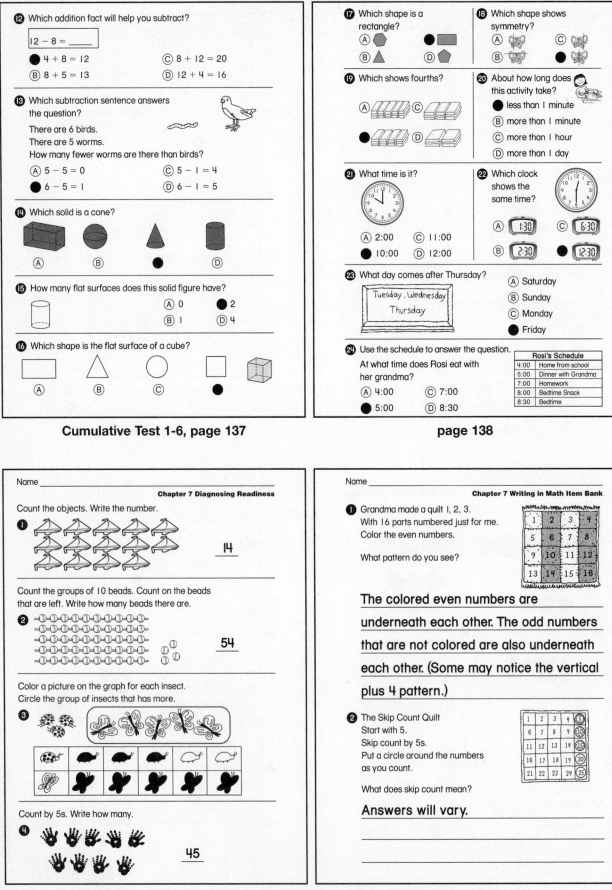

12 Which addition fact will help you subtract?

12 − 8 = ____

● 4 + 8 = 12   Ⓒ 8 + 12 = 20
Ⓑ 8 + 5 = 13   Ⓓ 12 + 4 = 16

13 Which subtraction sentence answers the question?

There are 6 birds.
There are 5 worms.
How many fewer worms are there than birds?

Ⓐ 5 − 5 = 0   Ⓒ 5 − 1 = 4
● 6 − 5 = 1   Ⓓ 6 − 1 = 5

14 Which solid is a cone?

Ⓐ   Ⓑ   ●   Ⓓ

15 How many flat surfaces does this solid figure have?

Ⓐ 0   ● 2
Ⓑ 1   Ⓓ 4

16 Which shape is the flat surface of a cube?

Ⓐ   Ⓑ   Ⓒ   ●

Cumulative Test 1-6, page 137

17 Which shape is a rectangle?

Ⓐ   ● ■
Ⓑ ▲   Ⓓ ⬠

18 Which shape shows symmetry?

Ⓐ   Ⓒ
Ⓑ   ●

19 Which shows fourths?

Ⓐ   Ⓒ
●   Ⓓ

20 About how long does this activity take?

● less than 1 minute
Ⓑ more than 1 minute
Ⓒ more than 1 hour
Ⓓ more than 1 day

21 What time is it?

Ⓐ 2:00   Ⓒ 11:00
● 10:00   Ⓓ 12:00

22 Which clock shows the same time?

Ⓐ 1:30   Ⓒ 6:30
Ⓑ 2:30   ● 12:30

23 What day comes after Thursday?

Tuesday, Wednesday
Thursday

Ⓐ Saturday
Ⓑ Sunday
Ⓒ Monday
● Friday

24 Use the schedule to answer the question.
At what time does Rosi eat with her grandma?

Ⓐ 4:00   Ⓒ 7:00
● 5:00   Ⓓ 8:30

Rosi's Schedule	
4:00	Home from school
5:00	Dinner with Grandma
7:00	Homework
8:00	Bedtime Snack
8:30	Bedtime

page 138

Name ____

Chapter 7 Diagnosing Readiness

Count the objects. Write the number.

1 14

Count the groups of 10 beads. Count on the beads that are left. Write how many beads there are.

2 54

Color a picture on the graph for each insect. Circle the group of insects that has more.

3

Count by 5s. Write how many.

4 45

Chapter 7 DR, page 139

Name ____

Chapter 7 Writing in Math Item Bank

1 Grandma made a quilt 1, 2, 3.
With 16 parts numbered just for me.
Color the even numbers.

What pattern do you see?

1	2	3	4
5	6	7	8
9	10	11	12
13	14	15	16

The colored even numbers are underneath each other. The odd numbers that are not colored are also underneath each other. (Some may notice the vertical plus 4 pattern.)

2 The Skip Count Quilt
Start with 5.
Skip count by 5s.
Put a circle around the numbers as you count.

1	2	3	4	5
6	7	8	9	10
11	12	13	14	15
16	17	18	19	20
21	22	23	24	25

What does skip count mean?

Answers will vary.

Item Bank, page 140

Chapter 7 Form A and Form B

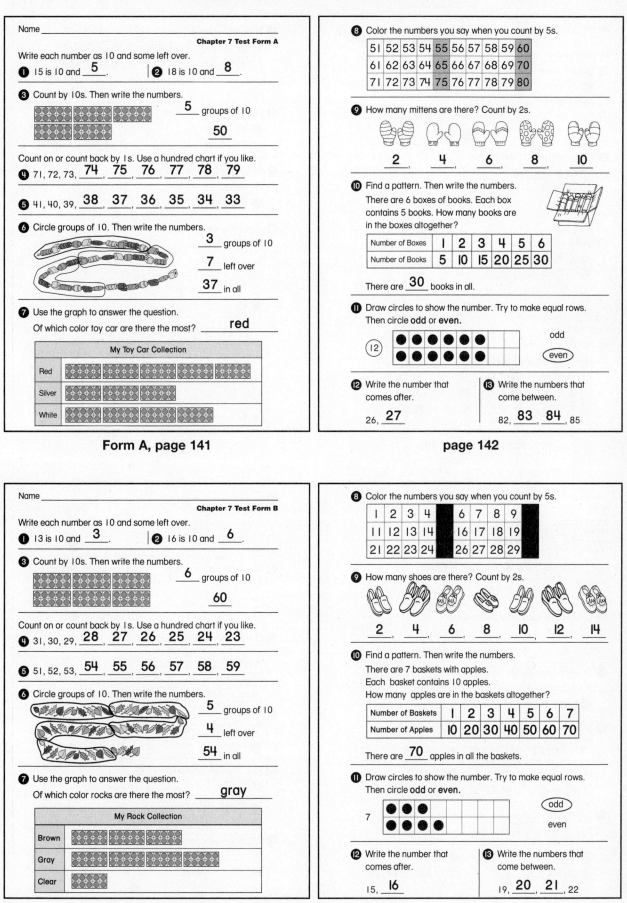

Name _____

Chapter 7 Test Form A

Write each number as 10 and some left over.

1 15 is 10 and __5__. | **2** 18 is 10 and __8__.

3 Count by 10s. Then write the numbers.

__5__ groups of 10

__50__

Count on or count back by 1s. Use a hundred chart if you like.

4 71, 72, 73, __74__ __75__ __76__ __77__ __78__ __79__

5 41, 40, 39, __38__ __37__ __36__ __35__ __34__ __33__

6 Circle groups of 10. Then write the numbers.

__3__ groups of 10

__7__ left over

__37__ in all

7 Use the graph to answer the question.

Of which color toy car are there the most? __red__

My Toy Car Collection	
Red	
Silver	
White	

Form A, page 141

8 Color the numbers you say when you count by 5s.

51	52	53	54	55	56	57	58	59	60
61	62	63	64	65	66	67	68	69	70
71	72	73	74	75	76	77	78	79	80

9 How many mittens are there? Count by 2s.

__2__, __4__, __6__, __8__, __10__

10 Find a pattern. Then write the numbers.

There are 6 boxes of books. Each box contains 5 books. How many books are in the boxes altogether?

Number of Boxes	1	2	3	4	5	6
Number of Books	5	10	15	20	25	30

There are __30__ books in all.

11 Draw circles to show the number. Try to make equal rows. Then circle **odd** or **even**.

(12)

odd

(even)

12 Write the number that comes after.

26, __27__

13 Write the numbers that come between.

82, __83__, __84__, 85

page 142

Name _____

Chapter 7 Test Form B

Write each number as 10 and some left over.

1 13 is 10 and __3__. | **2** 16 is 10 and __6__.

3 Count by 10s. Then write the numbers.

__6__ groups of 10

__60__

Count on or count back by 1s. Use a hundred chart if you like.

4 31, 30, 29, __28__ __27__ __26__ __25__ __24__ __23__

5 51, 52, 53, __54__ __55__ __56__ __57__ __58__ __59__

6 Circle groups of 10. Then write the numbers.

__5__ groups of 10

__4__ left over

__54__ in all

7 Use the graph to answer the question.

Of which color rocks are there the most? __gray__

My Rock Collection	
Brown	
Gray	
Clear	

Form B, page 143

8 Color the numbers you say when you count by 5s.

1	2	3	4	5	6	7	8	9	10
11	12	13	14	15	16	17	18	19	20
21	22	23	24	25	26	27	28	29	30

9 How many shoes are there? Count by 2s.

__2__, __4__, __6__, __8__, __10__, __12__, __14__

10 Find a pattern. Then write the numbers.

There are 7 baskets with apples. Each basket contains 10 apples. How many apples are in the baskets altogether?

Number of Baskets	1	2	3	4	5	6	7
Number of Apples	10	20	30	40	50	60	70

There are __70__ apples in all the baskets.

11 Draw circles to show the number. Try to make equal rows. Then circle **odd** or **even**.

7

(odd)

even

12 Write the number that comes after.

15, __16__

13 Write the numbers that come between.

19, __20__, __21__, 22

page 144

Chapter Tests Forms A and B in the Assessment Sourcebook parallel Chapter Tests in the Student Edition item for item. See the Teacher's Edition for item analysis of these tests.

Chapter 7 Form C

Name _____

Chapter 7 Test Form C

Mark the best answer.

1 Which number is 10 and 7 left over?

7	10	17	27
Ⓐ	Ⓑ	●	Ⓓ

2 Which number is 10 and 1 left over?

1	5	10	11
Ⓐ	Ⓑ	Ⓒ	●

3 Which number is 10 and 5 left over?

5	10	15	20
Ⓐ	Ⓑ	●	Ⓓ

Count by 10s.

4 What is the number?

Ⓐ 4
Ⓑ 10
Ⓒ 20
● 40

Form C, page 145

5 What is the number?

3	10	13	30
Ⓐ	Ⓑ	Ⓒ	●

6 Which group counts on by 1s?
- ● 24, 25, 26, 27
- Ⓒ 27, 26, 25, 24
- Ⓑ 24, 26, 28, 30
- Ⓓ 24, 25, 27, 28

7 Which group counts back by 1s?
- Ⓐ 34, 35, 36, 37
- Ⓒ 1, 3, 5, 7
- ● 37, 36, 35, 34
- Ⓓ 38, 37, 36, 34

8 How many apples are there in all?
- Ⓐ 20
- Ⓒ 62
- ● 26
- Ⓓ 206

9 How many oranges are there in all?
- Ⓐ 9
- Ⓒ 60
- Ⓑ 36
- ● 63

page 146

Use the graph to answer the following questions.

My Leaf Collection	
Yellow	▨▨
Red	▨
Green	▨▨▨▨
Orange	▨▨▨

10 Of which color leaf are there the most?
- Ⓐ Yellow
- ● Green
- Ⓑ Red
- Ⓓ Orange

11 Of which color leaf are there the fewest?
- Ⓐ Yellow
- Ⓒ Green
- ● Red
- Ⓓ Orange

12 Which numbers do you say when you count by 5s?

80	81	82	83	84	85	86	87	88	89	90

- Ⓐ 80, 82, 84, 86, 88, 90
- ● 80, 85, 90
- Ⓑ 80, 81, 82, 83, 84, 85
- Ⓓ 83, 86, 89

13 Which numbers do you say when you count by 5s?

21	22	23	24	25	26	27	28	29	30	31

- Ⓐ 25
- ● 25, 30
- Ⓑ 21, 30
- Ⓓ 21, 22, 23, 24, 25

page 147

14 How many mittens are there? Count by 2s.

1	2	3	6
Ⓐ	Ⓑ	Ⓒ	●

15 How many hats are there? Count by 5s.

4	5	10	20
Ⓐ	Ⓑ	Ⓒ	●

16 There are 4 shelves in a bookshelf with 10 books on each shelf. How many books are there in all?

Number of Shelves	1	2	3	4
Number of Books	10	20	30	40

- Ⓐ 4
- Ⓑ 10
- ● 40
- Ⓓ 44

17 Which number is odd?
- Ⓐ 16
- Ⓒ 18
- ● 17
- Ⓓ 20

18 Which number is even?
- Ⓐ 3
- Ⓒ 15
- Ⓑ 9
- ● 20

19 Which number comes after?
17, ____
- Ⓐ 15
- ● 18
- Ⓑ 16
- Ⓓ 19

20 Which number comes before?
____, 53
- Ⓐ 45
- ● 52
- Ⓑ 50
- Ⓓ 54

21 Which numbers come between?
32, ____, ____, 35

36, 37	34, 35	33, 34	30, 31
Ⓐ	Ⓑ	●	Ⓓ

page 148

258

Chapter 7 Form D

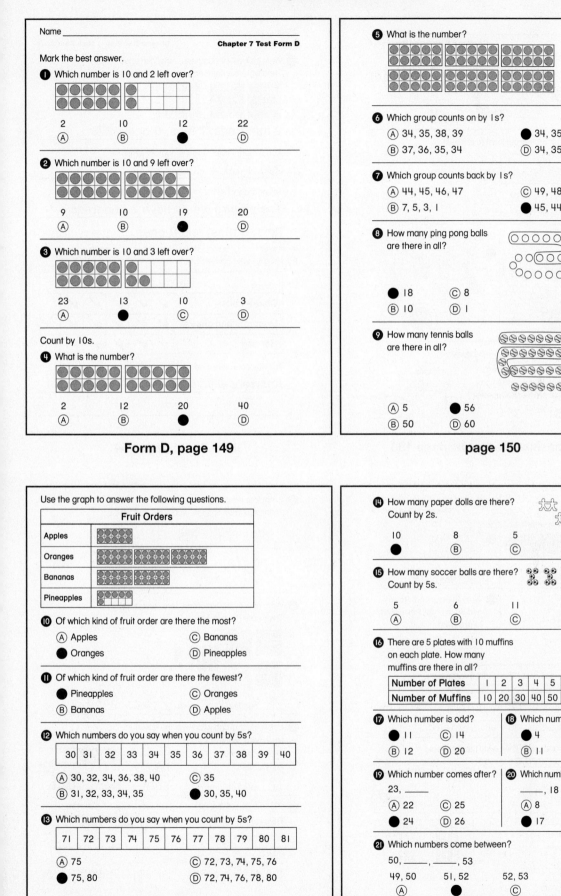

Name _____

Mark the best answer.

1 Which number is 10 and 2 left over?

2	10	12	22
Ⓐ	Ⓑ	●	Ⓓ

2 Which number is 10 and 9 left over?

9	10	19	20
Ⓐ	Ⓑ	●	Ⓓ

3 Which number is 10 and 3 left over?

23	13	10	3
Ⓐ	●	Ⓒ	Ⓓ

Count by 10s.

4 What is the number?

2	12	20	40
Ⓐ	Ⓑ	●	Ⓓ

Form D, page 149

5 What is the number?

Ⓐ 6
Ⓑ 10
Ⓒ 30
● 60

6 Which group counts on by 1s?
Ⓐ 34, 35, 38, 39   ● 34, 35, 36, 37
Ⓑ 37, 36, 35, 34   Ⓓ 34, 35, 37, 38

7 Which group counts back by 1s?
Ⓐ 44, 45, 46, 47   Ⓒ 49, 48, 46, 44
Ⓑ 7, 5, 3, 1   ● 45, 44, 43, 42

8 How many ping pong balls are there in all?
● 18   Ⓒ 8
Ⓑ 10   Ⓓ 1

9 How many tennis balls are there in all?
Ⓐ 5   ● 56
Ⓑ 50   Ⓓ 60

page 150

Use the graph to answer the following questions.

Fruit Orders

Apples	
Oranges	
Bananas	
Pineapples	

10 Of which kind of fruit order are there the most?
Ⓐ Apples   Ⓒ Bananas
● Oranges   Ⓓ Pineapples

11 Of which kind of fruit order are there the fewest?
● Pineapples   Ⓒ Oranges
Ⓑ Bananas   Ⓓ Apples

12 Which numbers do you say when you count by 5s?

30	31	32	33	34	35	36	37	38	39	40

Ⓐ 30, 32, 34, 36, 38, 40   Ⓒ 35
Ⓑ 31, 32, 33, 34, 35   ● 30, 35, 40

13 Which numbers do you say when you count by 5s?

71	72	73	74	75	76	77	78	79	80	81

Ⓐ 75   Ⓒ 72, 73, 74, 75, 76
● 75, 80   Ⓓ 72, 74, 76, 78, 80

page 151

14 How many paper dolls are there?
Count by 2s.

10	8	5	2
●	Ⓑ	Ⓒ	Ⓓ

15 How many soccer balls are there?
Count by 5s.

5	6	11	30
Ⓐ	Ⓑ	Ⓒ	●

16 There are 5 plates with 10 muffins on each plate. How many muffins are there in all?

Ⓐ 5
Ⓑ 10
Ⓒ 15
● 50

Number of Plates	1	2	3	4	5
Number of Muffins	10	20	30	40	50

17 Which number is odd?
● 11   Ⓒ 14
Ⓑ 12   Ⓓ 20

18 Which number is even?
● 4   Ⓒ 15
Ⓑ 11   Ⓓ 21

19 Which number comes after?
23, _____
Ⓐ 22   Ⓒ 25
● 24   Ⓓ 26

20 Which number comes before?
_____, 18
Ⓐ 8   Ⓒ 19
● 17   Ⓓ 20

21 Which numbers come between?
50, _____, _____, 53

49, 50	51, 52	52, 53	53, 54
Ⓐ	●	Ⓒ	Ⓓ

page 152

259

Chapter 8

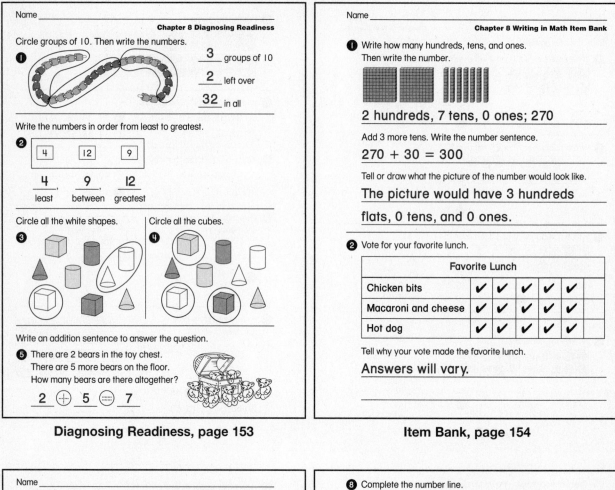

Chapter 8 Diagnosing Readiness

Circle groups of 10. Then write the numbers.

❶ __3__ groups of 10

__2__ left over

__32__ in all

Write the numbers in order from least to greatest.

❷ | 4 | 12 | 9 |

__4__ , __9__ , __12__
least between greatest

❸ Circle all the white shapes.

❹ Circle all the cubes.

Write an addition sentence to answer the question.

❺ There are 2 bears in the toy chest.
There are 5 more bears on the floor.
How many bears are there altogether?

2 ⊕ 5 ⊙ 7

Diagnosing Readiness, page 153

Chapter 8 Writing in Math Item Bank

❶ Write how many hundreds, tens, and ones.
Then write the number.

2 hundreds, 7 tens, 0 ones; 270

Add 3 more tens. Write the number sentence.

270 + 30 = 300

Tell or draw what the picture of the number would look like.

The picture would have 3 hundreds flats, 0 tens, and 0 ones.

❷ Vote for your favorite lunch.

Favorite Lunch					
Chicken bits	✔	✔	✔	✔	✔
Macaroni and cheese	✔	✔	✔	✔	✔
Hot dog	✔	✔	✔	✔	✔

Tell why your vote made the favorite lunch.

Answers will vary.

Item Bank, page 154

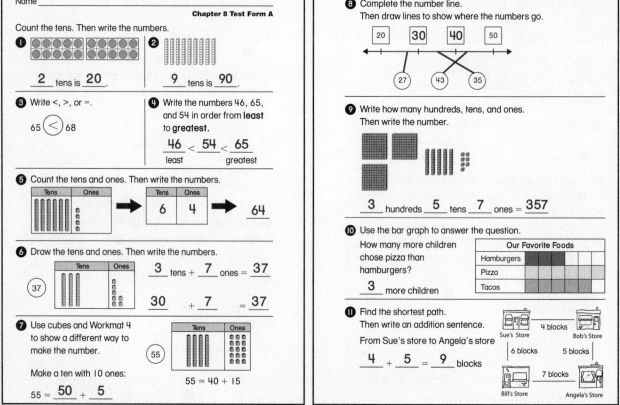

Chapter 8 Test Form A

Count the tens. Then write the numbers.

❶ __2__ tens is __20__

❷ __9__ tens is __90__

❸ Write <, >, or =.

65 < 68

❹ Write the numbers 46, 65, and 54 in order from **least** to **greatest**.

__46__ < __54__ < __65__
least   greatest

❺ Count the tens and ones. Then write the numbers.

Tens	Ones
6	4

→ 64

❻ Draw the tens and ones. Then write the numbers.

(37)

__3__ tens + __7__ ones = __37__

__30__ + __7__ = __37__

❼ Use cubes and Workmat 4 to show a different way to make the number.

(55)

Make a ten with 10 ones:

55 = 40 + 15

55 = __50__ + __5__

Form A, page 155

---

❽ Complete the number line.
Then draw lines to show where the numbers go.

20 30 40 50

27 43 35

❾ Write how many hundreds, tens, and ones.
Then write the number.

__3__ hundreds __5__ tens __7__ ones = __357__

❿ Use the bar graph to answer the question.

How many more children chose pizza than hamburgers?

__3__ more children

Our Favorite Foods				
Hamburgers				
Pizza				
Tacos				

⓫ Find the shortest path.
Then write an addition sentence.

From Sue's store to Angela's store

__4__ + __5__ = __9__ blocks

Sue's Store — 4 blocks — Bob's Store
6 blocks 5 blocks
Bill's Store — 7 blocks — Angela's Store

page 156

Chapter 8 Form B and Form C

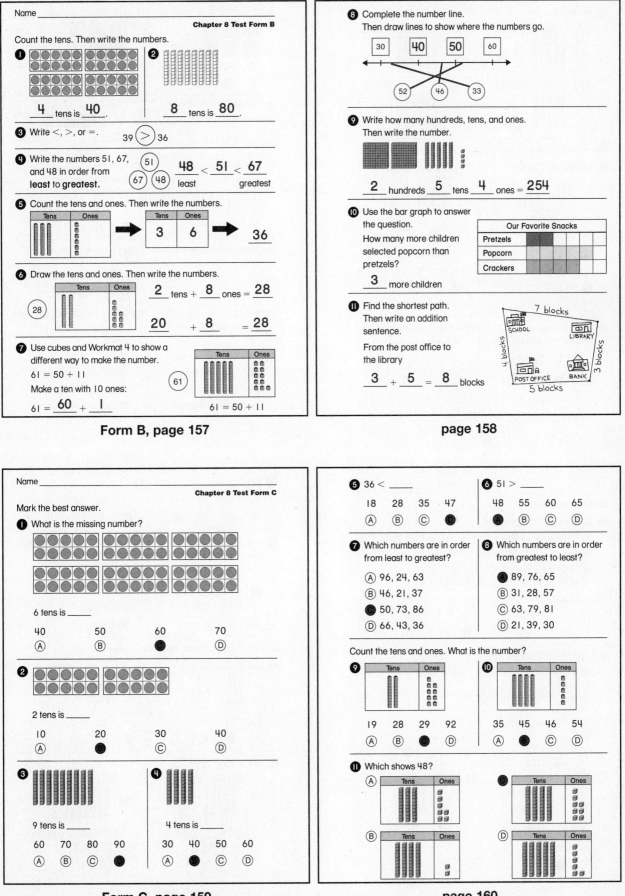

Name _____

Chapter 8 Test Form B

Count the tens. Then write the numbers.

1 _4_ tens is _40_.

2 _8_ tens is _80_.

3 Write <, >, or =.   39 ⊙> 36

4 Write the numbers 51, 67, and 48 in order from **least** to **greatest**.
⊙51 ⊙67 ⊙48
_48_ < _51_ < _67_
least   greatest

5 Count the tens and ones. Then write the numbers.
Tens | Ones → Tens 3 | Ones 6 → _36_

6 Draw the tens and ones. Then write the numbers.
⊙28
_2_ tens + _8_ ones = _28_
_20_ + _8_ = _28_

7 Use cubes and Workmat 4 to show a different way to make the number.
61 = 50 + 11
Make a ten with 10 ones:
61 = _60_ + _1_
⊙61   Tens | Ones   61 = 50 + 11

Form B, page 157

8 Complete the number line.
Then draw lines to show where the numbers go.
30 **40** **50** 60
52 46 33

9 Write how many hundreds, tens, and ones. Then write the number.
_2_ hundreds _5_ tens _4_ ones = _254_

10 Use the bar graph to answer the question.
How many more children selected popcorn than pretzels?
_3_ more children

Our Favorite Snacks
Pretzels
Popcorn
Crackers

11 Find the shortest path. Then write an addition sentence.
From the post office to the library
_3_ + _5_ = _8_ blocks

7 blocks
SCHOOL LIBRARY
4 blocks   3 blocks
POST OFFICE BANK
5 blocks

page 158

Name _____

Chapter 8 Test Form C

Mark the best answer.

1 What is the missing number?

6 tens is _____
40   50   60   70
Ⓐ   Ⓑ   ●   Ⓓ

2
2 tens is _____
10   20   30   40
Ⓐ   ●   Ⓒ   Ⓓ

3
9 tens is _____
60 70 80 90
Ⓐ Ⓑ Ⓒ ●

4
4 tens is _____
30 40 50 60
Ⓐ ● Ⓒ Ⓓ

Form C, page 159

5 36 < _____
18   28   35   47
Ⓐ   Ⓑ   Ⓒ   ●

6 51 > _____
48   55   60   65
●   Ⓑ   Ⓒ   Ⓓ

7 Which numbers are in order from least to greatest?
Ⓐ 96, 24, 63
Ⓑ 46, 21, 37
● 50, 73, 86
Ⓓ 66, 43, 36

8 Which numbers are in order from greatest to least?
● 89, 76, 65
Ⓑ 31, 28, 57
Ⓒ 63, 79, 81
Ⓓ 21, 39, 30

Count the tens and ones. What is the number?

9 Tens | Ones
19   28   29   92
Ⓐ   Ⓑ   ●   Ⓓ

10 Tens | Ones
35   45   46   54
Ⓐ   ●   Ⓒ   Ⓓ

11 Which shows 48?
Ⓐ Tens | Ones
Ⓑ Tens | Ones
● Tens | Ones
Ⓓ Tens | Ones

page 160

Chapter Tests Forms A and B in the Assessment Sourcebook parallel Chapter Tests in the Student Edition item for item. See the Teacher's Edition for item analysis of these tests.

261

Chapter 8 Form C and Form D

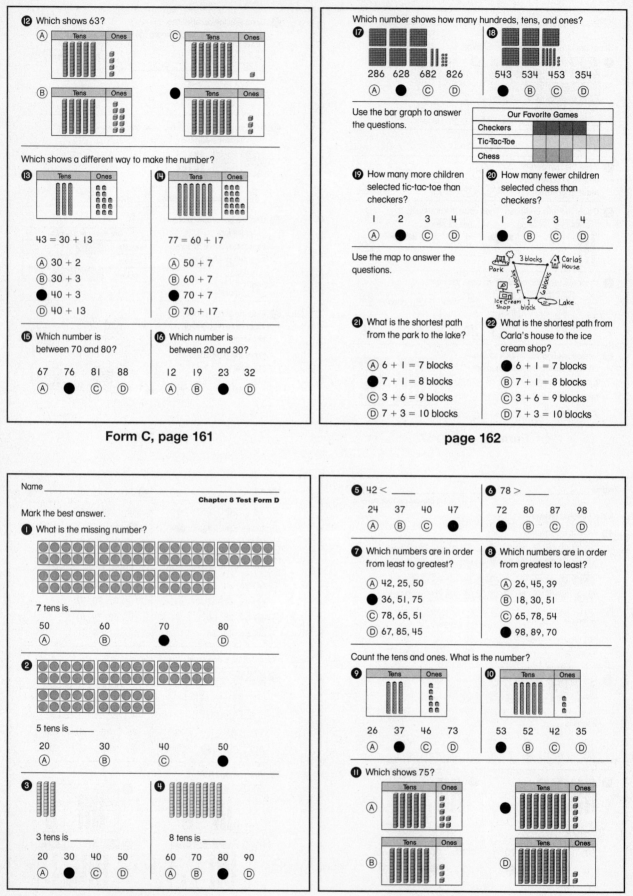

12 Which shows 63?

Ⓐ Tens | Ones
Ⓒ Tens | Ones
Ⓑ Tens | Ones
● Tens | Ones

Which shows a different way to make the number?

13 Tens | Ones

$43 = 30 + 13$

Ⓐ $30 + 2$
Ⓑ $30 + 3$
● $40 + 3$
Ⓓ $40 + 13$

14 Tens | Ones

$77 = 60 + 17$

Ⓐ $50 + 7$
Ⓑ $60 + 7$
● $70 + 7$
Ⓓ $70 + 17$

15 Which number is between 70 and 80?

67   76   81   88
Ⓐ   ●   Ⓒ   Ⓓ

16 Which number is between 20 and 30?

12   19   23   32
Ⓐ   Ⓑ   ●   Ⓓ

Form C, page 161

Which number shows how many hundreds, tens, and ones?

17
286   628   682   826
Ⓐ   ●   Ⓒ   Ⓓ

18
543   534   453   354
●   Ⓑ   Ⓒ   Ⓓ

Use the bar graph to answer the questions.

Our Favorite Games					
Checkers					
Tic-Tac-Toe					
Chess					

19 How many more children selected tic-tac-toe than checkers?

1   2   3   4
Ⓐ   ●   Ⓒ   Ⓓ

20 How many fewer children selected chess than checkers?

1   2   3   4
●   Ⓑ   Ⓒ   Ⓓ

Use the map to answer the questions.

21 What is the shortest path from the park to the lake?

Ⓐ $6 + 1 = 7$ blocks
● $7 + 1 = 8$ blocks
Ⓒ $3 + 6 = 9$ blocks
Ⓓ $7 + 3 = 10$ blocks

22 What is the shortest path from Carla's house to the ice cream shop?

● $6 + 1 = 7$ blocks
Ⓑ $7 + 1 = 8$ blocks
Ⓒ $3 + 6 = 9$ blocks
Ⓓ $7 + 3 = 10$ blocks

page 162

Name _____

Chapter 8 Test Form D

Mark the best answer.

1 What is the missing number?

7 tens is _____

50   60   70   80
Ⓐ   Ⓑ   ●   Ⓓ

2

5 tens is _____

20   30   40   50
Ⓐ   Ⓑ   Ⓒ   ●

3

3 tens is _____

20   30   40   50
Ⓐ   ●   Ⓒ   Ⓓ

4

8 tens is _____

60   70   80   90
Ⓐ   Ⓑ   ●   Ⓓ

Form D, page 163

5 $42 < $ _____

24   37   40   47
Ⓐ   Ⓑ   Ⓒ   ●

6 $78 > $ _____

72   80   87   98
●   Ⓑ   Ⓒ   Ⓓ

7 Which numbers are in order from least to greatest?

Ⓐ 42, 25, 50
● 36, 51, 75
Ⓒ 78, 65, 51
Ⓓ 67, 85, 45

8 Which numbers are in order from greatest to least?

Ⓐ 26, 45, 39
Ⓑ 18, 30, 51
Ⓒ 65, 78, 54
● 98, 89, 70

Count the tens and ones. What is the number?

9 Tens | Ones

26   37   46   73
Ⓐ   ●   Ⓒ   Ⓓ

10 Tens | Ones

53   52   42   35
●   Ⓑ   Ⓒ   Ⓓ

11 Which shows 75?

Ⓐ Tens | Ones
● Tens | Ones
Ⓑ Tens | Ones
Ⓓ Tens | Ones

page 164

262

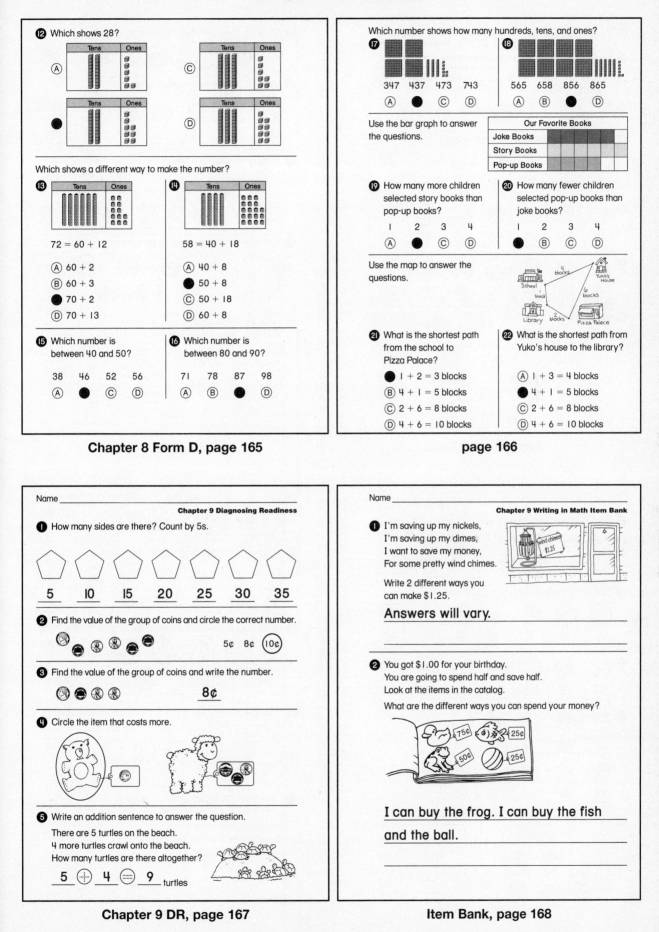

12 Which shows 28?

(A) Tens | Ones

(C) Tens | Ones

● Tens | Ones

(D) Tens | Ones

Which shows a different way to make the number?

13 Tens | Ones

$72 = 60 + 12$

(A) 60 + 2
(B) 60 + 3
● 70 + 2
(D) 70 + 13

14 Tens | Ones

$58 = 40 + 18$

(A) 40 + 8
● 50 + 8
(C) 50 + 18
(D) 60 + 8

15 Which number is between 40 and 50?

38   46   52   56
(A)   ●   (C)   (D)

16 Which number is between 80 and 90?

71   78   87   98
(A)   (B)   ●   (D)

Chapter 8 Form D, page 165

Which number shows how many hundreds, tens, and ones?

17

347   437   473   743
(A)   ●   (C)   (D)

18

565   658   856   865
(A)   (B)   ●   (D)

Use the bar graph to answer the questions.

Our Favorite Books
Joke Books
Story Books
Pop-up Books

19 How many more children selected story books than pop-up books?

1   2   3   4
(A) ●   (C) (D)

20 How many fewer children selected pop-up books than joke books?

1   2   3   4
●   (B) (C) (D)

Use the map to answer the questions.

21 What is the shortest path from the school to Pizza Palace?

● 1 + 2 = 3 blocks
(B) 4 + 1 = 5 blocks
(C) 2 + 6 = 8 blocks
(D) 4 + 6 = 10 blocks

22 What is the shortest path from Yuko's house to the library?

(A) 1 + 3 = 4 blocks
● 4 + 1 = 5 blocks
(C) 2 + 6 = 8 blocks
(D) 4 + 6 = 10 blocks

page 166

Name _____

Chapter 9 Diagnosing Readiness

1 How many sides are there? Count by 5s.

5   10   15   20   25   30   35

2 Find the value of the group of coins and circle the correct number.

5¢   8¢   ⑩¢

3 Find the value of the group of coins and write the number.

8¢

4 Circle the item that costs more.

5 Write an addition sentence to answer the question.

There are 5 turtles on the beach.
4 more turtles crawl onto the beach.
How many turtles are there altogether?

__5__ ⊕ __4__ ⊜ __9__ turtles

Chapter 9 DR, page 167

Name _____

Chapter 9 Writing in Math Item Bank

1 I'm saving up my nickels,
I'm saving up my dimes,
I want to save my money,
For some pretty wind chimes.

Write 2 different ways you can make $1.25.

Answers will vary.

2 You got $1.00 for your birthday.
You are going to spend half and save half.
Look at the items in the catalog.

What are the different ways you can spend your money?

I can buy the frog. I can buy the fish and the ball.

Item Bank, page 168

Chapter 9 Form A and Form B

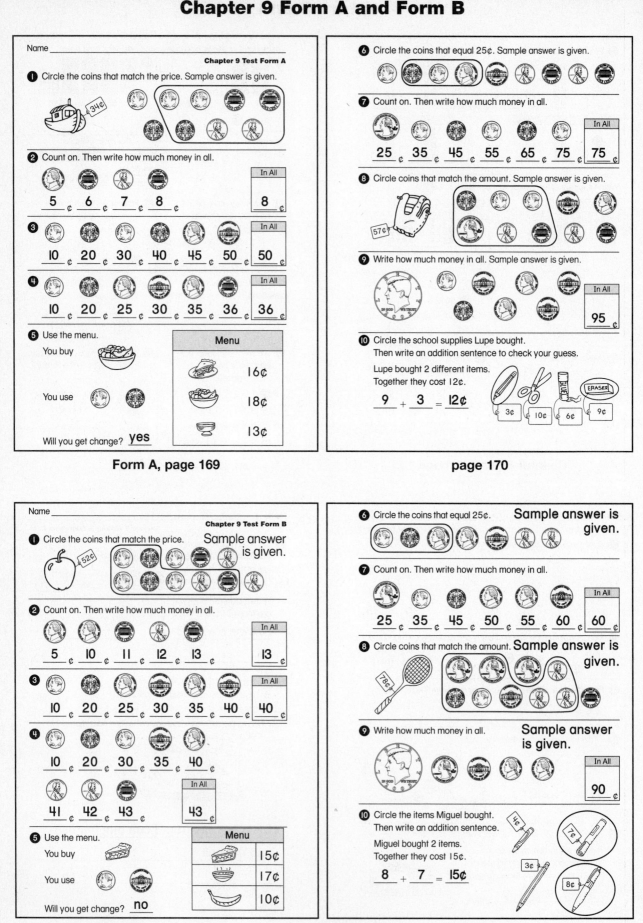

Name _____

Chapter 9 Test Form A

① Circle the coins that match the price. Sample answer is given.

② Count on. Then write how much money in all.

5 ¢   6 ¢   7 ¢   8 ¢ | In All: 8 ¢

③ 10 ¢   20 ¢   30 ¢   40 ¢   45 ¢   50 ¢ | In All: 50 ¢

④ 10 ¢   20 ¢   25 ¢   30 ¢   35 ¢   36 ¢ | In All: 36 ¢

⑤ Use the menu.
You buy
You use
Will you get change? **yes**

Menu	
	16¢
	18¢
	13¢

Form A, page 169

⑥ Circle the coins that equal 25¢. Sample answer is given.

⑦ Count on. Then write how much money in all.

25 ¢   35 ¢   45 ¢   55 ¢   65 ¢   75 ¢ | In All: 75 ¢

⑧ Circle coins that match the amount. Sample answer is given.

57¢

⑨ Write how much money in all. Sample answer is given.

In All: 95

⑩ Circle the school supplies Lupe bought.
Then write an addition sentence to check your guess.

Lupe bought 2 different items.
Together they cost 12¢.

_9_ + _3_ = 12¢

3¢   10¢   6¢   9¢ ERASER

page 170

Name _____

Chapter 9 Test Form B

① Circle the coins that match the price. **Sample answer is given.**

52¢

② Count on. Then write how much money in all.

5 ¢   10 ¢   11 ¢   12 ¢   13 ¢ | In All: 13 ¢

③ 10 ¢   20 ¢   25 ¢   30 ¢   35 ¢   40 ¢ | In All: 40 ¢

④ 10 ¢   20 ¢   30 ¢   35 ¢   40 ¢
41 ¢   42 ¢   43 ¢ | In All: 43 ¢

⑤ Use the menu.
You buy
You use
Will you get change? **no**

Menu	
	15¢
	17¢
	10¢

Form B, page 171

⑥ Circle the coins that equal 25¢. **Sample answer is given.**

⑦ Count on. Then write how much money in all.

25 ¢   35 ¢   45 ¢   50 ¢   55 ¢   60 ¢ | In All: 60 ¢

⑧ Circle coins that match the amount. **Sample answer is given.**

78¢

⑨ Write how much money in all. **Sample answer is given.**

In All: 90

⑩ Circle the items Miguel bought.
Then write an addition sentence.

Miguel bought 2 items.
Together they cost 15¢.

_8_ + _7_ = 15¢

4¢   7¢   3¢   8¢

page 172

Chapter 9 Form C

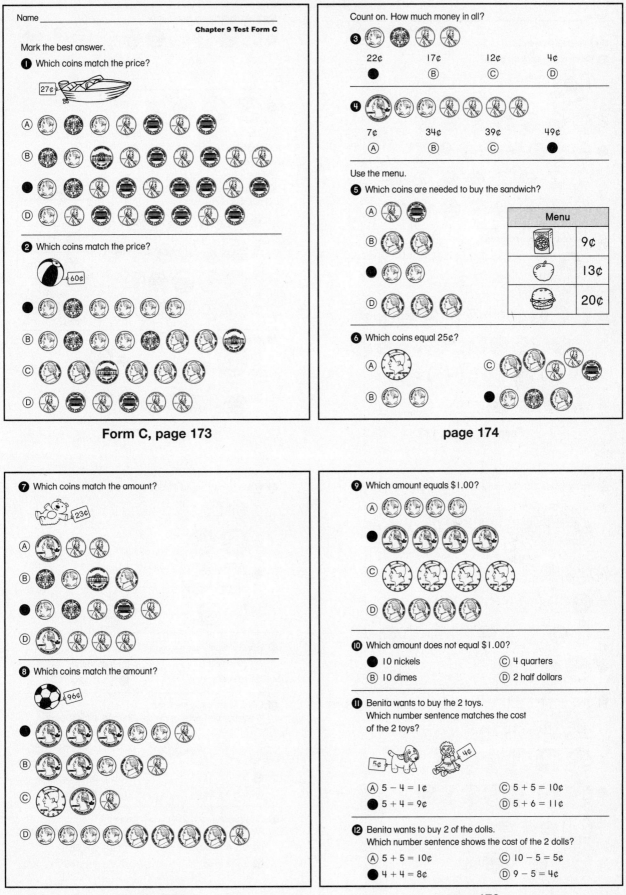

Name _____

Chapter 9 Test Form C

Mark the best answer.

1 Which coins match the price?

27¢

Ⓐ
Ⓑ
●
Ⓓ

2 Which coins match the price?

60¢

●
Ⓑ
Ⓒ
Ⓓ

Form C, page 173

Count on. How much money in all?

3

22¢	17¢	12¢	4¢
●	Ⓑ	Ⓒ	Ⓓ

4

7¢	34¢	39¢	49¢
Ⓐ	Ⓑ	Ⓒ	●

Use the menu.

5 Which coins are needed to buy the sandwich?

Ⓐ
Ⓑ
●
Ⓓ

Menu	
(crackers)	9¢
(apple)	13¢
(hamburger)	20¢

6 Which coins equal 25¢?

Ⓐ   Ⓒ

Ⓑ   ●

page 174

---

7 Which coins match the amount?

23¢

Ⓐ
Ⓑ
●
Ⓓ

8 Which coins match the amount?

96¢

●
Ⓑ
Ⓒ
Ⓓ

page 175

---

9 Which amount equals $1.00?

Ⓐ
●
Ⓒ
Ⓓ

10 Which amount does not equal $1.00?

● 10 nickels   Ⓒ 4 quarters

Ⓑ 10 dimes   Ⓓ 2 half dollars

11 Benita wants to buy the 2 toys.
Which number sentence matches the cost
of the 2 toys?

5¢   4¢

Ⓐ 5 − 4 = 1¢   Ⓒ 5 + 5 = 10¢

● 5 + 4 = 9¢   Ⓓ 5 + 6 = 11¢

12 Benita wants to buy 2 of the dolls.
Which number sentence shows the cost of the 2 dolls?

Ⓐ 5 + 5 = 10¢   Ⓒ 10 − 5 = 5¢

● 4 + 4 = 8¢   Ⓓ 9 − 5 = 4¢

page 176

Chapter 9 Form D

Name _____

Chapter 9 Test Form D

Mark the best answer.

1 Which coins match the price?

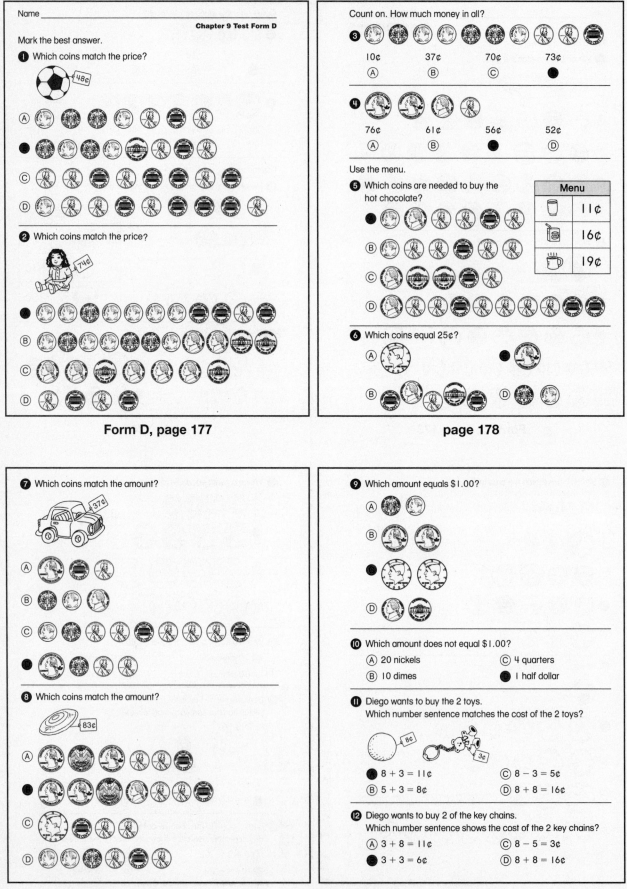

Ⓐ

● (filled)

Ⓒ

Ⓓ

2 Which coins match the price?

● (filled)

Ⓑ

Ⓒ

Ⓓ

Form D, page 177

Count on. How much money in all?

3

10¢	37¢	70¢	73¢
Ⓐ	Ⓑ	Ⓒ	●

4

76¢	61¢	56¢	52¢
Ⓐ	Ⓑ	●	Ⓓ

Use the menu.

5 Which coins are needed to buy the hot chocolate?

● (filled)

Ⓑ

Ⓒ

Ⓓ

Menu	
🥛	11¢
🧃	16¢
☕	19¢

6 Which coins equal 25¢?

Ⓐ

● (filled)

Ⓑ

Ⓓ

page 178

---

7 Which coins match the amount?

Ⓐ

Ⓑ

Ⓒ

● (filled)

8 Which coins match the amount?

Ⓐ

● (filled)

Ⓒ

Ⓓ

page 179

---

9 Which amount equals $1.00?

Ⓐ

Ⓑ

● (filled)

Ⓓ

10 Which amount does not equal $1.00?

Ⓐ 20 nickels   Ⓒ 4 quarters

Ⓑ 10 dimes   ● 1 half dollar

11 Diego wants to buy the 2 toys.
Which number sentence matches the cost of the 2 toys?

● 8 + 3 = 11¢   Ⓒ 8 − 3 = 5¢

Ⓑ 5 + 3 = 8¢   Ⓓ 8 + 8 = 16¢

12 Diego wants to buy 2 of the key chains.
Which number sentence shows the cost of the 2 key chains?

Ⓐ 3 + 8 = 11¢   Ⓒ 8 − 5 = 3¢

● 3 + 3 = 6¢   Ⓓ 8 + 8 = 16¢

page 180

Cumulative Test 1–9

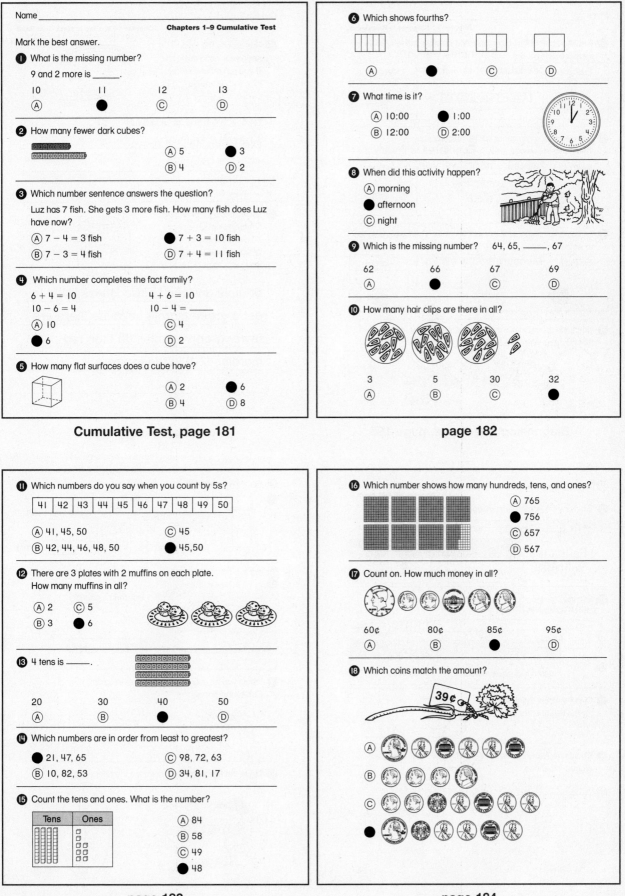

Name _____

Chapters 1–9 Cumulative Test

Mark the best answer.

1 What is the missing number?

9 and 2 more is _____.

10   11   12   13
Ⓐ   ●   Ⓒ   Ⓓ

2 How many fewer dark cubes?

Ⓐ 5   ● 3
Ⓑ 4   Ⓓ 2

3 Which number sentence answers the question?

Luz has 7 fish. She gets 3 more fish. How many fish does Luz have now?

Ⓐ $7 - 4 = 3$ fish   ● $7 + 3 = 10$ fish
Ⓑ $7 - 3 = 4$ fish   Ⓓ $7 + 4 = 11$ fish

4 Which number completes the fact family?

$6 + 4 = 10$ $4 + 6 = 10$
$10 - 6 = 4$ $10 - 4 = $ _____

Ⓐ 10   Ⓒ 4
● 6   Ⓓ 2

5 How many flat surfaces does a cube have?

Ⓐ 2   ● 6
Ⓑ 4   Ⓓ 8

Cumulative Test, page 181

6 Which shows fourths?

Ⓐ   ●   Ⓒ   Ⓓ

7 What time is it?

Ⓐ 10:00   ● 1:00
Ⓑ 12:00   Ⓓ 2:00

8 When did this activity happen?

Ⓐ morning
● afternoon
Ⓒ night

9 Which is the missing number?   64, 65, _____, 67

62   66   67   69
Ⓐ   ●   Ⓒ   Ⓓ

10 How many hair clips are there in all?

3   5   30   32
Ⓐ   Ⓑ   Ⓒ   ●

page 182

11 Which numbers do you say when you count by 5s?

| 41 | 42 | 43 | 44 | 45 | 46 | 47 | 48 | 49 | 50 |

Ⓐ 41, 45, 50   Ⓒ 45
Ⓑ 42, 44, 46, 48, 50   ● 45, 50

12 There are 3 plates with 2 muffins on each plate. How many muffins in all?

Ⓐ 2   Ⓒ 5
Ⓑ 3   ● 6

13 4 tens is _____.

20   30   40   50
Ⓐ   Ⓑ   ●   Ⓓ

14 Which numbers are in order from least to greatest?

● 21, 47, 65   Ⓒ 98, 72, 63
Ⓑ 10, 82, 53   Ⓓ 34, 81, 17

15 Count the tens and ones. What is the number?

Tens	Ones

Ⓐ 84
Ⓑ 58
Ⓒ 49
● 48

page 183

16 Which number shows how many hundreds, tens, and ones?

Ⓐ 765
● 756
Ⓒ 657
Ⓓ 567

17 Count on. How much money in all?

60¢   80¢   85¢   95¢
Ⓐ   Ⓑ   ●   Ⓓ

18 Which coins match the amount?

39¢

Ⓐ
Ⓑ
Ⓒ
●

page 184

Item Analysis for Diagnosis and Intervention: Chapters 1–9 Cumulative Test is on page 283 in the Assessment Sourcebook.

267

Chapter 10

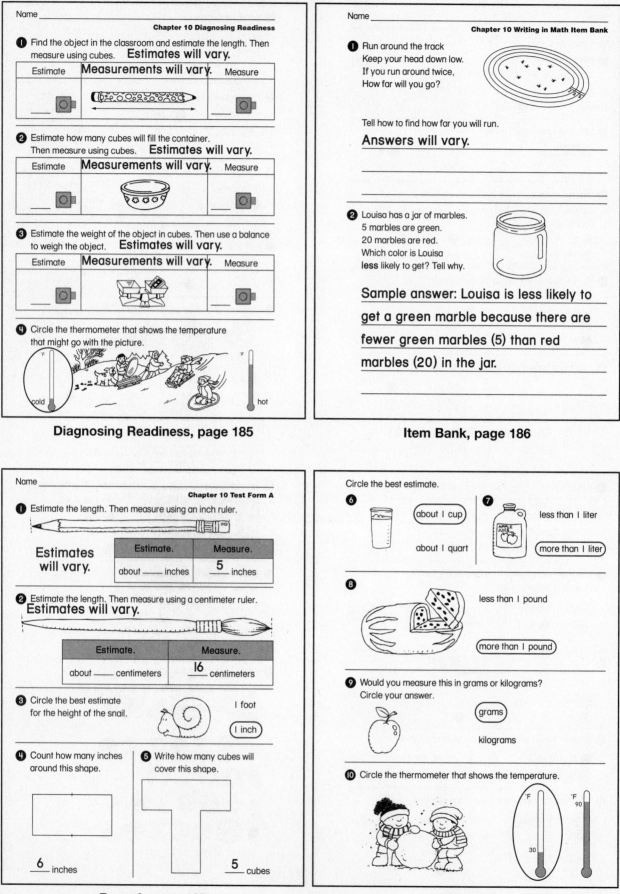

Diagnosing Readiness, page 185

Name _____

Chapter 10 Diagnosing Readiness

❶ Find the object in the classroom and estimate the length. Then measure using cubes. **Estimates will vary.**

Estimate	**Measurements will vary.**	Measure

❷ Estimate how many cubes will fill the container. Then measure using cubes. **Estimates will vary.**

Estimate	**Measurements will vary.**	Measure

❸ Estimate the weight of the object in cubes. Then use a balance to weigh the object. **Estimates will vary.**

Estimate	**Measurements will vary.**	Measure

❹ Circle the thermometer that shows the temperature that might go with the picture.

cold   hot

Item Bank, page 186

Name _____

Chapter 10 Writing in Math Item Bank

❶ Run around the track
Keep your head down low.
If you run around twice,
How far will you go?

Tell how to find how far you will run.

Answers will vary.

❷ Louisa has a jar of marbles.
5 marbles are green.
20 marbles are red.
Which color is Louisa
less likely to get? Tell why.

Sample answer: Louisa is less likely to get a green marble because there are fewer green marbles (5) than red marbles (20) in the jar.

Form A, page 187

Name _____

Chapter 10 Test Form A

❶ Estimate the length. Then measure using an inch ruler.

Estimates will vary.

Estimate.	Measure.
about ____ inches	5 inches

❷ Estimate the length. Then measure using a centimeter ruler.
Estimates will vary.

Estimate.	Measure.
about ____ centimeters	16 centimeters

❸ Circle the best estimate for the height of the snail.

1 foot
(1 inch)

❹ Count how many inches around this shape.

6 inches

❺ Write how many cubes will cover this shape.

5 cubes

page 188

Circle the best estimate.

❻ (about 1 cup)
about 1 quart

❼ less than 1 liter
(more than 1 liter)

❽ less than 1 pound
(more than 1 pound)

❾ Would you measure this in grams or kilograms? Circle your answer.

(grams)
kilograms

❿ Circle the thermometer that shows the temperature.

Chapter Tests Forms A and B in the Assessment Sourcebook parallel Chapter Tests in the Student Edition item for item. See the Teacher's Edition for item analysis of these tests.

Chapter 10 Form B and Form C

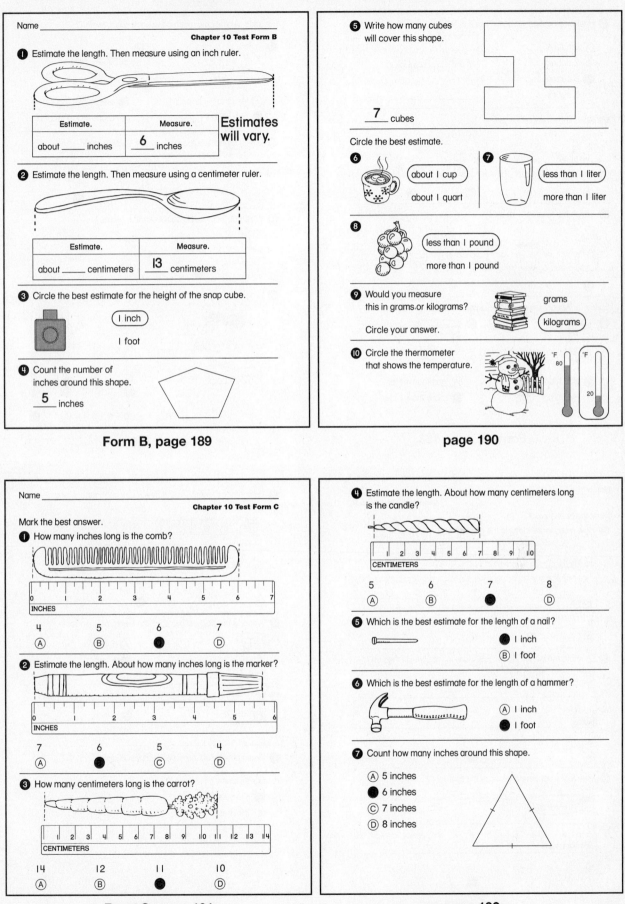

Name _____

1 Estimate the length. Then measure using an inch ruler.

Estimate.	Measure.
about _____ inches	**6** inches

Estimates will vary.

2 Estimate the length. Then measure using a centimeter ruler.

Estimate.	Measure.
about _____ centimeters	**13** centimeters

3 Circle the best estimate for the height of the snap cube.

(1 inch)

1 foot

4 Count the number of inches around this shape.

___5___ inches

Form B, page 189

5 Write how many cubes will cover this shape.

___7___ cubes

Circle the best estimate.

6 (about 1 cup)

about 1 quart

7 (less than 1 liter)

more than 1 liter

8 (less than 1 pound)

more than 1 pound

9 Would you measure this in grams or kilograms?

grams

(kilograms)

Circle your answer.

10 Circle the thermometer that shows the temperature.

°F 80

°F 20

page 190

Name _____

Mark the best answer.

1 How many inches long is the comb?

4	5	6	7
Ⓐ	Ⓑ	⬤	Ⓓ

2 Estimate the length. About how many inches long is the marker?

7	6	5	4
Ⓐ	⬤	Ⓒ	Ⓓ

3 How many centimeters long is the carrot?

14	12	11	10
Ⓐ	Ⓑ	⬤	Ⓓ

Form C, page 191

4 Estimate the length. About how many centimeters long is the candle?

5	6	7	8
Ⓐ	Ⓑ	⬤	Ⓓ

5 Which is the best estimate for the length of a nail?

⬤ 1 inch

Ⓑ 1 foot

6 Which is the best estimate for the length of a hammer?

Ⓐ 1 inch

⬤ 1 foot

7 Count how many inches around this shape.

Ⓐ 5 inches

⬤ 6 inches

Ⓒ 7 inches

Ⓓ 8 inches

page 192

Chapter Tests Forms A and B in the Assessment Sourcebook parallel Chapter Tests in the Student Edition item for item. See the Teacher's Edition for item analysis of these tests.

269

Chapter 10 Form C and Form D

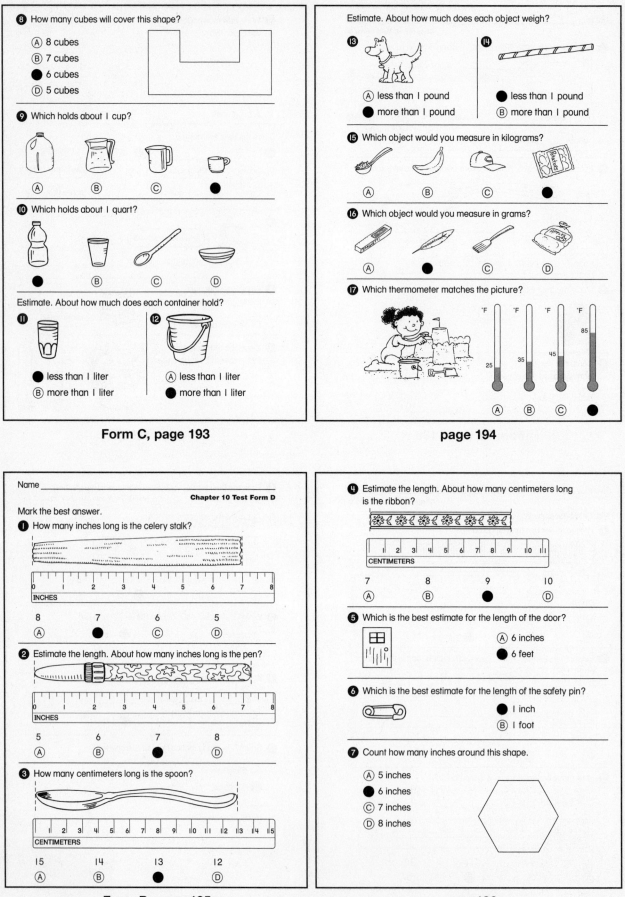

8 How many cubes will cover this shape?
- Ⓐ 8 cubes
- Ⓑ 7 cubes
- ● 6 cubes
- Ⓓ 5 cubes

9 Which holds about I cup?
Ⓐ   Ⓑ   Ⓒ   ●

10 Which holds about I quart?
●   Ⓑ   Ⓒ   Ⓓ

Estimate. About how much does each container hold?

11
- ● less than I liter
- Ⓑ more than I liter

12
- Ⓐ less than I liter
- ● more than I liter

Form C, page 193

Estimate. About how much does each object weigh?

13
- Ⓐ less than I pound
- ● more than I pound

14
- ● less than I pound
- Ⓑ more than I pound

15 Which object would you measure in kilograms?
Ⓐ   Ⓑ   Ⓒ   ●

16 Which object would you measure in grams?
Ⓐ   ●   Ⓒ   Ⓓ

17 Which thermometer matches the picture?
Ⓐ   Ⓑ   Ⓒ   ●

page 194

Name _____

Chapter 10 Test Form D

Mark the best answer.

1 How many inches long is the celery stalk?

INCHES

8   7   6   5
Ⓐ   ●   Ⓒ   Ⓓ

2 Estimate the length. About how many inches long is the pen?

INCHES

5   6   7   8
Ⓐ   Ⓑ   ●   Ⓓ

3 How many centimeters long is the spoon?

CENTIMETERS

15   14   13   12
Ⓐ   Ⓑ   ●   Ⓓ

Form D, page 195

4 Estimate the length. About how many centimeters long is the ribbon?

CENTIMETERS

7   8   9   10
Ⓐ   Ⓑ   ●   Ⓓ

5 Which is the best estimate for the length of the door?
- Ⓐ 6 inches
- ● 6 feet

6 Which is the best estimate for the length of the safety pin?
- ● I inch
- Ⓑ I foot

7 Count how many inches around this shape.
- Ⓐ 5 inches
- ● 6 inches
- Ⓒ 7 inches
- Ⓓ 8 inches

page 196

270

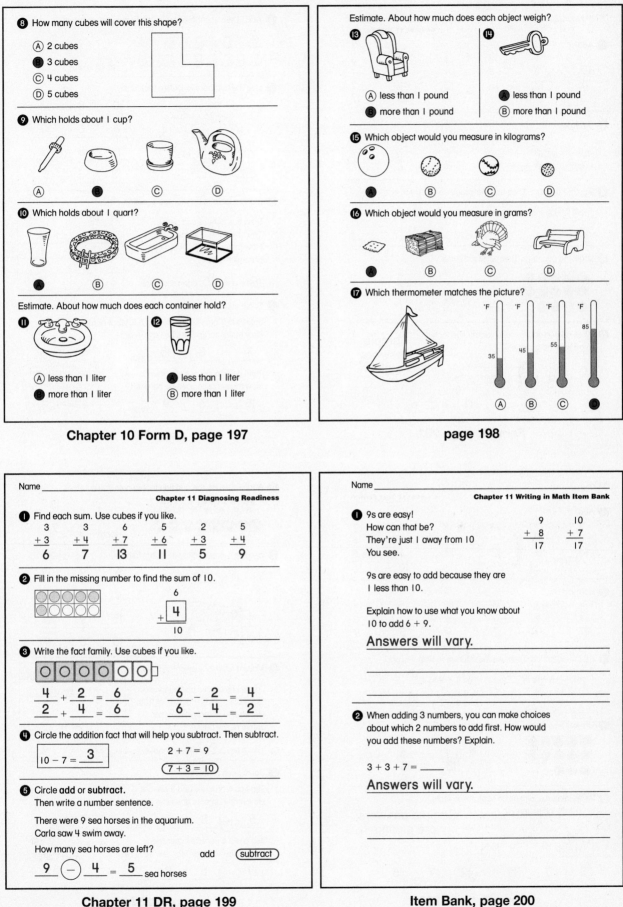

8 How many cubes will cover this shape?

Ⓐ 2 cubes
Ⓑ 3 cubes
Ⓒ 4 cubes
Ⓓ 5 cubes

9 Which holds about 1 cup?

Ⓐ   **Ⓑ**   Ⓒ   Ⓓ

10 Which holds about 1 quart?

Ⓐ   Ⓑ   Ⓒ   Ⓓ

Estimate. About how much does each container hold?

11
Ⓐ less than 1 liter
Ⓑ more than 1 liter

12
Ⓐ less than 1 liter
Ⓑ more than 1 liter

Chapter 10 Form D, page 197

Estimate. About how much does each object weigh?

13
Ⓐ less than 1 pound
Ⓑ more than 1 pound

14
Ⓐ less than 1 pound
Ⓑ more than 1 pound

15 Which object would you measure in kilograms?

Ⓐ   Ⓑ   Ⓒ   Ⓓ

16 Which object would you measure in grams?

Ⓐ   Ⓑ   Ⓒ   Ⓓ

17 Which thermometer matches the picture?

Ⓐ   Ⓑ   Ⓒ   **Ⓓ**

page 198

Name _____

Chapter 11 Diagnosing Readiness

1 Find each sum. Use cubes if you like.

3	3	6	5	2	5
+3	+4	+7	+6	+3	+4
6	7	13	11	5	9

2 Fill in the missing number to find the sum of 10.

6
+ **4**
10

3 Write the fact family. Use cubes if you like.

$\frac{4}{2} + \frac{2}{4} = \frac{6}{6}$ $\frac{6}{6} - \frac{2}{4} = \frac{4}{2}$

4 Circle the addition fact that will help you subtract. Then subtract.

10 − 7 = **3**

2 + 7 = 9
(7 + 3 = 10)

5 Circle **add** or **subtract**.
Then write a number sentence.

There were 9 sea horses in the aquarium.
Carla saw 4 swim away.

How many sea horses are left?   add   (subtract)

9 ⊖ **4** = **5** sea horses

Chapter 11 DR, page 199

Name _____

Chapter 11 Writing in Math Item Bank

1 9s are easy!
How can that be?
They're just 1 away from 10
You see.

9   10
+ 8   + 7
17   17

9s are easy to add because they are
1 less than 10.

Explain how to use what you know about
10 to add 6 + 9.

Answers will vary. _____

_____

_____

2 When adding 3 numbers, you can make choices
about which 2 numbers to add first. How would
you add these numbers? Explain.

3 + 3 + 7 = _____

Answers will vary. _____

_____

_____

Item Bank, page 200

Chapter 11 Form A and Form B

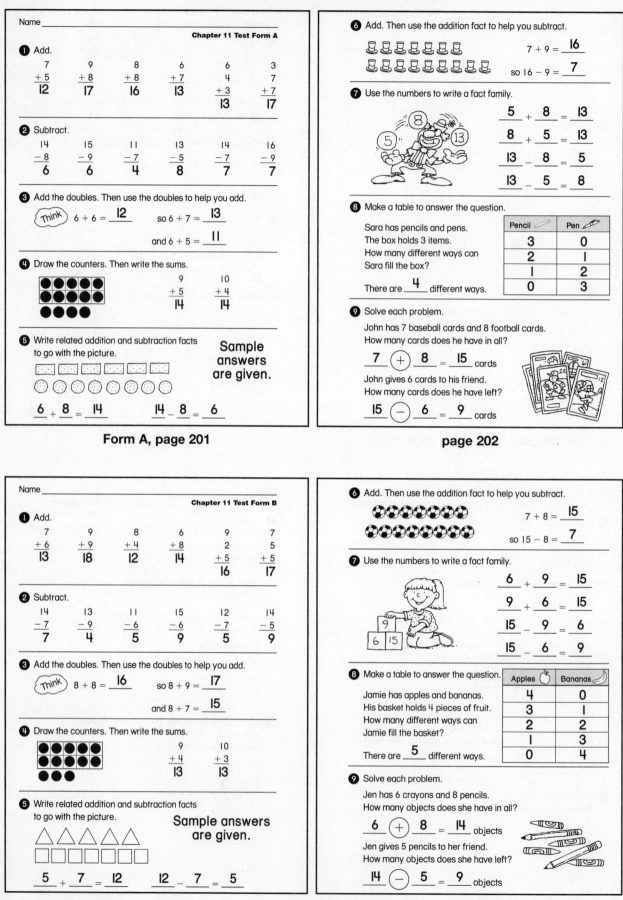

Name _____

Chapter 11 Test Form A

① Add.

7	9	8	6	6	3
+5	+8	+8	+7	4	7
12	17	16	13	+3	+7
				13	17

② Subtract.

14	15	11	13	14	16
−8	−9	−7	−5	−7	−9
6	6	4	8	7	7

③ Add the doubles. Then use the doubles to help you add.

Think 6 + 6 = 12   so 6 + 7 = 13

and 6 + 5 = 11

④ Draw the counters. Then write the sums.

9	10
+5	+4
14	14

⑤ Write related addition and subtraction facts to go with the picture.

Sample answers are given.

6 + 8 = 14   14 − 8 = 6

Form A, page 201

---

⑥ Add. Then use the addition fact to help you subtract.

7 + 9 = 16

so 16 − 9 = 7

⑦ Use the numbers to write a fact family.

5 + 8 = 13

8 + 5 = 13

13 − 8 = 5

13 − 5 = 8

⑧ Make a table to answer the question.

Sara has pencils and pens.
The box holds 3 items.
How many different ways can
Sara fill the box?

There are __4__ different ways.

Pencil	Pen
3	0
2	1
1	2
0	3

⑨ Solve each problem.

John has 7 baseball cards and 8 football cards.
How many cards does he have in all?

7 ⊕ 8 = 15 cards

John gives 6 cards to his friend.
How many cards does he have left?

15 ⊖ 6 = 9 cards

page 202

Name _____

Chapter 11 Test Form B

① Add.

7	9	8	6	9	7
+6	+9	+4	+8	2	5
13	18	12	14	+5	+5
				16	17

② Subtract.

14	13	11	15	12	14
−7	−9	−6	−6	−7	−5
7	4	5	9	5	9

③ Add the doubles. Then use the doubles to help you add.

Think 8 + 8 = 16   so 8 + 9 = 17

and 8 + 7 = 15

④ Draw the counters. Then write the sums.

9	10
+4	+3
13	13

⑤ Write related addition and subtraction facts to go with the picture.

Sample answers are given.

5 + 7 = 12   12 − 7 = 5

Form B, page 203

---

⑥ Add. Then use the addition fact to help you subtract.

7 + 8 = 15

so 15 − 8 = 7

⑦ Use the numbers to write a fact family.

6 + 9 = 15

9 + 6 = 15

15 − 9 = 6

15 − 6 = 9

⑧ Make a table to answer the question.

Jamie has apples and bananas.
His basket holds 4 pieces of fruit.
How many different ways can
Jamie fill the basket?

There are __5__ different ways.

Apples	Bananas
4	0
3	1
2	2
1	3
0	4

⑨ Solve each problem.

Jen has 6 crayons and 8 pencils.
How many objects does she have in all?

6 ⊕ 8 = 14 objects

Jen gives 5 pencils to her friend.
How many objects does she have left?

14 ⊖ 5 = 9 objects

page 204

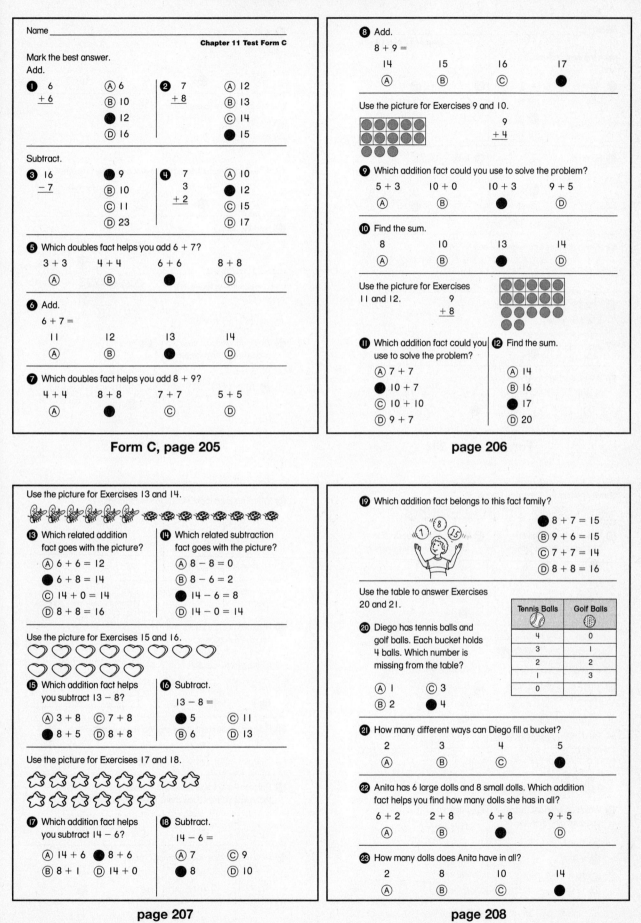

Name _____

Chapter 11 Test Form C

Mark the best answer.
Add.

1 6
+ 6
- (A) 6
- (B) 10
- ● 12
- (D) 16

2 7
+ 8
- (A) 12
- (B) 13
- (C) 14
- ● 15

Subtract.

3 16
− 7
- ● 9
- (B) 10
- (C) 11
- (D) 23

4 7
3
+ 2
- (A) 10
- ● 12
- (C) 15
- (D) 17

5 Which doubles fact helps you add 6 + 7?

3 + 3   4 + 4   6 + 6   8 + 8
(A)   (B)   ●   (D)

6 Add.

6 + 7 =

11   12   13   14
(A)   (B)   ●   (D)

7 Which doubles fact helps you add 8 + 9?

4 + 4   8 + 8   7 + 7   5 + 5
(A)   ●   (C)   (D)

Form C, page 205

8 Add.

8 + 9 =

14   15   16   17
(A)   (B)   (C)   ●

Use the picture for Exercises 9 and 10.

9
+ 4

9 Which addition fact could you use to solve the problem?

5 + 3   10 + 0   10 + 3   9 + 5
(A)   (B)   ●   (D)

10 Find the sum.

8   10   13   14
(A)   (B)   ●   (D)

Use the picture for Exercises 11 and 12.

9
+ 8

11 Which addition fact could you use to solve the problem?
- (A) 7 + 7
- ● 10 + 7
- (C) 10 + 10
- (D) 9 + 7

12 Find the sum.
- (A) 14
- (B) 16
- ● 17
- (D) 20

page 206

Use the picture for Exercises 13 and 14.

13 Which related addition fact goes with the picture?
- (A) 6 + 6 = 12
- ● 6 + 8 = 14
- (C) 14 + 0 = 14
- (D) 8 + 8 = 16

14 Which related subtraction fact goes with the picture?
- (A) 8 − 8 = 0
- (B) 8 − 6 = 2
- ● 14 − 6 = 8
- (D) 14 − 0 = 14

Use the picture for Exercises 15 and 16.

15 Which addition fact helps you subtract 13 − 8?
- (A) 3 + 8   (C) 7 + 8
- ● 8 + 5   (D) 8 + 8

16 Subtract.

13 − 8 =
- ● 5   (C) 11
- (B) 6   (D) 13

Use the picture for Exercises 17 and 18.

17 Which addition fact helps you subtract 14 − 6?
- (A) 14 + 6   ● 8 + 6
- (B) 8 + 1   (D) 14 + 0

18 Subtract.

14 − 6 =
- (A) 7   (C) 9
- ● 8   (D) 10

page 207

19 Which addition fact belongs to this fact family?
- ● 8 + 7 = 15
- (B) 9 + 6 = 15
- (C) 7 + 7 = 14
- (D) 8 + 8 = 16

Use the table to answer Exercises 20 and 21.

20 Diego has tennis balls and golf balls. Each bucket holds 4 balls. Which number is missing from the table?

- (A) 1   (C) 3
- (B) 2   ● 4

Tennis Balls	Golf Balls
4	0
3	1
2	2
1	3
0	

21 How many different ways can Diego fill a bucket?

2   3   4   5
(A)   (B)   (C)   ●

22 Anita has 6 large dolls and 8 small dolls. Which addition fact helps you find how many dolls she has in all?

6 + 2   2 + 8   6 + 8   9 + 5
(A)   (B)   ●   (D)

23 How many dolls does Anita have in all?

2   8   10   14
(A)   (B)   (C)   ●

page 208

273

Chapter 11 Form D

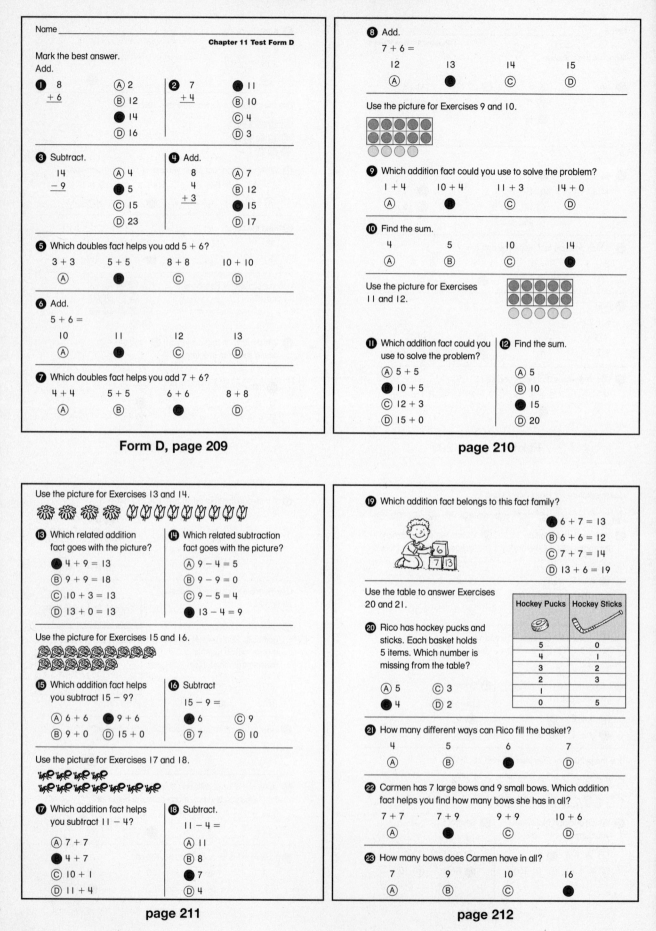

Name _____

Mark the best answer.
Add.

1. 8
+ 6
- (A) 2
- (B) 12
- ● 14
- (D) 16

2. 7
+ 4
- ● 11
- (B) 10
- (C) 4
- (D) 3

3. Subtract.
14
− 9
- (A) 4
- ● 5
- (C) 15
- (D) 23

4. Add.
8
4
+ 3
- (A) 7
- (B) 12
- ● 15
- (D) 17

5. Which doubles fact helps you add 5 + 6?
- 3 + 3 (A)
- 5 + 5 ●
- 8 + 8 (C)
- 10 + 10 (D)

6. Add.
5 + 6 =
- 10 (A)
- 11 ●
- 12 (C)
- 13 (D)

7. Which doubles fact helps you add 7 + 6?
- 4 + 4 (A)
- 5 + 5 (B)
- 6 + 6 ●
- 8 + 8 (D)

Form D, page 209

8. Add.
7 + 6 =
- 12 (A)
- 13 ●
- 14 (C)
- 15 (D)

Use the picture for Exercises 9 and 10.

9. Which addition fact could you use to solve the problem?
- 1 + 4 (A)
- 10 + 4 ●
- 11 + 3 (C)
- 14 + 0 (D)

10. Find the sum.
- 4 (A)
- 5 (B)
- 10 (C)
- 14 ●

Use the picture for Exercises 11 and 12.

11. Which addition fact could you use to solve the problem?
- (A) 5 + 5
- ● 10 + 5
- (C) 12 + 3
- (D) 15 + 0

12. Find the sum.
- (A) 5
- (B) 10
- ● 15
- (D) 20

page 210

Use the picture for Exercises 13 and 14.

13. Which related addition fact goes with the picture?
- ● 4 + 9 = 13
- (B) 9 + 9 = 18
- (C) 10 + 3 = 13
- (D) 13 + 0 = 13

14. Which related subtraction fact goes with the picture?
- (A) 9 − 4 = 5
- (B) 9 − 9 = 0
- (C) 9 − 5 = 4
- ● 13 − 4 = 9

Use the picture for Exercises 15 and 16.

15. Which addition fact helps you subtract 15 − 9?
- (A) 6 + 6
- ● 9 + 6
- (B) 9 + 0
- (D) 15 + 0

16. Subtract.
15 − 9 =
- ● 6
- (C) 9
- (B) 7
- (D) 10

Use the picture for Exercises 17 and 18.

17. Which addition fact helps you subtract 11 − 4?
- (A) 7 + 7
- ● 4 + 7
- (C) 10 + 1
- (D) 11 + 4

18. Subtract.
11 − 4 =
- (A) 11
- (B) 8
- ● 7
- (D) 4

page 211

19. Which addition fact belongs to this fact family?
- ● 6 + 7 = 13
- (B) 6 + 6 = 12
- (C) 7 + 7 = 14
- (D) 13 + 6 = 19

Use the table to answer Exercises 20 and 21.

20. Rico has hockey pucks and sticks. Each basket holds 5 items. Which number is missing from the table?
- (A) 5
- (C) 3
- ● 4
- (D) 2

Hockey Pucks	Hockey Sticks
5	0
4	1
3	2
2	3
1	
0	5

21. How many different ways can Rico fill the basket?
- 4 (A)
- 5 (B)
- 6 ●
- 7 (D)

22. Carmen has 7 large bows and 9 small bows. Which addition fact helps you find how many bows she has in all?
- 7 + 7 (A)
- 7 + 9 ●
- 9 + 9 (C)
- 10 + 6 (D)

23. How many bows does Carmen have in all?
- 7 (A)
- 9 (B)
- 10 (C)
- 16 ●

page 212

274

Chapter 12

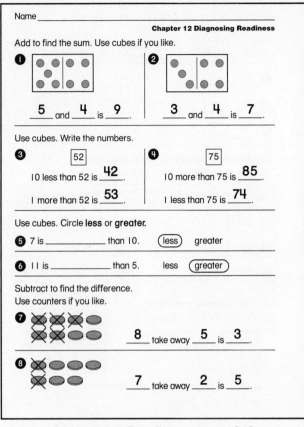

Chapter 12 Diagnosing Readiness

Name _____

Add to find the sum. Use cubes if you like.

❶ __5__ and __4__ is __9__.

❷ __3__ and __4__ is __7__.

Use cubes. Write the numbers.

❸ [52]
10 less than 52 is __42__.
1 more than 52 is __53__.

❹ [75]
10 more than 75 is __85__.
1 less than 75 is __74__.

Use cubes. Circle **less** or **greater**.

❺ 7 is _____ than 10. (less) greater

❻ 11 is _____ than 5. less (greater)

Subtract to find the difference.
Use counters if you like.

❼ __8__ take away __5__ is __3__.

❽ __7__ take away __2__ is __5__.

Diagnosing Readiness, page 213

Chapter 12 Writing in Math Item Bank

Name _____

❶ All of the grade 1 classes wanted to sell the most popcorn. Which class sold the most? Which class sold the least? How much popcorn did the first graders sell?

Popcorn Sales

Grade 1 Class	Week 1	Week 2	Week 3	Total
Miss Riley	$11.00	$22.00	$30.00	$63.00
Mrs. Scott	$12.00	$31.00	$42.00	$85.00
Mr. Bell	$12.00	$24.00	$35.00	$71.00
Total				$219.00

Mrs. Scott's class sold the most popcorn.

Miss Riley's class sold the least popcorn.

The First Graders sold a total of $219.00 of popcorn.

❷ Popcorn Sale Totals

Grade 1	$289.00
Grade 2	$168.00
Difference	

Tell how to find the difference. Write a number sentence that shows the difference between the total sales.

Subtract to find the difference.

$289 − $168 = $121.00.

Item Bank, page 214

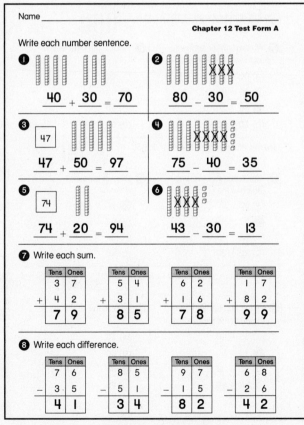

Chapter 12 Test Form A

Name _____

Write each number sentence.

❶ __40__ + __30__ = __70__

❷ __80__ − __30__ = __50__

❸ [47] __47__ + __50__ = __97__

❹ __75__ − __40__ = __35__

❺ [74] __74__ + __20__ = __94__

❻ __43__ − __30__ = __13__

❼ Write each sum.

Tens	Ones
3	7
+ 4	2
7	**9**

Tens	Ones
5	4
+ 3	1
8	**5**

Tens	Ones
6	2
+ 1	6
7	**8**

Tens	Ones
1	7
+ 8	2
9	**9**

❽ Write each difference.

Tens	Ones
7	6
− 3	5
4	**1**

Tens	Ones
8	5
− 5	1
3	**4**

Tens	Ones
9	7
− 1	5
8	**2**

Tens	Ones
6	8
− 2	6
4	**2**

Form A, page 215

Use cubes and Workmat 4. Do you need to regroup?
Circle **yes** or **no**. Then write the sum.

Show.	Add.	Do you need to regroup?	Find the sum.
❾ 86	9	(yes) no	86 + 9 = __95__
❿ 53	6	yes (no)	53 + 6 = __59__
⓫ 67	8	(yes) no	67 + 8 = __75__

Use cubes and Workmat 4. Do you need to regroup?
Circle **yes** or **no**. Then write the difference.

Show.	Subtract.	Do you need to regroup?	Find the difference.
⓬ 78	6	yes (no)	78 − 6 = __72__
⓭ 81	8	(yes) no	81 − 8 = __73__
⓮ 94	5	(yes) no	94 − 5 = __89__

⓯ Circle **exact answer** or **estimate**.

Juanita has 2 sheets of stickers.
Each sheet has 15 stickers.
There are 27 children in her class.
Are there enough stickers for all of the children in her class?

Do we need an exact answer or an estimate?

exact answer (estimate)

page 216

Chapter Tests Forms A and B in the Assessment Sourcebook parallel Chapter Tests in the Student Edition item for item. See the Teacher's Edition for item analysis of these tests.

Chapter 12 Form B and Form C

Form B, page 217

Name _____

Chapter 12 Test Form B

Write each number sentence.

1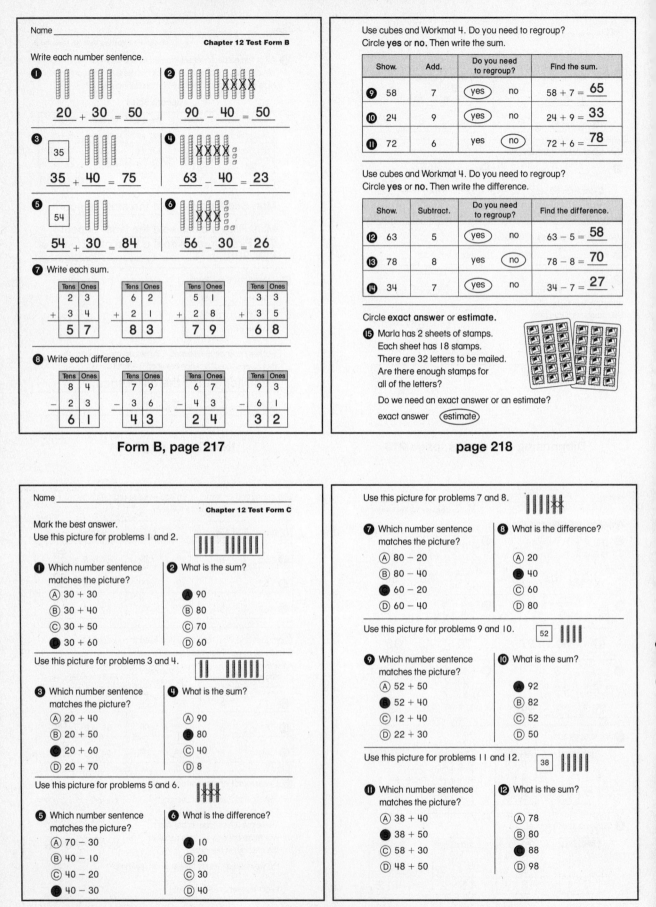

$20 + 30 = 50$

2

$90 - 40 = 50$

3 35

$35 + 40 = 75$

4

$63 - 40 = 23$

5 54

$54 + 30 = 84$

6

$56 - 30 = 26$

7 Write each sum.

Tens	Ones
2	3
+ 3	4
5	7

Tens	Ones
6	2
+ 2	1
8	3

Tens	Ones
5	1
+ 2	8
7	9

Tens	Ones
3	3
+ 3	5
6	8

8 Write each difference.

Tens	Ones
8	4
− 2	3
6	1

Tens	Ones
7	9
− 3	6
4	3

Tens	Ones
6	7
− 4	3
2	4

Tens	Ones
9	3
− 6	1
3	2

page 218

Use cubes and Workmat 4. Do you need to regroup?
Circle **yes** or **no**. Then write the sum.

Show.	Add.	Do you need to regroup?		Find the sum.
9 58	7	(yes)	no	$58 + 7 = $ 65
10 24	9	(yes)	no	$24 + 9 = $ 33
11 72	6	yes	(no)	$72 + 6 = $ 78

Use cubes and Workmat 4. Do you need to regroup?
Circle **yes** or **no**. Then write the difference.

Show.	Subtract.	Do you need to regroup?		Find the difference.
12 63	5	(yes)	no	$63 - 5 = $ 58
13 78	8	yes	(no)	$78 - 8 = $ 70
14 34	7	(yes)	no	$34 - 7 = $ 27

Circle **exact answer** or **estimate**.

15 Marla has 2 sheets of stamps.
Each sheet has 18 stamps.
There are 32 letters to be mailed.
Are there enough stamps for
all of the letters?

Do we need an exact answer or an estimate?

exact answer   (estimate)

Form C, page 219

Name _____

Chapter 12 Test Form C

Mark the best answer.
Use this picture for problems 1 and 2.

1 Which number sentence
matches the picture?
- Ⓐ $30 + 30$
- Ⓑ $30 + 40$
- Ⓒ $30 + 50$
- ● $30 + 60$

2 What is the sum?
- ● 90
- Ⓑ 80
- Ⓒ 70
- Ⓓ 60

Use this picture for problems 3 and 4.

3 Which number sentence
matches the picture?
- Ⓐ $20 + 40$
- Ⓑ $20 + 50$
- ● $20 + 60$
- Ⓓ $20 + 70$

4 What is the sum?
- Ⓐ 90
- ● 80
- Ⓒ 40
- Ⓓ 8

Use this picture for problems 5 and 6.

5 Which number sentence
matches the picture?
- Ⓐ $70 - 30$
- Ⓑ $40 - 10$
- Ⓒ $40 - 20$
- ● $40 - 30$

6 What is the difference?
- ● 10
- Ⓑ 20
- Ⓒ 30
- Ⓓ 40

page 220

Use this picture for problems 7 and 8.

7 Which number sentence
matches the picture?
- Ⓐ $80 - 20$
- Ⓑ $80 - 40$
- ● $60 - 20$
- Ⓓ $60 - 40$

8 What is the difference?
- Ⓐ 20
- ● 40
- Ⓒ 60
- Ⓓ 80

Use this picture for problems 9 and 10.   52

9 Which number sentence
matches the picture?
- Ⓐ $52 + 50$
- ● $52 + 40$
- Ⓒ $12 + 40$
- Ⓓ $22 + 30$

10 What is the sum?
- ● 92
- Ⓑ 82
- Ⓒ 52
- Ⓓ 50

Use this picture for problems 11 and 12.   38

11 Which number sentence
matches the picture?
- Ⓐ $38 + 40$
- ● $38 + 50$
- Ⓒ $58 + 30$
- Ⓓ $48 + 50$

12 What is the sum?
- Ⓐ 78
- Ⓑ 80
- ● 88
- Ⓓ 98

Chapter Tests Forms A and B in the Assessment Sourcebook parallel Chapter Tests in the Student
Edition item for item. See the Teacher's Edition for item analysis of these tests.

Chapter 12 Form C and Form D

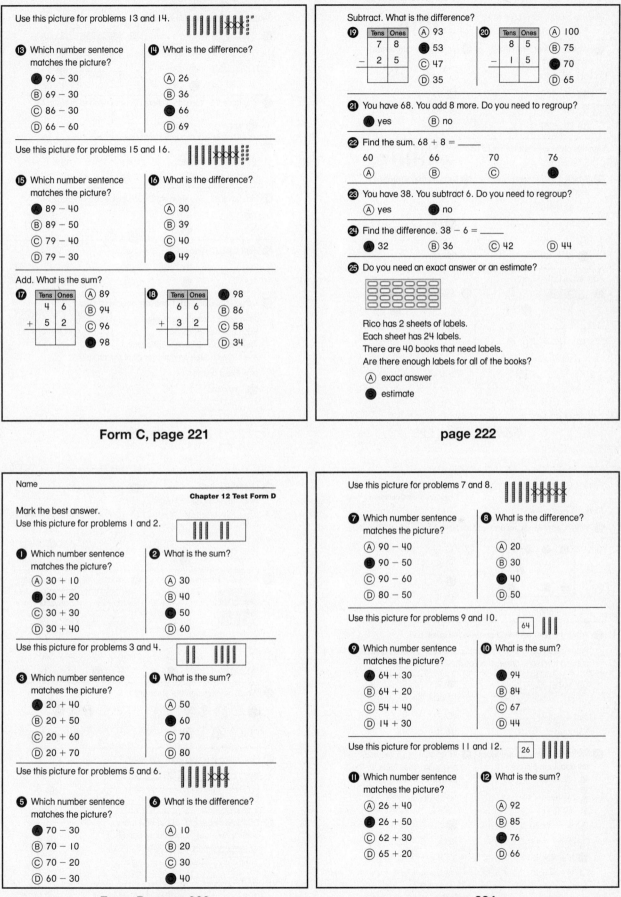

Use this picture for problems 13 and 14.

13 Which number sentence matches the picture?
- Ⓐ 96 − 30
- Ⓑ 69 − 30
- Ⓒ 86 − 30
- Ⓓ 66 − 60

14 What is the difference?
- Ⓐ 26
- Ⓑ 36
- Ⓒ 66
- Ⓓ 69

Use this picture for problems 15 and 16.

15 Which number sentence matches the picture?
- Ⓐ 89 − 40
- Ⓑ 89 − 50
- Ⓒ 79 − 40
- Ⓓ 79 − 30

16 What is the difference?
- Ⓐ 30
- Ⓑ 39
- Ⓒ 40
- Ⓓ 49

Add. What is the sum?

17
Tens	Ones
4	6
+ 5	2
- Ⓐ 89
- Ⓑ 94
- Ⓒ 96
- Ⓓ 98

18
Tens	Ones
6	6
+ 3	2
- Ⓐ 98
- Ⓑ 86
- Ⓒ 58
- Ⓓ 34

Form C, page 221

Subtract. What is the difference?

19
Tens	Ones
7	8
− 2	5
- Ⓐ 93
- Ⓑ 53
- Ⓒ 47
- Ⓓ 35

20
Tens	Ones
8	5
− 1	5
- Ⓐ 100
- Ⓑ 75
- Ⓒ 70
- Ⓓ 65

21 You have 68. You add 8 more. Do you need to regroup?
- Ⓐ yes
- Ⓑ no

22 Find the sum. 68 + 8 = _____
- 60 Ⓐ
- 66 Ⓑ
- 70 Ⓒ
- 76 Ⓓ

23 You have 38. You subtract 6. Do you need to regroup?
- Ⓐ yes
- Ⓑ no

24 Find the difference. 38 − 6 = _____
- Ⓐ 32
- Ⓑ 36
- Ⓒ 42
- Ⓓ 44

25 Do you need an exact answer or an estimate?

Rico has 2 sheets of labels.
Each sheet has 24 labels.
There are 40 books that need labels.
Are there enough labels for all of the books?
- Ⓐ exact answer
- Ⓑ estimate

page 222

Name _____

Chapter 12 Test Form D

Mark the best answer.
Use this picture for problems 1 and 2.

1 Which number sentence matches the picture?
- Ⓐ 30 + 10
- Ⓑ 30 + 20
- Ⓒ 30 + 30
- Ⓓ 30 + 40

2 What is the sum?
- Ⓐ 30
- Ⓑ 40
- Ⓒ 50
- Ⓓ 60

Use this picture for problems 3 and 4.

3 Which number sentence matches the picture?
- Ⓐ 20 + 40
- Ⓑ 20 + 50
- Ⓒ 20 + 60
- Ⓓ 20 + 70

4 What is the sum?
- Ⓐ 50
- Ⓑ 60
- Ⓒ 70
- Ⓓ 80

Use this picture for problems 5 and 6.

5 Which number sentence matches the picture?
- Ⓐ 70 − 30
- Ⓑ 70 − 10
- Ⓒ 70 − 20
- Ⓓ 60 − 30

6 What is the difference?
- Ⓐ 10
- Ⓑ 20
- Ⓒ 30
- Ⓓ 40

Form D, page 223

Use this picture for problems 7 and 8.

7 Which number sentence matches the picture?
- Ⓐ 90 − 40
- Ⓑ 90 − 50
- Ⓒ 90 − 60
- Ⓓ 80 − 50

8 What is the difference?
- Ⓐ 20
- Ⓑ 30
- Ⓒ 40
- Ⓓ 50

Use this picture for problems 9 and 10.   64

9 Which number sentence matches the picture?
- Ⓐ 64 + 30
- Ⓑ 64 + 20
- Ⓒ 54 + 40
- Ⓓ 14 + 30

10 What is the sum?
- Ⓐ 94
- Ⓑ 84
- Ⓒ 67
- Ⓓ 44

Use this picture for problems 11 and 12.   26

11 Which number sentence matches the picture?
- Ⓐ 26 + 40
- Ⓑ 26 + 50
- Ⓒ 62 + 30
- Ⓓ 65 + 20

12 What is the sum?
- Ⓐ 92
- Ⓑ 85
- Ⓒ 76
- Ⓓ 66

page 224

Chapter 12 Form D and Cumulative Test

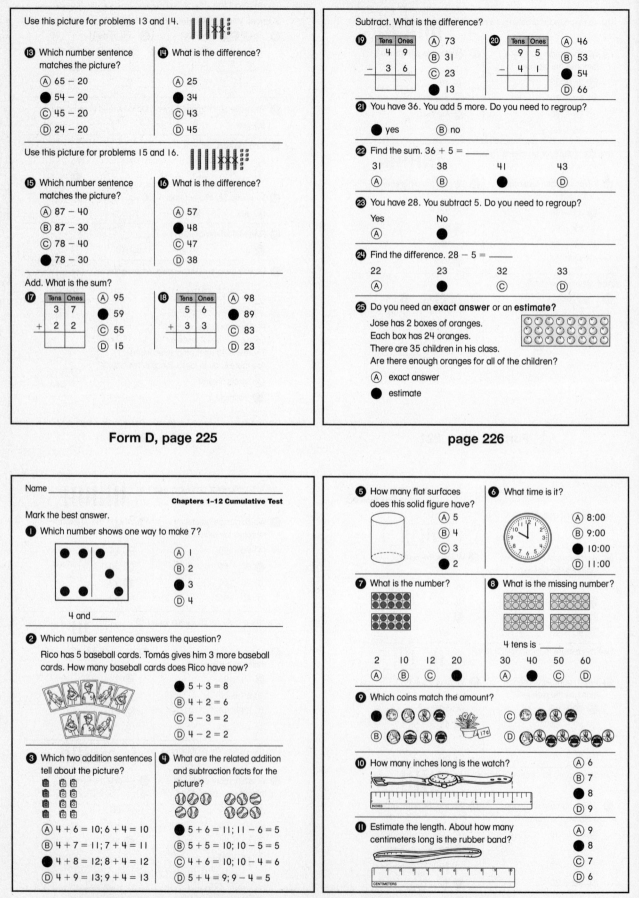

Use this picture for problems 13 and 14.

13 Which number sentence matches the picture?
- Ⓐ 65 − 20
- ● 54 − 20
- Ⓒ 45 − 20
- Ⓓ 24 − 20

14 What is the difference?
- Ⓐ 25
- ● 34
- Ⓒ 43
- Ⓓ 45

Use this picture for problems 15 and 16.

15 Which number sentence matches the picture?
- Ⓐ 87 − 40
- Ⓑ 87 − 30
- Ⓒ 78 − 40
- ● 78 − 30

16 What is the difference?
- Ⓐ 57
- ● 48
- Ⓒ 47
- Ⓓ 38

Add. What is the sum?

17

Tens	Ones
3	7
+ 2	2

- Ⓐ 95
- ● 59
- Ⓒ 55
- Ⓓ 15

18

Tens	Ones
5	6
+ 3	3

- Ⓐ 98
- ● 89
- Ⓒ 83
- Ⓓ 23

Form D, page 225

Subtract. What is the difference?

19

Tens	Ones
4	9
− 3	6

- Ⓐ 73
- Ⓑ 31
- Ⓒ 23
- ● 13

20

Tens	Ones
9	5
− 4	1

- Ⓐ 46
- Ⓑ 53
- ● 54
- Ⓓ 66

21 You have 36. You add 5 more. Do you need to regroup?
- ● yes
- Ⓑ no

22 Find the sum. 36 + 5 = _____

31	38	41	43
Ⓐ	Ⓑ	●	Ⓓ

23 You have 28. You subtract 5. Do you need to regroup?

Yes	No
Ⓐ	●

24 Find the difference. 28 − 5 = _____

22	23	32	33
Ⓐ	●	Ⓒ	Ⓓ

25 Do you need an **exact answer** or an **estimate**?

Jose has 2 boxes of oranges.
Each box has 24 oranges.
There are 35 children in his class.
Are there enough oranges for all of the children?

- Ⓐ exact answer
- ● estimate

page 226

Name _____

Mark the best answer.

1 Which number shows one way to make 7?

- Ⓐ 1
- Ⓑ 2
- ● 3
- Ⓓ 4

4 and _____

2 Which number sentence answers the question?

Rico has 5 baseball cards. Tomás gives him 3 more baseball cards. How many baseball cards does Rico have now?

- ● 5 + 3 = 8
- Ⓑ 4 + 2 = 6
- Ⓒ 5 − 3 = 2
- Ⓓ 4 − 2 = 2

3 Which two addition sentences tell about the picture?

- Ⓐ 4 + 6 = 10; 6 + 4 = 10
- Ⓑ 4 + 7 = 11; 7 + 4 = 11
- ● 4 + 8 = 12; 8 + 4 = 12
- Ⓓ 4 + 9 = 13; 9 + 4 = 13

4 What are the related addition and subtraction facts for the picture?

- ● 5 + 6 = 11; 11 − 6 = 5
- Ⓑ 5 + 5 = 10; 10 − 5 = 5
- Ⓒ 4 + 6 = 10; 10 − 4 = 6
- Ⓓ 5 + 4 = 9; 9 − 4 = 5

Cumulative Test 1–12, page 227

---

5 How many flat surfaces does this solid figure have?
- Ⓐ 5
- Ⓑ 4
- Ⓒ 3
- ● 2

6 What time is it?
- Ⓐ 8:00
- Ⓑ 9:00
- ● 10:00
- Ⓓ 11:00

7 What is the number?

2	10	12	20
Ⓐ	Ⓑ	Ⓒ	●

8 What is the missing number?

4 tens is _____

30	40	50	60
Ⓐ	●	Ⓒ	Ⓓ

9 Which coins match the amount?

10 How many inches long is the watch?
- Ⓐ 6
- Ⓑ 7
- ● 8
- Ⓓ 9

11 Estimate the length. About how many centimeters long is the rubber band?
- Ⓐ 9
- ● 8
- Ⓒ 7
- Ⓓ 6

page 228

Item Analysis for Diagnosis and Intervention: Chapters 1–12 Cumulative Test is on page 284 in the Assessment Sourcebook.

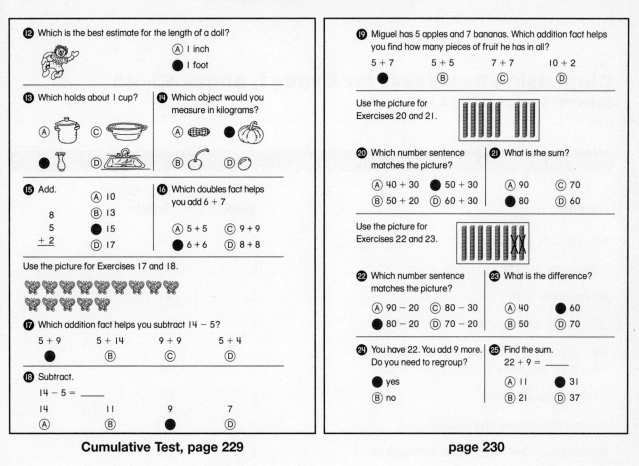

12 Which is the best estimate for the length of a doll?

- (A) I inch
- ● I foot

13 Which holds about I cup?

- (A)
- (C)
- ●
- (D)

14 Which object would you measure in kilograms?

- (A)
- ●
- (B)
- (D)

15 Add.

8
5
+ 2

- (A) 10
- (B) 13
- ● 15
- (D) 17

16 Which doubles fact helps you add 6 + 7?

- (A) 5 + 5
- (C) 9 + 9
- ● 6 + 6
- (D) 8 + 8

Use the picture for Exercises 17 and 18.

17 Which addition fact helps you subtract 14 − 5?

5 + 9	5 + 14	9 + 9	5 + 4
●	(B)	(C)	(D)

18 Subtract.

14 − 5 = _____

14	11	9	7
(A)	(B)	●	(D)

19 Miguel has 5 apples and 7 bananas. Which addition fact helps you find how many pieces of fruit he has in all?

5 + 7	5 + 5	7 + 7	10 + 2
●	(B)	(C)	(D)

Use the picture for Exercises 20 and 21.

20 Which number sentence matches the picture?

- (A) 40 + 30
- ● 50 + 30
- (B) 50 + 20
- (D) 60 + 30

21 What is the sum?

- (A) 90
- (C) 70
- ● 80
- (D) 60

Use the picture for Exercises 22 and 23.

22 Which number sentence matches the picture?

- (A) 90 − 20
- (C) 80 − 30
- ● 80 − 20
- (D) 70 − 20

23 What is the difference?

- (A) 40
- ● 60
- (B) 50
- (D) 70

24 You have 22. You add 9 more. Do you need to regroup?

- ● yes
- (B) no

25 Find the sum.

22 + 9 = _____

- (A) 11
- ● 31
- (B) 21
- (D) 37

Cumulative Test, page 229

page 230

Item Analysis for Diagnosis and Intervention: Chapters 1–12 Cumulative Test is on page 284 in the Assessment Sourcebook.

279

Diagnosing Readiness for Grade 1, pages 43–46
(Answers on page 234.)

Item Analysis for Diagnosis and Intervention

Objective	Items	Intervention System
Sort objects by shape.	1	D42
Extend shape patterns.	2	D1
Read a picture graph.	3	D1
Use the word *fifth* to identify an ordinal position.	4	A1
Solve problems by performing probability experiments and making tally marks in a table to record data.	5	A3
Compare objects by height.	6	D20
Compare containers by their capacity.	7	D20
Represent and count the quantities 11 through 20.	8	A3
Identify cubes.	9	D43
Identify equal parts of a whole.	10	D43
Tell time to the hour on an analog clock.	11	D2
Write and solve addition sentences to represent joining situations.	12	B2
Solve addition sentences to represent joining situations.	13	B2
Solve subtractions sentences to represent take-away situations.	14	B3
Subtract pennies, write subtractions sentences, and use the ¢ sign.	15	B3
Write and solve addition sentences to represent joining situations.	16	B2
Count and write numbers to 100.	17	A4

Chapters 1-3 Cumulative Test, pages 89-92
(Answers on pages 244-245.)

Item Analysis for Diagnosis and Intervention

Objective	Items	Student Book Pages	Intervention System
Identify the pattern unit in a repeating pattern, and extend the pattern.	1	3–4 or 27–28	D44
Show ways that the number 7 can be divided into two parts.	3	11–12 or 5–6	A5
Show ways that the number 8 can be divided into two parts.	2	13–14 or 7–8	A5
Solve problems by using objects to act them out.	7	21–22 or 13–14	E29
Find the number that is 2 more than a given number.	4	25–26 or 17–18	A7
Find the number that is 2 fewer than a given number.	5	27–28 or 19–20	A7
Compare and order numbers through 12.	6, 8	31–32 or 23–24	A9
Write an addition sentence to find the sum in a joining situation.	9	49–50	B7
Solve problems by writing addition sentences.	11	57–58	E36
Write the differences for horizontal and vertical forms of subtraction.	10	69–70	B14
Solve problems by choosing addition or subtraction.	12, 17	71–72	E4
Compare two groups to find out how many fewer.	13	75–76	B15
Write subtraction sentences to compare and tell how many more.	14	77–78	B15
Use the commutative property to find sums.	15	93–94	B18
Use a number line to count on 2.	16	97–98	B20
Solve problems by identifying unnecessary information and writing number sentences.	19, 20	99–100	E8
Use doubles facts to learn doubles-plus-1 facts.	18	105–106	B22

Chapters 1–6 Cumulative Test, pages 135–138
(Answers on pages 255–256.)

Item Analysis for Diagnosis and Intervention

Objective	Items	Student Book Pages	Intervention System
Identify the pattern unit in a repeating pattern, and extend the pattern.	1	3–4	D44
Show ways that the number 8 can be divided into two parts.	2	13–14	A5
Write an addition sentence to find the sum in a joining situation.	3	49–50	B7
Write the sums for the horizontal and vertical forms of addition.	7	53–54	B9
Write the differences for horizontal and vertical forms of subtraction.	4	69–70	B14
Solve problems by choosing addition or subtraction.	8	71–72	E4
Write subtraction sentences to compare and tell how many more.	5	77–78	B15
Recognize facts that have sums of 10.	6	107–108	B23
Use a number line to count back 1 or 2.	9, 10	125–126	B24
Solve problems by writing subtraction sentences.	13	133–134	E36
Write the addition and subtraction sentences that make up a fact family.	11	139–140	B28
Find differences by using known addition facts.	12	141–142	B29
Identify and name standard geometric solids.	14	157–158	D45
Count the number of flat surfaces on geometric solids.	15	159–160	D46
Match a geometric solid to an outline of one of its flat surfaces.	16	161–162	D47, D48
Identify and name standard plane shapes.	17	165–166	D49
Identify objects that show symmetry.	18	171–172	D52
Identify fourths of a region.	19	185–186	A60
Determine if an event takes more or less than 1 minute.	20	205–206	D3
Tell the time to the hour.	21	207–208	D4
Tell and write time to the half hour.	22	211–212	D6
Solve problems by reading and using the information in a schedule.	24	223–224	E1
Name the days of the week.	23	225–226	D8

Chapters 1-9 Cumulative Test, pages 181-184
(Answers on page 267.)

Item Analysis for Diagnosis and Intervention

Objective	Items	Student Book Pages	Intervention System
Find the number that is 2 more than a given number.	1	25–26	A7
Solve problems by choosing addition or subtraction.	3	71–72	E4
Compare two groups to find out how many fewer.	2	75–76	B15
Write the addition and subtraction sentences that make up a fact family.	4	139–140	B28
Count the number of flat surfaces on geometric figures.	5	159–160	D46
Identify fourths of a region.	6	185–186	A60
Tell time to the hour.	7	207–208	D4
Determine whether an event takes place in the *morning, afternoon, or night.*	8	219–220	D7
Count and write numbers to 100.	9	245–246	A11
Count sets that are grouped in 10s and leftover ones.	10	247–248	A12
Use a hundred chart to skip count by 5s.	11	255–256	A14
Skip count to find the total number of items arranged in sets of 2s.	12	257–258	A15
Count tens to find how many there are in all.	13	281–282	A19
Given a quantity shown with tens and ones, tell how many tens and ones there are, and write the number.	15	283–284	A20
Given three two-digit numbers, order them from least to greatest.	14	301–302	A29
Write a three-digit number for a given model of hundreds, tens, and ones.	16	303–304	A30
Count collections of coins including a quarter, dimes, nickels, and pennies.	18	345–346	A37
Identify a half-dollar coin and combinations of coins worth amounts up to $ 1.00.	17	347–348	A38, A39

Chapters 1-12 Cumulative Test, pages 227-230
(Answers on pages 278-279.)

Item Analysis for Diagnosis and Intervention

Objective	Items	Student Book Pages	Intervention System
Show ways that the number 7 can be divided into two parts.	1	11–12	A5
Solve problems by choosing addition or subtraction.	2	71–72	E4
Use the commutative property to find sums.	3	93–94	B18
Write related addition and subtraction facts.	4	137–138	B27
Count the number of flat surfaces on geometric solids.	5	159–160	D46
Tell time to the hour.	6	207–208	D4
Count groups of 10 and write how many.	7	243–244	A11
Count tens to find how many there are in all.	8	281–282	A19
Identify the value of a group of dimes, nickels, and pennies through 99¢.	9	337–338	A35
Measure the lengths of objects to the nearest inch using a ruler.	10	371–372	D22
Estimate the length of objects to the nearest foot.	12	373–374	D22
Estimate the length of objects in centimeters using a ruler.	11	375–376	D23
Estimate and compare the capacities of containers.	13	383–384	D24
Select the appropriate unit for measuring, given the choice of grams or kilograms.	14	393–394	D29
Use doubles facts to learn doubles-plus-1 facts.	16	419–420	B31
Use the associative property to find sums of three numbers.	15	427–428	B35
Write related addition and subtraction facts with sums through 18.	17, 18, 19	435–436	B36
Add two multiples of 10 for sums to 100.	20, 21	459–460	C1
Use models to add a one-digit quantity to a two-digit quantity with regrouping.	24, 25	465–466	C3
Subtract a multiple of 10 from a multiple of 10, 100 or less.	22, 23	471–472	C5